Student Edition

SpringBoard®

Mathematics

Course 1

CollegeBoard

About the College Board

The College Board is a mission-driven not-for-profit organization that connects students to college success and opportunity. Founded in 1900, the College Board was created to expand access to higher education. Today, the membership association is made up of over 6,000 of the world's leading educational institutions and is dedicated to promoting excellence and equity in education. Each year, the College Board helps more than seven million students prepare for a successful transition to college through programs and services in college readiness and college success—including the SAT® and the Advanced Placement Program®. The organization also serves the education community through research and advocacy on behalf of students, educators, and schools.

For further information, visit www.collegeboard.org.

ISBN: 1-4573-0148-2
ISBN: 978-1-4573-0148-3

4 5 6 7 8 9   16 17 18 19 20 21 22
Printed in the United States of America

Acknowledgments

The College Board gratefully acknowledges the outstanding work of the classroom teachers and writers who have been integral to the development of this revised program. The end product is testimony to their expertise, understanding of student learning needs, and dedication to rigorous but accessible mathematics instruction.

Michael Allwood
Brunswick School
Greenwich, Connecticut

Shawn Harris
Ronan Middle School
Ronan, Montana

Dr. Roxy Peck
California Polytechnic Institute
San Luis Obispo, California

Floyd Bullard
North Carolina School of Science
and Mathematics
Durham, North Carolina

Marie Humphrey
David W. Butler High School
Charlotte, North Carolina

Katie Sheets
Harrisburg School
Harrisburg, South Dakota

Marcia Chumas
East Mecklenburg High School
Charlotte, North Carolina

Brian Kotz
Montgomery College
Monrovia, Maryland

Andrea Sukow
Mathematics Consultant
Nashville, Tennessee

Kathy Fritz
Plano Independent School
District
Plano, Texas

Chris Olsen
Prairie Lutheran School
Cedar Rapids, Iowa

Stephanie Tate
Hillsborough School District
Tampa, Florida

SpringBoard Mathematics Product Development

Betty Barnett
Executive Director
Content Development

Allen M. D. von Pallandt, Ph.D.
Senior Director
Mathematics Content Development

John Nelson
Mathematics Editor

Judy Windle
Senior Math Instructional Specialist

Acknowledgments *continued*

Research and Planning Advisors

We also wish to thank the members of our SpringBoard Advisory Council and the many educators who gave generously of their time and their ideas as we conducted research for both the print and online programs. Your suggestions and reactions to ideas helped immeasurably as we planned the revisions. We gratefully acknowledge the teachers and administrators in the following districts.

ABC Unified
Cerritos, California

Albuquerque Public Schools
Albuquerque, New Mexico

Amarillo School District
Amarillo, Texas

Baltimore County Public Schools
Baltimore, Maryland

Bellevue School District 405
Bellevue, Washington

Charlotte Mecklenburg Schools
Charlotte, North Carolina

Clark County School District
Las Vegas, Nevada

Cypress Fairbanks ISD
Houston, Texas

District School Board of Collier
County
Collier County, Florida

Denver Public Schools
Denver, Colorado

Frisco ISD
Frisco, Texas

Gilbert Unified School District
Gilbert, Arizona

Grand Prairie ISD
Grand Prairie, Texas

Hillsborough County Public
Schools
Tampa, Florida

Houston Independent School
District
Houston, Texas

Hobbs Municipal Schools
Hobbs, New Mexico

Irving Independent School
District
Irving, Texas

Kenton County School District
Fort Wright, Kentucky

Lee County Public Schools
Fort Myers, Florida

Newton County Schools
Covington, Georgia

Noblesville Schools
Noblesville, Indiana

Oakland Unified School District
Oakland, California

Orange County Public Schools
Orlando, Florida

School District of Palm Beach
County
Palm Beach, Florida

Peninsula School District
Gig Harbor, Washington

Polk County Public Schools
Bartow, Florida

Quakertown Community School
District
Quakertown, Pennsylvania

Rio Rancho Public Schools
Rio Rancho, New Mexico

Ronan School District
Ronan, Montana

St. Vrain Valley School District
Longmont, Colorado

Scottsdale Public Schools
Phoenix, Arizona

Seminole County Public Schools
Sanford, Florida

Southwest ISD
San Antonio, Texas

Spokane Public Schools
Spokane, Washington

Volusia County Schools
DeLand, Florida

Contents

Contents *continued*

Contents *continued*

To the Student

Welcome to the SpringBoard program. We hope you will discover how SpringBoard can help you achieve high academic standards, reach your learning goals, and prepare for success in future mathematics studies.

The program has been created with you in mind: the content you need to learn, the tools to help you learn, and the critical thinking skills that help you build confidence in your own knowledge of mathematics. The College Board publishes the SpringBoard program. It also publishes the PSAT/NMSQT, the SAT, and the Advanced Placement exams—all exams that you are likely to encounter in your student years. Preparing you to perform well on those exams and to develop the mathematics skills needed for high school success is the primary purpose of this program.

Standards-Based Mathematics Learning

Knowledge of mathematics helps prepare you for future success in college, in work, and in your personal life. We all encounter some form of mathematics daily, from calculating the cost of groceries to determining the cost of materials and labor needed to build a new road. The SpringBoard program is based on learning standards that identify the mathematics skills and knowledge that you should master to succeed in high school and in future college-level work. In this course, the standards follow these broad areas of mathematics knowledge:

- Mathematical practices
- Number and operations
- Ratio and proportionality
- Expressions, equations, and relationships
- Geometry
- Statistics and probability

Mathematical practice standards guide your study of mathematics. They are actions you take to help you understand mathematical concepts rather than just mathematical procedures. For example, the mathematical practice standards suggest the following:

- Make sense of and connect mathematics concepts to everyday life and situations around you.
- Model with mathematics to solve problems, justify solutions and their reasonableness, and communicate mathematical ideas.
- Use appropriate tools, such as number lines, protractors, technology, or paper and pencil, strategically to help you solve problems.
- Communicate abstract and quantitative reasoning both orally and in writing through arguments and critiques.
- Analyze mathematical relationships through structure and repeated reasoning to connect ideas.
- Attend to precision in both written and oral communication of your mathematical ideas.

In the middle school years, your study of mathematics begins with a basic understanding of fractions and the operations performed with them. Your study continues with the development of a deep understanding of the rational numbers, their different representations, and the connections between these numbers and other number systems and operations. You will need a broad understanding of addition, subtraction, and multiplication with rational numbers, along with computational fluency with whole-number operations.

As you continue your studies, you will examine ratios and rates, which will allow you to make comparisons between numbers. Ratios and rates represent proportionality. Understanding the concept of proportionality is critical to future success in your study of algebra and the rest of the high school mathematics curriculum.

See pages xiii–xvi for a complete list of the College and Career Readiness Standards for Mathematics for this course.

Strategies for Learning Mathematics

Some tools to help you learn are built into every activity. At the beginning of each activity, you will see suggested learning strategies. Each of these strategies is explained in full in the Resources section of your book. As you learn to use each strategy, you'll have the opportunity to decide which strategies work best for you. Suggested learning strategies include:

- Reading strategies, which help you learn to look at problem descriptions in different ways, from marking the text to highlight key information to turning problem information into questions that help you break the problem down into its separate parts.
- Writing strategies, which help you focus on your purpose for writing and what you're writing about.
- Problem-solving strategies, which give you multiple ways to approach the problem, from learning to identify the tasks within a problem to looking for patterns or working backward to see how the problem is set up.
- Collaborative strategies, which you'll use with your classmates to explore concepts and problems in group discussions and working with partners.

Building Mathematics Knowledge and Skills

Whether it is mathematics or sports or cooking, one way we learn something really well is by practice and repetition. To help you learn mathematics, the SpringBoard program is built around problem solving, reasoning and justification, communication, connections between concepts and ideas, and visual representation of mathematical concepts.

Problem Solving Many of the problems in this book are based on real-life situations that require you to *analyze* the situation and the information in the problem, *make decisions*, *determine the strategies* you'll use to solve the problem, and *justify* your solution. Having a real-world focus helps you see how mathematics is used in everyday life.

Reasoning and Justification One part of learning mathematics, or any subject, is learning not only how to solve problems but also why you solved them the way you did. You will have many opportunities to predict possible solutions and then to verify solutions. You will be asked to explain the reasoning behind how you solved the problem, the mathematics concepts involved, and why your approach was appropriate for solving the problem.

Communication When learning a language, saying words out loud helps you learn to pronounce the words and to remember them. Communicating about mathematics, orally and in writing, with your classmates and teachers helps you organize your learning and explain mathematics concepts and problem-solving strategies more precisely. Sharing your ideas and thoughts allows you and your classmates to build on each other's ideas and expand your own understanding.

Mathematics Connections As you study mathematics, you will learn many different concepts and ways of solving problems. Reading the problem descriptions will take you into the real-life applications of mathematics. As you develop your mathematics knowledge, you will see the many connections between mathematics concepts and between mathematics and your own life.

Representations Artists create representations through drawings and paintings. In mathematics, representations can take many forms, such as numeric, verbal, graphic, or symbolic. In this course, you are encouraged to use representations to organize problem information, present possible solutions, and communicate your reasoning. Creating representations is a tool you can use to gain understanding of concepts and communicate that understanding to others.

We hope you enjoy your study of mathematics using the SpringBoard program. We, the writers, are all classroom teachers, and we created this program because we love mathematics. We wanted to inspire you to learn mathematics *and* build confidence that you can be successful in your math studies and in using mathematics in daily life.

College and Career Readiness Standards

Grade 6

Standards for Mathematical Practice

MP.1 Make sense of problems and persevere in solving them.

MP.2 Reason abstractly and quantitatively.

MP.3 Construct viable arguments and critique the reasoning of others.

MP.4 Model with mathematics.

MP.5 Use appropriate tools strategically.

MP.6 Attend to precision.

MP.7 Look for and make use of structure.

MP.8 Look for and express regularity in repeated reasoning.

6.RP Ratios and Proportional Relationships

6.RP.A.1 Understand the concept of a ratio and use ratio language to describe a ratio relationship between two quantities. *For example, "The ratio of wings to beaks in the bird house at the zoo was 2:1, because for every 2 wings there was 1 beak." "For every vote candidate A received, candidate C received nearly three votes."*

6.RP.A.2 Understand the concept of a unit rate a/b associated with a ratio a:b with b ≠ 0, and use rate language in the context of a ratio relationship. *For example, "This recipe has a ratio of 3 cups of flour to 4 cups of sugar, so there is $\frac{3}{4}$ cup of flour for each cup of sugar." "We paid $75 for 15 hamburgers, which is a rate of $5 per hamburger."*[1]

6.RP.A.3 Use ratio and rate reasoning to solve real-world and mathematical problems, e.g., by reasoning about tables of equivalent ratios, tape diagrams, double number line diagrams, or equations.

> **6.RP.A.3a** Make tables of equivalent ratios relating quantities with whole-number measurements, find missing values in the tables, and plot the pairs of values on the coordinate plane. Use tables to compare ratios.

> **6.RP.A.3b** Solve unit rate problems including those involving unit pricing and constant speed. *For example, if it took 7 hours to mow 4 lawns, then at that rate, how many lawns could be mowed in 35 hours? At what rate were lawns being mowed?*

> **6.RP.A.3c** Find a percent of a quantity as a rate per 100 (e.g., 30% of a quantity means $\frac{30}{100}$ times the quantity); solve problems involving finding the whole, given a part and the percent.

> **6.RP.A.3d** Use ratio reasoning to convert measurement units; manipulate and transform units appropriately when multiplying or dividing quantities.

6.NS The Number System

6.NS.A.1 Interpret and compute quotients of fractions, and solve word problems involving division of fractions by fractions, e.g., by using visual fraction models and equations to represent the problem. *For example, create a story context for $\left(\frac{2}{3}\right) \div \left(\frac{3}{4}\right)$ and use a visual fraction model to show the quotient; use the relationship between multiplication and division to explain that $\left(\frac{2}{3}\right) \div \left(\frac{3}{4}\right) = \frac{8}{9}$ because $\frac{3}{4}$ of $\frac{8}{9}$ is $\frac{2}{3}$. (In general, $\left(\frac{a}{b}\right) \div \left(\frac{c}{d}\right) = \frac{ad}{bc}$.) How much chocolate will each person get if 3 people* share $\frac{1}{2}$ lb of chocolate equally? How many $\frac{3}{4}$-cup servings are in $\frac{2}{3}$ of a cup of yogurt? How wide is a rectangular strip of land with length $\frac{3}{4}$ mi and area $\frac{1}{2}$ square mi?.

6.NS.B.2 Fluently divide multi-digit numbers using the standard algorithm.

6.NS.B.3 Fluently add, subtract, multiply, and divide multi-digit decimals using the standard algorithm for each operation.

6.NS.B.4 Find the greatest common factor of two whole numbers less than or equal to 100 and the least common multiple of two whole numbers less than or equal to 12. Use the distributive property to express a sum of two whole numbers 1–100 with a common factor as a multiple of a sum of two whole numbers with no common factor. *For example, express 36 + 8 as 4(9 + 2).*

6.NS.C.5 Understand that positive and negative numbers are used together to describe quantities having opposite directions or values (e.g., temperature above/below zero, elevation above/below sea level, credits/debits, positive/negative electric charge); use positive and negative numbers to represent quantities in real-world contexts, explaining the meaning of 0 in each situation.

6.NS.C.6 Understand a rational number as a point on the number line. Extend number line diagrams and coordinate axes familiar from previous grades to represent points on the line and in the plane with negative number coordinates.

> **6.NS.C.6a** Recognize opposite signs of numbers as indicating locations on opposite sides of 0 on the number line; recognize that the opposite of the opposite of a number is the number itself, e.g., $-(-3) = 3$, and that 0 is its own opposite.

> **6.NS.C.6b** Understand signs of numbers in ordered pairs as indicating locations in quadrants of the coordinate plane; recognize that when two ordered pairs differ only by signs, the locations of the points are related by reflections across one or both axes.

> **6.NS.C.6c** Find and position integers and other rational numbers on a horizontal or vertical number line diagram; find and position pairs of integers and other rational numbers on a coordinate plane.

6.NS.C.7 Understand ordering and absolute value of rational numbers.

> **6.NS.C.7a** Interpret statements of inequality as statements about the relative position of two numbers on a number line diagram. *For example, interpret $-3 > -7$ as a statement that -3 is located to the right of -7 on a number line oriented from left to right.*

> **6.NS.C.7b** Write, interpret, and explain statements of order for rational numbers in real-world contexts. *For example, write $-3\ ^{\circ}C > -7\ ^{\circ}C$ to express the fact that $-3°C$ is warmer than $-7\ ^{\circ}C$.*

> **6.NS.C.7c** Understand the absolute value of a rational number as its distance from 0 on the number line; interpret absolute value as magnitude for a positive or negative quantity in a real-world situation. *For example, for an account balance of -30 dollars, write $|-30| = 30$ to describe the size of the debt in dollars.*

> **6.NS.C.7d** Distinguish comparisons of absolute value from statements about order. *For example, recognize that an account balance less than -30 dollars represents a debt greater than 30 dollars.*

6.NS.C.8 Solve real-world and mathematical problems by graphing points in all four quadrants of the coordinate plane. Include use of coordinates and absolute value to find distances between points with the same first coordinate or the same second coordinate.

6.EE Expressions and Equations

6.EE.A.1 Write and evaluate numerical expressions involving whole-number exponents.

6.EE.A.2 Write, read, and evaluate expressions in which letters stand for numbers.

> **6.EE.A.2a** Write expressions that record operations with numbers and with letters standing for numbers. *For example, express the calculation "Subtract y from 5" as $5 - y$.*

> **6.EE.A.2b** Identify parts of an expression using mathematical terms (sum, term, product, factor, quotient, coefficient); view one or more parts of an expression as a single entity. *For example, describe the expression $2(8 + 7)$ as a product of two factors; view $(8 + 7)$ as both a single entity and a sum of two terms.*

> **6.EE.A.2c** Evaluate expressions at specific values of their variables. Include expressions that arise from formulas used in real-world problems. Perform arithmetic operations, including those involving whole-number exponents, in the conventional order when there are no parentheses to specify a particular order (Order of Operations). *For example, use the formulas $V = s^3$ and $A = 6s^2$ to find the volume and surface area of a cube with sides of length $s = \frac{1}{2}$.*

6.EE.A.3 Apply the properties of operations to generate equivalent expressions. *For example, apply the distributive property to the expression $3(2 + x)$ to produce the equivalent expression $6 + 3x$; apply the distributive property to the expression $24x + 18y$ to produce the equivalent expression $6(4x + 3y)$; apply properties of operations to $y + y + y$ to produce the equivalent expression $3y$.*

6.EE.A.4 Identify when two expressions are equivalent (i.e., when the two expressions name the same number regardless of which value is substituted into them). *For example, the expressions $y + y + y$ and $3y$ are equivalent because they name the same number regardless of which number y stands for.*

6.EE.B.5 Understand solving an equation or inequality as a process of answering a question: which values from a specified set, if any, make the equation or inequality true? Use substitution to determine whether a given number in a specified set makes an equation or inequality true.

6.EE.B.6 Use variables to represent numbers and write expressions when solving a real-world or mathematical problem; understand that a variable can represent an unknown number, or, depending on the purpose at hand, any number in a specified set.

6.EE.B.7 Solve real-world and mathematical problems by writing and solving equations of the form $x + p = q$ and $px = q$ for cases in which p, q and x are all nonnegative rational numbers.

6.EE.B.8 Write an inequality of the form $x > c$ or $x < c$ to represent a constraint or condition in a real-world or mathematical problem. Recognize that inequalities of the form $x > c$ or $x < c$ have infinitely many solutions; represent solutions of such inequalities on number line diagrams.

6.EE.C.9 Use variables to represent two quantities in a real-world problem that change in relationship to one another; write an equation to express one quantity, thought of as the dependent variable, in terms of the other quantity, thought of as the independent variable. Analyze the relationship between the dependent and independent variables using graphs and tables, and relate these to the equation. For example, in a problem involving motion at constant speed, list and graph ordered pairs of distances and times, and write the equation $d = 65t$ to represent the relationship between distance and time.

6.G Geometry

6.G.A.1 Find the area of right triangles, other triangles, special quadrilaterals, and polygons by composing into rectangles or decomposing into triangles and other shapes; apply these techniques in the context of solving real-world and mathematical problems.

6.G.A.2 Find the volume of a right rectangular prism with fractional edge lengths by packing it with unit cubes of the appropriate unit fraction edge lengths, and show that the volume is the same as would be found by multiplying the edge lengths of the prism. Apply the formulas $V = lwh$ and $V = bh$ to find volumes of right rectangular prisms with fractional edge lengths in the context of solving real-world and mathematical problems.

6.G.A.3 Draw polygons in the coordinate plane given coordinates for the vertices; use coordinates to find the length of a side joining points with the same first coordinate or the same second coordinate. Apply these techniques in the context of solving real-world and mathematical problems.

6.G.A.4 Represent three-dimensional figures using nets made up of rectangles and triangles, and use the nets to find the surface area of these figures. Apply these techniques in the context of solving real-world and mathematical problems.

6.SP Statistics and Probability

6.SP.A.1 Recognize a statistical question as one that anticipates variability in the data related to the question and accounts for it in the answers. *For example, "How old am I?" is not a statistical question, but "How old are the students in my school?" is a statistical question because one anticipates variability in students' ages.*

6.SP.A.2 Understand that a set of data collected to answer a statistical question has a distribution which can be described by its center, spread, and overall shape.

6.SP.A.3 Recognize that a measure of center for a numerical data set summarizes all of its values with a single number, while a measure of variation describes how its values vary with a single number.

6.SP.B.4 Display numerical data in plots on a number line, including dot plots, histograms, and box plots.

6.SP.B.5 Summarize numerical data sets in relation to their context, such as by:

6.SP.B.5a Reporting the number of observations.

6.SP.B.5b Describing the nature of the attribute under investigation, including how it was measured and its units of measurement.

6.SP.B.5c Giving quantitative measures of center (median and/or mean) and variability (interquartile range and/or mean absolute deviation), as well as describing any overall pattern and any striking deviations from the overall pattern with reference to the context in which the data were gathered.

6.SP.B.5d Relating the choice of measures of center and variability to the shape of the data distribution and the context in which the data were gathered.

Number Concepts

Unit Overview
In this unit you will extend your knowledge of numbers as you solve problems using whole numbers, decimals, and fractions. You will also study factorization and exponents.

Key Terms
As you study this unit, add these and other terms to your math notebook. Include in your notes your prior knowledge of each word, as well as your experiences in using the word in different mathematical examples. If needed, ask for help in pronouncing new words and add information on pronunciation to your math notebook. It is important that you learn new terms and use them correctly in your class discussions and in your problem solutions.

Academic Vocabulary
- annex
- algorithm
- conjecture
- simulate

Math Terms
- visual representation
- prime number
- evaluate
- least common multiple (LCM)
- proper fraction
- mixed number
- factor
- composite number
- greatest common factor (GCF)
- least common denominator
- improper fraction
- reciprocal

ESSENTIAL QUESTIONS

? Why is it important to be able to use whole numbers, fractions, and decimals to solve problems?

? How can you use visualization and estimation to solve problems?

EMBEDDED ASSESSMENTS

These assessments, following Activities 1, 3, and 6, will give you an opportunity to demonstrate how you can use your understanding of number concepts to solve mathematical and real-world problems.

Embedded Assessment 1:

Comparing and Computing with Whole Numbers and Decimals   p. 25

Embedded Assessment 2:

Prime Factorization, Exponents, GCF, and LCM   p. 43

Embedded Assessment 3:

Multiplying and Dividing Fractions and Mixed Numbers p. 79

1. Order the following numbers from least to greatest:

   30   303   11   31   1,111   313   333

2. Why is 4×9 equal to 9×4?

3. The grid below represents the number 1. Write the number shown by the shaded part of the grid as a fraction and as a decimal.

   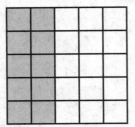

4. Use a model to represent the fraction $\frac{5}{8}$. Then explain why your model represents $\frac{5}{8}$.

5. Is $1\frac{3}{4}$ closer to 1 or to 2? Explain your answer.

6. List three numbers that are divisible by:
   a. 3   **b.** 4   **c.** 5

7. What is a divisibility rule for 2?

8. Give three numbers that satisfy each set of given conditions.
   a. whole numbers that are less than 7
   b. decimals that are greater than 5
   c. fractions that are less than 1

Whole Numbers and Decimals

Science, Shopping, and Society

Lesson 1-1 Comparing and Ordering Whole Numbers and Decimals

Learning Targets:

- Locate whole numbers and decimals on a number line.
- Interpret statements of inequality of whole numbers and positive decimals.
- Order a set of positive whole numbers and decimals.

> **SUGGESTED LEARNING STRATEGIES:** Create Representations, Look for a Pattern, Think-Pair-Share, Sharing and Responding

Paramecia are tiny one-celled organisms commonly found in freshwater environments. They are shaped like a grain of rice. If you have excellent eyesight you might see a paramecium as a tiny moving speck, but to see one in detail you need a microscope. The lengths of four specimens of common types of paramecia were measured and are given in the table.

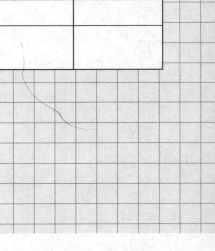

My Notes

Type	Length (meters)
Aurelia	0.00156
Bursaria	0.00097
Caudatum	0.00181
Multimicronucleatum	0.002

1. **Model with mathematics.** Complete the table below showing the lengths of each type of paramecium.

	ones		tenths	hundredths	thousandths	ten thousandths	hundred thousandths
	1	.	0.1	0.01	0.001	0.0001	0.00001
Aurelia							
Bursaria							
Caudatum							
Multimicro-nucleatum							

2. The table shows zeros in both the tenths and hundredths place for aurelia. Name the value of the 1, the 5, and the 6.

My Notes

ACADEMIC VOCABULARY

The verb *annex* means to attach or to add something.

MATH TIP

If you *annex* or add zeros to the right of the last digit in a decimal, you do not change the value of the decimal. Annexing zeros can help you compare decimals.

For example, to compare 1.53 and 1.5342, you can add two 0s to 1.53:

1.5300 < 1.5342, so
1.53 < 1.5342.

3. **Make use of structure.** Which paramecium was longer, aurelia or bursaria? Explain how you found the answer.

4. Which paramecium was shorter, aurelia or caudatum? Explain how you found the answer.

5. Which paramecium was longest? Explain how you found the answer.

6. **Make use of structure.** Another way to compare decimals is to use a number line. Paramecia have cilia (hairlike structures) that act like oars and propel them through the water. The table below shows the times in which different paramecia swam 10 mm.

Swimmer	Time (sec)
Aurelia	11.6
Bursaria	11.3
Caudatum	13.4
Multimicronucleatum	12.7
Jenningsi	13.0

Plot each paramecium's time on the number line below. Write the first letter of the paramecium's name above the point representing its time.

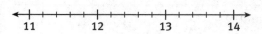

7. Name the paramecia with times faster than 12 seconds and those with slower times. Explain how you made your decisions.

8. How can you tell which of two numbers plotted on a number line is the greater number?

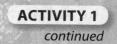

My Notes

9. How can a number line be used to explain why 11.6 > 11.3?

10. Insert > or < between each pair of numbers to create a true inequality statement.

    a. 11.3   13.4   **b.** 13   12.7   **c.** 11.3   11.6

Check Your Understanding

11. Insert > or < between each pair of numbers to create a true inequality statement. Identify the larger number.
    a. 0.7 and 0.652   **b.** 31 and 31.59
    c. 6.700 and 6.8   **d.** 377.151 and 377.1509

12. Order the numbers in each group from least to greatest.
    a. 76, 34, 85.2, 37.5, 34.8
    b. 2.31, 0.231, 23.1, 0.23, 3.21
    c. 5.78, 5.7001, 5.701, 5.71, 5.7

13. **Make use of structure.** Describe the steps you would follow to compare two decimals. Use an example.

LESSON 1-1 PRACTICE

14. Radon is a gas that occurs in nature. It is considered to be a health hazard. Radon is measured in "pico Curies per liter" or pCi/L. One city considers 3.85 pCi/L of radon to be the maximum safe level of radon in public buildings. The table gives the measured levels in four buildings. Order the radon levels from least to greatest.

Building	Radon Level (pCi/L)
City Hall	3.855
Library	3.8095
Art Museum	3.839
Police Station	3.850
Fire Station	4.08

Which buildings, if any, exceeded the recommended level?

15. All cheeses in Blake's Grocery sell for no less than $3.95 per pound but less than $4 per pound. List all possible cheese prices at the store from least to greatest.

16. **Reason quantitatively.** If you were to plot 36.948516 on a number line, would it be closer to 36.9 or to 37? Explain your reasoning.

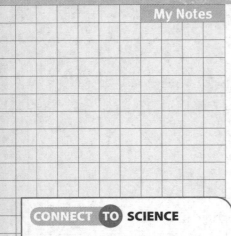

My Notes

WRITING MATH

Subscripts are small numbers written below and to the right of letters. Subscripts indicate different members of a group. For instance, three different places of resistance can be labeled R_1, R_2, and R_3.

MATH TERMS

A **visual representation** is a model that uses pictures in order to help solve a problem.

Learning Targets:

- Add and subtract multidigit decimals.
- Solve real-world problems by adding and subtracting decimals.

> **SUGGESTED LEARNING STRATEGIES:** Marking the Text, Think-Pair-Share, Discussion Groups, Visualization, Create Representations

George is going to join his father at work on "Bring Your Son to Work Day." To understand his dad's work as an electrician, George needs to know how to add and subtract decimals.

George's dad works on heaters. He gives George the following problem for practice.

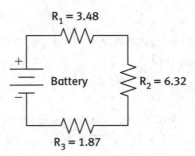

The control circuit for the heater circuit (shown above) is not working properly. George needs to troubleshoot to find where the problem is. The heater elements are represented by R_1, R_2, and R_3. If $R_1 = 3.48$ ohms, $R_2 = 6.32$ ohms, and $R_3 = 1.87$ ohms, George must figure out how much total resistance (measured in ohms) the circuit has.

1. The total resistance in the circuit is found using the formula $R_1 + R_2 + R_3$. Using the numbers George's dad gave him, write an expression for the total resistance.

George needs to find the sum so that he can determine which heater element is not working properly.

You can use a ***visual representation*** to find a decimal sum like this one.

Example A

Find the sum of 4.25 and 9.42.

Step 1: Add the whole numbers to the left of the decimal point.

$$4 + 9 = 13$$

Step 2: Find the sum of the decimal parts of each addend, using a 10-by-10 grid.

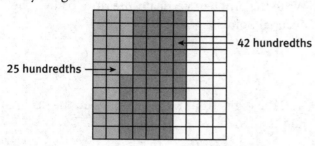

25 hundredths

42 hundredths

Since 67 of the boxes are shaded, the sum is 0.67.

Step 3: Combine your sums from Step 1 and Step 2.

$$13 + 0.67 = 13.67$$

Solution: The sum of 4.25 and 9.42 is 13.67.

Try These A

Find each sum. Use the My Notes section to create and shade 10-by-10 grids.

a. $1.45 + 2.15$

b. $4.2 + 3.25$

Now find the sum of the resistances in George's circuit. Remember that $R_1 = 3.48$, $R_2 = 6.32$, and $R_3 = 1.87$.

2. Find the sum of the whole numbers in the three addends.

3. Find the sum of the decimal parts on the 10-by-10 grids below.

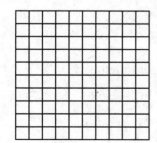 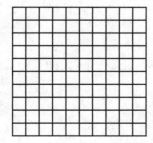

sum = _____

4. To find the total resistance in George's circuit, find the sum of the whole numbers and the decimals.

total resistance = _____ ohms

My Notes

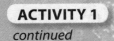

My Notes

Another way to find the sum is to use an *algorithm*. As you discuss the following examples be sure to use the academic vocabulary precisely. Make notes to help you remember the meaning of new words.

Example B

Find the sum of 4.8 and 12.75.

Step 1: Write the problem vertically. Be sure to align the decimal points.

$$
\begin{array}{r}
12.75 \\
+\ 4.80 \\
\hline
\end{array}
$$

Step 2: Add the digits from right to left. Keep the decimal points aligned.

$$
\begin{array}{r}
12.75 \\
+\ 4.80 \\
\hline
17.55
\end{array}
$$

Solution: The sum of 4.8 and 12.75 is 17.55.

Try These B

a. $32.8 + 9.25$　　　　**b.** $9.8 + 12.41 + 4.32$

The algorithm for subtracting decimals is similar to the algorithm for subtracting whole numbers.

Example C

Find the difference: $27.6 - 12.24$

Step 1: Write the problem vertically. Align the decimal points.

$$
\begin{array}{r}
27.60 \\
-12.24 \\
\hline
\end{array}
$$

Step 2: Subtract the digits from right to left.

$$
\begin{array}{r}
27.60 \\
-12.24 \\
\hline
15.36
\end{array}
$$

Solution: $27.6 - 12.24 = 15.36$

Try These C

Find each difference.

a. $27.16 - 7.52$　　　　**b.** $42.56 - 9.7$　　　　**c.** $36.3 - 13.48$

Lesson 1-2
Adding and Subtracting Decimals

Work with your group on items 5 through 8.

5. In Item 1, the total resistance in George's circuit should be $R_1 + R_2 + R_3 = 3.48 + 6.32 + 1.87$ ohms. However, measurements show that the total resistance is only 9.8 ohms. Predict which of the three heater elements, R_1, R_2, or R_3, is not working. Explain how you made your prediction.

6. Confirm your prediction by showing that the sum of the resistances of the two working heater elements is 9.8.

In order to make sure George is ready for the day tomorrow, George's dad wants to challenge him with one more problem.

The place where multiple electric currents intercept is called a node.

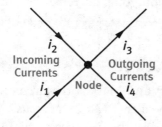

Kirchhoff's Current Law states that the sum of all the currents at any node must equal zero. This means that at any node, the sum of the incoming currents will be equal to the sum of the outgoing currents.

George's dad gives him the following information about an electrical circuit:

$$i_1 = 0.45 \text{ amps} \quad i_2 = 0.67 \text{ amps} \quad i_3 = 0.34 \text{ amps}$$

7. Reason quantitatively. Use the given information and the diagram to find i_4. Show your work.

8. Describe four real-life situations in which you might need to add or subtract decimals.

DISCUSSION GROUP TIPS

If you do not understand something in group discussions, ask for help or raise your hand for help. Describe your questions as clearly as possible, using synonyms or other words when you do not know the precise words to use.

CONNECT TO SCIENCE

A *node* is a place on a circuit where two or more wires connect.

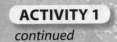

My Notes

Check Your Understanding

9. Find the sum or difference. Use any method you like.
 a. $3.86 + 0.98$ **b.** $76.31 - 48.55$
 c. $126 + 87.457$ **d.** $17 - 8.63$
 e. $0.55 + 4 + 13.708$ **f.** $90.01 - 5.77$
 g. $0.045 + 0.39 + 0.7$ **h.** $2,006 - 29.95$

10. The total resistance in an electrical circuit consisting of three heater elements is 14.7 ohms. The resistances of two of the heater elements are 5.57 ohms and 4.91 ohms. Find the resistance of the third heater element.

11. The three incoming currents at a node in an electrical circuit measure 0.38 amps, 0.75 amps, and 0.29 amps. Two of the three outgoing currents measure 0.48 amps and 0.6 amps. Find the measure of the third outgoing current.

LESSON 1-2 PRACTICE

12. Reason quantitatively. Mark and Marcus ate dinner in a restaurant. Mark's meal cost $34.16. Marcus's meal cost $3.68 less than Mark's. Sales tax on the two meals was $4.52. Mark paid with a $100 bill. How much change did he receive?

13. The map shows the road from Abbott (A) to Baxter (B) to Carlton (C) to Dalton (D). The total distance from Abbott to Dalton is 233 km.

A   76.59 km   B   79.8 km   C   76.61   D
                                    ?

 a. How far is it from Carlton to Dalton?
 b. The new freeway shortens the distance from Baxter to Dalton by 10.8 km. How far is it from Baxter to Dalton if you take the freeway?

14. Julie's scores in all but her final event at a gymnastics meet are given below. The current leader has a total score of 104.1 for all the events. How many points must Julie score on her final vault to win the meet?

> Floor: 8.3, 8.9, 9.2   Beam: 7.2, 7.7, 8.1
> Bars: 8.8, 8.8, 8.7   Vault: 9.8, 9.7, [?]

Learning Targets:
- Multiply multidigit decimals.
- Estimate products of decimals.
- Solve real-world problems by multiplying decimal numbers.

SUGGESTED LEARNING STRATEGIES: Marking the Text, Predict and Confirm, Paraphrasing, Quickwrite, Simplify the Problem

Amanda is going to a family reunion and is in charge of bringing a fruit salad. She has budgeted $35 for the salad. She plans to buy apples, blueberries, strawberries, kiwis, and yogurt. Since she is not sure how much it will cost, she decides to estimate the price.

She knows from her previous trips to the grocery store that the following prices are what each item should cost.

Item	Price
Apples	$1.99 per pound
Blueberries	$1.25 per pound
Strawberries	$2.99 per pound
Kiwis	$1.75 per pound
Yogurt	$2.75 per container

For her recipe, Amanda needs 3.25 pounds of apples, 1.75 pounds of blueberries, 3.5 pounds of strawberries, 1.2 pounds of kiwis, and 5 containers of yogurt. Work with your group to answer items 1-5. If you need help expressing your ideas to your group, make notes about what you want to say, listen to others, and ask for the meanings of any words they use that you don't understand.

1. Predict the total cost. Does your prediction put Amanda over or under budget?

2. Round the number of pounds of apples that Amanda needs to the nearest pound and the price of apples to the nearest dollar. Then write an expression you can use to estimate the total cost of the apples.

3. Evaluate the expression to estimate the total cost of the apples.

4. Use the method given in item 2 to estimate the total cost of each ingredient. Then find the total cost.
   Blueberries
   Strawberries
   Kiwis
   Yogurt

My Notes

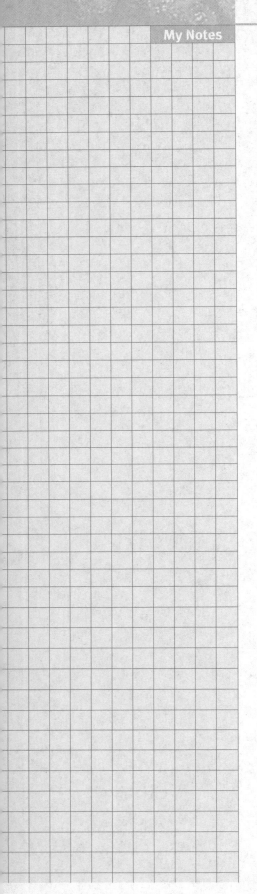

My Notes

5. Based on the estimated costs in Item 4, would you change your prediction from Item 1? Why or why not?

To find the exact costs, Amanda will need to multiply decimal numbers. One way to multiply decimals is to use a decimal model like the one at the right.

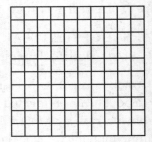

6. The entire 10-by-10 grid represents 1. What does each small square represent?

7. Model with mathematics.

a. To find the product 0.7×0.3, represent 0.7 by shading the first 7 columns of the grid. Then, using a different color, represent 0.3 by shading the first 3 rows of the grid.

b. The number of squares in the region where the shaded columns and rows overlap represents the product. Write a number sentence to show the product of 0.7 and 0.3.

c. How does the total number of decimal places in the product compare with the total number of decimal places in the two factors?

You can also use the multiplication algorithm.

Example A

Find the product: 1.8×2.35

| Step 1: | Write the factors vertically, placing the number with more digits on the top line | $\begin{array}{r} 2.35 \\ \times\ 1.8 \\ \hline \end{array}$ |

| Step 2: | Multiply the numbers. | $\begin{array}{r} 2.35 \\ \times\ 1.8 \\ \hline 1880 \\ +2350 \\ \hline 4230 \end{array}$ |

| Step 3: | Count the total number of decimal places in the two factors. Put the decimal point in the product so that it has the total number of decimal places that the factors have. | $2.\boxed{35} \rightarrow 2$ decimal places
 $\times\ 1.\boxed{8} \rightarrow 1$ decimal place
 $\overline{4.\boxed{230}} \rightarrow 3$ decimal places |

Solution: The product is 4.230, or 4.23.

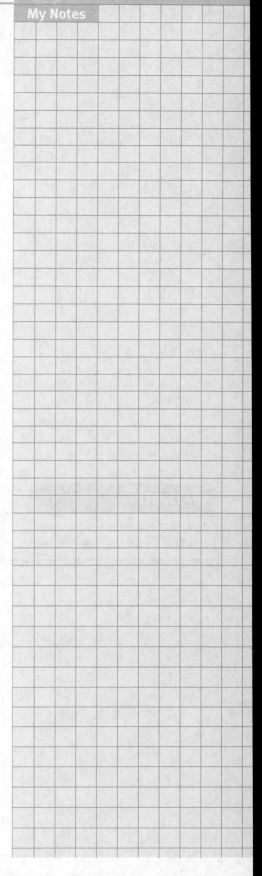

Try These A

Find the product.

a. 2.3×5 **b.** 4.27×1.3 **c.** 1.473×2.31

When Amanda arrives at the grocery store, she finds that the actual prices of the items she needs are slightly different from those she used in her estimate.

Item	Price
Apples	$2.25 per pound
Blueberries	$1.75 per pound
Strawberries	$2.89 per pound
Kiwis	$1.85 per pound
Yogurt	$2.50 per container

Remember that she needs 3.25 pounds of apples, 1.75 pounds of blueberries, 3.5 pounds of strawberries, 1.2 pounds of kiwis, and 5 containers of yogurt.

8. Calculate the total cost of each item. Since your answers will be in dollars, round each product to the nearest cent.

Apples

Blueberries

Strawberries

Kiwis

Yogurt

9. Find the total cost of the ingredients.

10. Will Amanda be within her $35 budget? How much over or under it will she be?

11. Before going to the store, Amanda estimated the total cost of the salad at $30. Was her estimate reasonable? Why or why not?

12. Was the prediction you made at the beginning of the lesson correct? If not, how much over or under the actual cost?

My Notes

Check Your Understanding

13. **Model with mathematics.** Use a decimal model to find the product. Model the first factor by shading columns and the second factor by shading rows.
    a. 0.4×0.6 b. 0.6×0.4
    c. What property of multiplication do your answers to Parts a and b illustrate? Explain.

14. Find the product.
    a. 6.7×4.2 b. 5.77×0.6 c. 9.23×17
    d. $0.045 \times 10,000$ e. 0.0071×0.34 f. 12.15×5.2

LESSON 1-3 PRACTICE

15. Damon works 32 hours per week and earns $10.75 per hour.
    a. Estimate his weekly earnings. Explain how you determined your estimate.
    b. Find the exact amount he earns per week.
    c. Is your answer reasonable based on your estimate? Explain.

16. a. Lyla wants to model 3×0.17 on a 10-by-10 grid. Show how she might do this.
    b. What is the product?

17. A rectangular soccer field is 70.75 meters wide and 105.25 meters long.
    a. Estimate the area of the field.
    b. Find the area of the field. Round your answer to the nearest hundredth.

18. On the morning of a business trip, Maria drove for 3.1 hours at an average rate of 63.8 miles per hour. In the afternoon, she drove for 3.5 hours at an average rate of 59.5 miles per hour.
    a. Did she travel farther in the morning or the afternoon?
    b. How much farther did she travel?

19. **Reason abstractly.** Can the product of a whole number and a decimal number less than 1 ever be greater than the whole number? Give examples to support your answer.

20. a. Describe two ways to find the product $4.2(6 + 0.43)$.
    b. What property of multiplication does your answer to Part a illustrate?

MATH TIP

To find the area of a rectangle, multiply the length and the width.

Learning Targets:
- Divide whole numbers by whole numbers.
- Estimate quotients of whole numbers.
- Solve real-world problems by dividing whole numbers.

SUGGESTED LEARNING STRATEGIES: Group Presentation, Quickwrite, Interactive Word Wall, Summarizing

Charley is researching population density for a science project. In order to find the population density of a location, she needs to divide the number of people who live there by the area they occupy.

Population Density = Number of People ÷ Area Occupied

In order for Charley to complete her project, she needs to review the algorithm for long division.

My Notes

CONNECT TO SOCIAL STUDIES

Population density is the average number of residents per some unit of measure, usually square mile or square meter.

Example A
Find the quotient: 3,375 ÷ 15

Step 1: Write the divisor and the dividend.

divisor
$15\overline{)3375}$ ← dividend

Step 2: Divide 15 into 33 and subtract.

$$15\overline{)\begin{array}{r} 2 \\ 3375 \\ -30 \\ \hline 3 \end{array}}$$

Step 3: Bring down the 7 in the dividend. Divide 15 into 37. Continue subtracting, bringing down the next digit in the dividend, and dividing.

$$15\overline{)\begin{array}{r} 225 \\ 3375 \\ -30 \\ \hline 37 \\ -30 \\ \hline 75 \\ -75 \\ \hline 0 \end{array}}$$

READING MATH

A quotient is calculated by dividing a dividend by a divisor.

quotient
$divisor\overline{)dividend}$

Solution: The quotient is 225.

Try These A
a. 5,841 ÷ 11   **b.** 2,898 ÷ 126   **c.** 58,650 ÷ 25

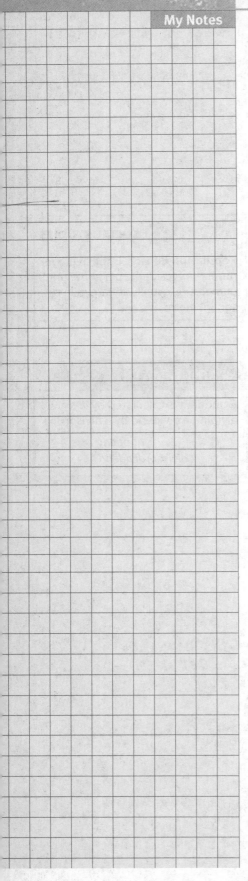

My Notes

1. In a recent census, the population of Orlando, Florida, was found to be 238,374. Orlando has an area of 102 square miles. Estimate the population density of Orlando. Explain how you made your estimate.

2. Use the table to find the population density of each city.

City	Population	Area (sq mi)
Dallas, TX	1,197,820	340
Sioux Falls, SD	153,957	73
Orlando, FL	238,374	102
Omaha, NE	409,067	127
Los Angeles, CA	3,792,900	470
New York, NY	8,175,140	302
Seattle, WA	608,664	84
Charlotte, NC	731,700	300

a. Dallas   **b.** Sioux Falls

c. Orlando   **d.** Omaha

e. Los Angeles   **f.** New York City

g. Seattle   **h.** Charlotte

3. Is your answer for Item 2c reasonable? Explain.

4. Order the cities by population density from greatest to least.

5. **Construct viable arguments.** The towns of Higby and Milton have the same population. Higby's area is greater than Milton's. Which town has the greater population density? Explain your reasoning.

Lesson 1-4
Dividing Whole Numbers

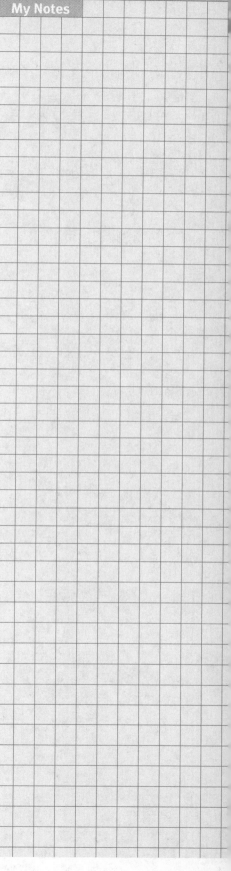

When you use the algorithm to find a quotient of two whole numbers, you may need to add a decimal point and zeros to the dividend. This will create a decimal quotient.

Example B

Estimate the quotient 245 ÷ 20. Then find the quotient and determine if it is reasonable.

Step 1: Estimate the quotient. Use the compatible numbers 240 and 20:

$$240 \div 20 = 12.$$

So, 12 is a good estimate of the quotient.

Step 2: Use the algorithm to divide.

```
        12
   20) 245
      −20
       45
      −40
        5
```

Step 3: The remainder is not zero, and there are no more digits in the dividend to bring down. So, write a decimal point after the 5 in the dividend and place a zero to its right. Place the decimal point in the quotient directly above the decimal point in the dividend.

```
        12.2
   20) 245.0
      −20
       45
      −40
       50
      −40
       10
```

Step 4: Continue to divide, adding zeros as necessary until the remainder is zero.

```
        12.25
   20) 245.00
      −20
       45
      −40
       50
      −40
      100
     −100
        0
```

Solution: 245 ÷ 20 = 12.25. This is reasonable because it is close to the estimate of 12.

Try These B

a. 305 ÷ 122

b. 10 ÷ 8

c. 82 ÷ 16

My Notes

Find each quotient.
  6. $325 \div 13$ **7.** $2,128 \div 28$ **8.** $48,184 \div 152$
  9. $221 \div 65$ **10.** $2,052 \div 240$ **11.** $297 \div 88$

LESSON 1-4 PRACTICE

12. Dexter drove 546 miles on one tank of gasoline. His car's gas tank holds 15 gallons of gas. Find the average number of miles he drove per gallon.

13. Crystal works 6 hours three days a week and 7 hours two days a week. She earns $472 per week. What is her hourly rate of pay?

14. Reasoning abstractly and quantitatively. The town of Brighton has a population of 12,096 and an area of 15 square miles. The town of Pauling has the same population density as Brighton and an area of 22.5 square miles. What is the population of Pauling?

15. Great Wilderness Animal Park is divided into four sections. Each section features animals from a single continent. The table shows the number of animals in each section and the area of the section, in square yards.

Continent	Number of Animals	Area (square yards)
North America	228	4,560
South America	684	11,400
Africa	912	18,240
Asia	456	11,400

a. Find the population density of each section of the park, in animals per square yard.
b. Find the population density of the entire park.
c. Explain how you found the population density of the entire park.

16. a. Use the fact that $8 \times 3.5 = 28$ to write two division problems relating 8, 3.5, and 28.
b. Describe the relationship between multiplication and division that allowed you to write the two division problems.

17. Construct viable arguments. Do $6 \div 3$ and $600 \div 300$ have the same quotient? Support your answer.

Learning Targets:

- Divide decimals by whole numbers.
- Divide whole numbers and decimals by decimals.
- Estimate quotients.
- Solve real-world problems by dividing decimals.

SUGGESTED LEARNING STRATEGIES: Close Reading, Marking the Text, Predict and Confirm, Create Representations, Shared Reading

In the last lesson, you learned that population density is the number of people per 1 square mile of area. There are many types of density. Like population density, other measures of density give the amount of one quantity that is contained in one unit of another quantity. At 50 degrees F, the density of water, for example, is about 62.4 pounds per cubic foot.

A chemist wanted to find the density of air, in pounds per cubic foot. You might be surprised to find out that air has weight. It does, but it is much lighter than water! You may also be surprised to know that the density of air changes when the temperature changes.

The chemist found that, at the current temperature, 9 cubic feet of air weighed 0.72 pounds. To write the density in pounds per cubic foot, find the quotient $0.72 \div 9$. Remember, 0.72 means 72 hundredths, or 72 out of 100.

1. **Model with mathematics.** This grid represents $\frac{100}{100}$ or 1 whole. To divide 0.72 by 9, you need to make 9 equal groups. Model 0.72 by shading a rectangle that is 9 units wide and 8 units high. Mark the shaded rectangle to show 9 groups of equal size. How many squares are in each group?

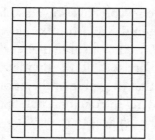

2. 0.72 divided by 9 equals _____.

3. So, at the temperature when the chemist performed the experiment, the density of air was _____ pounds per cubic foot.

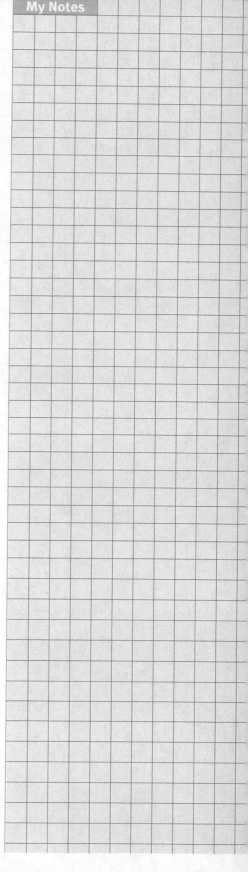
My Notes

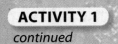

My Notes

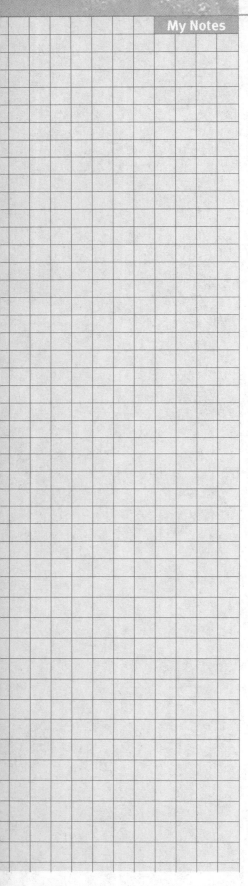

Example A

Thirty-two chemistry students raised $272.64 to purchase a precision electronic balance for their laboratory. What was the average amount of money raised per student?

Step 1: Estimate the quotient.
Use compatible numbers. 272.64 is about 300, and 32 is about 30. $300 \div 30 = 10$. So, $10 is a good estimate of the quotient.

Step 2: Use the algorithm for dividing whole numbers.

$$
\begin{array}{r}
8.52 \\
32\overline{)\ 272.64} \\
-256 \\
\hline
166 \\
-160 \\
\hline
64 \\
-64 \\
\hline
0
\end{array}
$$

Solution: The average amount raised per student was $8.52. The answer is reasonable because it is close to the estimate of $10.

Try These A

Estimate each quotient. Then find the quotient.

a. $25\overline{)168.75}$ Estimate: _____   Quotient: _____

b. $7\overline{)339.5}$ Estimate: _____   Quotient: _____

All of the division problems you have solved so far have had whole numbers as divisors. When the divisor is not a whole number, it has to be multiplied by 10, 100, 1,000, or some higher power of 10 to create a whole number. Both the divisor and the dividend have to be multiplied by the same number so that the value of the quotient is not affected. This can be done by moving the decimal points of the dividend and divisor an equal number of spaces to the right.

Example B

Find the quotient $103.5 \div 0.45$.

Step 1: Estimate the quotient.

Use compatible numbers. 103.5 is about 100; 0.45 is about 0.5. $100 \div 0.5 = 200$. So, 200 is a good estimate of the quotient.

Step 2: Think: I can rewrite 0.45 as a whole number by multiplying it by 100. I'll do the same thing to the dividend 103.5. I can do this by moving both decimal points two places to the right. This changes the problem from $103.5 \div 0.45$ to the equivalent problem $10{,}350 \div 45$.

$$
\begin{array}{r}
230 \\
0.45{\overline{\smash{\big)}\,103.50}} \\
\underline{-90} \\
135 \\
\underline{-135} \\
00 \\
\underline{-00} \\
0
\end{array}
$$

Solution: The quotient is 230. The answer is reasonable because it is close to the estimate of 200.

Try These B

Estimate each quotient. Then find the quotient.

a. $2.7{\overline{\smash{\big)}\,13.041}}$ Estimate: Quotient:

b. $0.31{\overline{\smash{\big)}\,682}}$ Estimate: Quotient:

Check Your Understanding

4. Complete.
   a. $231 \div 5.07 =$ _____ $\div 507$
   b. $0.4472 \div 0.315 =$ _____ $\div 315$
   c. $61 \div 0.9 =$ _____ $\div 9$

5. Imam makes bead bracelets. She can buy 12 beads for $2.04 or 17 beads for $3.57. Which deal gives her the lower cost for one bead? Explain.

6. Sam is saving $5.75 per week to buy a CD player that costs $46. How many weeks will he have to save before he can buy the player?

7. A 17.5-kilometer racecourse is divided into 2.5-kilometer portions. How many portions are there in the complete course?

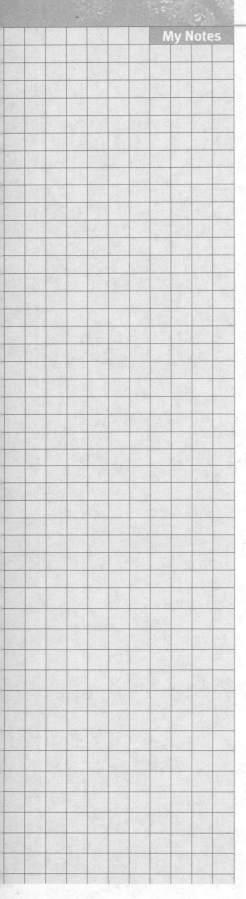

LESSON 1-5 PRACTICE

8. Write the mixed number $2\frac{5}{16}$ as a decimal. Explain your method.

9. **Attend to precision.** Find the quotient $0.8 \div 0.04 \div 0.002$. Explain how you found the answer.

The table below gives the densities of four gases.

Gas	Density (lb/cu ft)
Carbon Monoxide	0.08
Helium	0.012
Hydrogen Chloride	0.09
Ozone	0.125

10. How many times the density of helium is the density of hydrogen chloride?

11. How many times the density of carbon monoxide is the density of ozone?

ACTIVITY 1 PRACTICE
Write your answers on notebook paper.
Show your work.

Lesson 1-1

1. A geologist weighed four rocks, with these results: Rock A, 1.147 kg; Rock B, 1.15 kg; Rock C, 1.098 kg; Rock D, 0.884 kg. Order the rocks from heaviest to lightest.

2. Which number is closest to 51.4?
   A. 51.41   **B.** 51.041
   C. 51.39   **D.** 51.402

3. The table gives the heights of five South American mountains. List the mountains from highest to lowest.

Name	Country	Height (ft)
Solo	Argentina	20,492
Palermo	Argentina	20,079
Chimborazo	Ecuador	20,702
Solimana	Peru	20,068
El Condor	Argentina	20,669

4. Which number is greater, 10.6395 or 10.64? Explain how you decided.

5. On a number line, point K is to the left of point H and to the right of point R. Point T is between points R and K. Order the points from least to greatest.

Lesson 1-2

6. The total resistance in an electrical circuit consisting of three heater elements is 12.61 ohms. The resistances of two of the heater elements are 3.9 ohms and 5.04 ohms. Find the resistance of the third heater element.

7. Mike bought three shirts costing $15.98, $19, and $24.50. He paid for his purchase with a $100 bill. How much change did he receive?

8. The three incoming currents at a node in an electrical circuit measure 0.7 amps, 0.68 amps, and 0.47 amps. Two of the three outgoing currents measure 0.8 amps and 0.55 amps. Find the measure of the third outgoing current.

9. Find the difference $6 - 0.564$.
   A. 0.546   **B.** 5.546
   C. 5.436   **D.** 5.536

10. Find the sum $98.87 + 9.89$.
    A. 197.77   **B.** 108.76
    C. 107.66   **D.** 97.66

11. Complete.
    a. $4.79 + \underline{\hspace{1cm}} = 37$
    b. $100 - \underline{\hspace{1cm}} = 52.7$
    c. $\underline{\hspace{1cm}} + 8{,}477.6 = 10{,}248$
    d. $\underline{\hspace{1cm}} - 0.07 = 0.1$

12. Name the number property illustrated by this equation:
    $4.78 + (2.5 + 12.66) = 4.78 + (12.66 + 2.5)$

Lesson 1-3

13. Which multiplication problem is modeled by the grid?

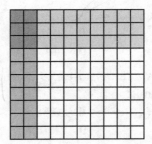

    A. $0.2 \times 0.3 = 0.6$ **B.** $0.2 \times 0.3 = 0.06$
    C. $0.02 \times 0.03 = 0.6$ **D.** $0.02 \times 0.03 = 0.06$

14. Find the product 3.6×2.05.
    A. 0.738   **B.** 1.845
    C. 7.38   **D.** 18.45

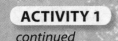

15. Marie bought 2.5 pounds of cheddar cheese, 3.2 pounds of jack cheese, and 1.9 pounds of Swiss cheese. Use the table to find the total cost of her purchase.

Cheese	Price per Pound
Cheddar	$4.92
Jack	$3.75
Swiss	$4.50

16. Margo drove for 3.85 hours at an average speed of 61.4 miles per hour.
   a. Estimate the total distance that she drove. Explain your method.
   b. Find the exact distance that she drove.
   c. Is your answer reasonable? Explain why or why not.

17. Centennial Park in Fernville is a rectangle measuring 87.5 meters by 56.2 meters.
   a. What is the perimeter of the park?
   b. What is the area of the park?

Lesson 1-4

18. Find the quotient: $10,404 \div 51$
   A. 24   **B.** 200
   C. 204   **D.** 240

19. One dozen donuts cost $6.96. What is the price of one donut?
   A. $0.55   **B.** $0.58
   C. $0.65   **D.** $1.16

20. a. A city of 6,688 residents has an area of 16 square miles. What is the population density of the city?
   b. A city of 82,080 residents has a population density of 2,160 residents per square mile. What is the area of the city?
   c. A city with an area of 87 square miles has a population density of 3,517 residents per square mile. What is the city's population?

21. The table shows the number of magazine subscriptions Craig sold in one week. His total sales were $2,628. What was the average price of a subscription?

Day	Subscriptions Sold
Monday	36
Tuesday	52
Wednesday	15
Thursday	29
Friday	87

Lesson 1-5

22. The table gives the costs for organizing Field Day at Montgomery Middle School. Thirty-two students will attend the event.

Expense	Total Cost ($)
Supplies	272.64
Announcer	168.84
Refreshments	113.40

   a. What is the cost per student for this event?
   b. What is the cost per student for supplies only?

23. Find the quotient $60.146 \div 0.58$.
   A. 1.037   **B.** 10.37
   C. 103.7   **D.** 1.037

24. A kangaroo weighs about 0.03 ounces at birth. Fully grown, it can weigh 180 pounds. How many times as heavy as a newborn kangaroo is a fully grown adult?

MATHEMATICAL PRACTICES
Model with Mathematics

25. Describe how to use a 10-by-10 decimal grid to show the quotient $0.48 \div 6$.

Write your answers on notebook paper. Show your work.

1. Ramon's hobby is raising parrots. The table gives the weights of five of his birds.

Parrot	Weight (oz)
Jack	6.102
Tippy	5.98
Fritz	6.058
Danny	6.8
Abe	6.06

   a. Order the weights from least to greatest.
   b. Explain how you decided which parrot was heavier, Fritz or Abe.
   c. Estimate the combined weight of the parrots. Explain how you made your estimate.
   d. What is the exact combined weight of all five parrots?
   e. Is your answer reasonable? Explain.
   f. What is the average weight of the parrots?
   g. Jack, Fritz, and a third parrot have a combined weight of 18.22 ounces. What is the name of the third parrot?

2. A female parrot that weighs 13.44 ounces has a chick that weighs 0.56 ounces. How many times the chick's weight is the weight of the mother?

3. Ramon has an African Grey parrot named Curly that weighs 17.4 ounces. How much heavier is Curly than Tippy?

4. Ramon buys five 3-pound bags of natural parrot food for $8.79 per bag and two 5-pound bags for $13.90 per bag.
   a. How many pounds of parrot food does he buy?
   b. What is the total cost?
   c. What is the average cost per pound of parrot food?

Scoring Guide	Exemplary	Proficient	Emerging	Incomplete
	The solution demonstrates these characteristics:			
Mathematics Knowledge and Thinking (Items 1a, 1c-d, 1f-g, 2, 3, 4a-c)	• Clear and accurate understanding of operations with decimals. • Effective understanding and accuracy in ordering and comparing decimals.	• Operations with decimals that are usually correct. • Correct comparison of decimals by ordering.	• Operations with decimals that are sometimes correct. • Partially correct comparison or ordering of decimals.	• Incorrect or incomplete computation in operations with decimals. • No comparison or ordering of decimals.
Problem Solving (Items 1c-g, 2, 3, 4a-c)	• An appropriate and efficient strategy that results in a correct answer. • A clear understanding of whether a solution is reasonable.	• A strategy that may include unnecessary steps but results in a correct answer. • Some understanding of whether a solution is reasonable.	• A strategy that results in some incorrect answers. • Uncertainty regarding the reasonableness of a solution.	• No clear strategy when solving problems. • No understanding of whether a solution is reasonable.
Mathematical Modeling / Representations (Items 1a, 1c-d, 1f-g, 2, 3, 4a-c)	• Clear and accurately written expressions for operations with decimals. • Clear and correct ordering and comparison of decimals.	• Some difficulty in writing the best expression for a problem situation, but still shows correct answers. • An understanding of ordering decimals.	• Errors in writing expressions for a given problem situation. • Errors in ordering decimals (for example, orders greatest to least instead of least to greatest).	• Inaccurately written expressions. • Incorrect ordering of decimals.
Reasoning and Communication (Items 1b-c, 1e)	• Precise use of appropriate math terms and language to explain comparing decimals, estimating a sum, and determining reasonableness.	• An adequate explanation of comparing decimals, estimating a sum, and determining reasonableness.	• A misleading or confusing explanation of comparing decimals, estimating a sum, and determining reasonableness.	• An incomplete or inaccurate description of comparing decimals, estimating a sum, and determining reasonableness.

Prime Factorization and Exponents
The Primes of Your Life
Lesson 2-1 Prime Factorization

Learning Targets:

- Determine whether a given whole number is a prime number or a composite number.
- Express a composite number as a product of prime numbers.

SUGGESTED LEARNING STRATEGIES: Create Representations, Note Taking, Think-Pair-Share, Visualization, Sharing and Responding

The *prime factorization* of a number shows the number as a product of factors that are all prime numbers. One way to find the prime factorization of a number is to use a visual model called a factor tree.

MATH TERMS

A **prime number** is a natural number greater than 1 that has exactly two factors, itself and 1. For example, 2 is a prime number ($2 = 2 \times 1$), as is 13 ($13 = 13 \times 1$).

A **factor** is one of the numbers you multiply to get a product.

A **prime factor** is a factor that is prime.

A **composite number** is a natural number that has more than two factors. For example, 15 is a composite number ($15 = 1 \times 3 \times 5$).

Example A

Find the prime factorization of 12.

Step 1: Use divisibility rules to find two factors of the number.

Try 3 and 4. Use branches to show the factors.

Step 2: If both numbers are prime, stop. If not, continue factoring until all factors are prime numbers.

3 is prime. Bring it down to the next branch. Continue by factoring 4.

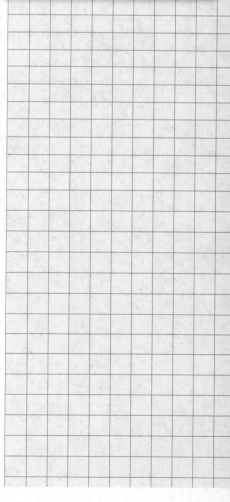

Step 3: Check again to be sure all factors are now prime numbers.

$$3 = 3 \times 1 \qquad 2 = 2 \times 1$$

There is no other way to factor these numbers, so 2 and 3 are prime.

Solution: The prime factorization of 12 is $3 \times 2 \times 2$.

Try These A

a. Reason quantitatively. Will the prime factorization of 12 be different if you start with the factors 2 and 6? Explain.

Find the prime factorization of each number.

b. 21   **c.** 16   **d.** 18

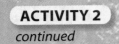
ACTIVITY 2
continued

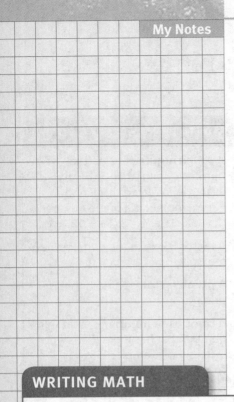

Here is another method for finding prime factors.

Example B

Find the prime factorization of 60.

Step 1: Write the number as the dividend inside a division symbol. Write one of the prime factors as the divisor on the outside.

$$
\begin{array}{r}
5 \quad \leftarrow\text{Step 4}\\
2)\overline{10}\\
3)\overline{30} \quad \leftarrow\text{Steps 2 \& 3}\\
2)\overline{60} \quad \leftarrow\text{Step 1}
\end{array}
$$

Step 2: Divide as you would if you were using long division.

Step 3: Repeat the steps, this time using the quotient on top of the division symbol as the new dividend.

Step 4: Stop when the quotient is a prime number.

Step 5: Use the divisors and the final quotient to write the prime factorization.

Solution: $60 = 2 \times 2 \times 3 \times 5$

Try These B

Find each prime factorization using the long division method.
a. 32   **b.** 45   **c.** 56

WRITING MATH

Prime factorizations are usually written with the factors ordered from least to greatest: $2 \times 3 \times 3 \times 7$, not $3 \times 7 \times 3 \times 2$

Even if a number is not divisible by any small natural numbers such as 2, 3, or 5, it may still be a composite number. To find its prime factorization, you may have to use larger numbers to guess and check with.

Example C

At After School Sports Club, 143 students are divided into teams, with the same number on each team. How many teams are there and how many students are on each team?

To solve, use divisibility rules to see if 143 is divisible by any prime numbers. Start with 2 and work upwards.

2? No. 143 is not even.

3? No. $1 + 4 + 3 = 8$, which is not divisible by 3.

5? No. The ones digit of 143 is not 0 or 5.

7? No. When you divide 143 by 7, there is a remainder.

11? Yes. $143 \div 11 = 13$.

Solution: Since $143 \div 11 = 13$, $143 = 11 \times 13$. That means there could by 11 teams with 13 on each team, or 13 teams with 11 on each team.

Try These C

a. Last year there were 133 students in After School Sports Club. How many teams were there, and how many students were on each team?

b. There are 221 math books in a closet arranged in equal stacks. How many stacks are there, and how many books are in each stack?

My Notes

Check Your Understanding

1. Determine the prime factorization of each number.

   a. 14   **b.** 30   **c.** 27

   d. 38   **e.** 84   **f.** 41

   g. 100   **h.** 77   **i.** 180

2. Why is every prime number greater than 2 an odd number?

3. Explain why numbers with a 5 in the ones place are not prime numbers.

4. List all the prime numbers from 1 to 50.

5. Explain why you cannot find the prime factorization of 4.8.

LESSON 2-1 PRACTICE

6. **Construct viable arguments.** $7{,}719 = 83 \times 93$. Explain why 83×93 is not the prime factorization of 7,719.

7. A *conjecture* is a statement that appears to be true, but which remains unproven. In 1976, a seventh-grade student named Arthur Hamann made a conjecture that every even number can be expressed as the difference between two prime numbers.

   $$6 = 19 - 13 \qquad 20 = 23 - 3$$

   No one has ever found an even number for which Arthur Hamann's conjecture is not true. Test the conjecture for these even numbers:
   a. 14   **b.** 18   **c.** 22

8. A famous conjecture by the eighteenth-century mathematician Christian Goldbach also remains unproven. Goldbach's conjecture states that every even number greater than 2 can be expressed as the sum of two prime numbers.

   $$12 = 5 + 7 \qquad 26 = 13 + 13$$

   Test Goldbach's conjecture for these even numbers:
   a. 16   **b.** 26   **c.** 34

ACADEMIC VOCABULARY

A *conjecture* is a statement that appears to be true but has not been proven.

Learning Targets:

- Evaluate a whole number or decimal raised to a whole number exponent.
- Express prime factorizations using exponents when a prime factor occurs more than once.

SUGGESTED LEARNING STRATEGIES: Note Taking, Think-Pair-Share, Vocabulary Organizer, Sharing and Responding, Discussion Group

An **exponent** tells how many times a **base** is to be used as a factor.

$$2^3 = 2 \times 2 \times 2 = 8$$

exponent

base

Powers are numbers expressed using exponents.

Power	Verbal Expression	Expanded Expression	Product
2^6	2 to the sixth power	$2 \times 2 \times 2 \times 2 \times 2 \times 2$	64
4.7^2	4.7 to the second power, or 4.7 **squared**	4.7×4.7	22.09
5^3	5 to the third power, or 5 **cubed**	$5 \times 5 \times 5$	125

A number written without an exponent is said to be in **standard** form. When it is written with an exponent, it is in **exponential** form.

$49 \rightarrow$ standard form $\qquad 7^2 \rightarrow$ exponential form

1. Write each power as an expanded *numeric expression*. Then *evaluate* the expression.

a. 3^4 **b.** 4^5 **c.** 5.3^2

d. eight squared   **e.** six cubed

2. Write each expanded expression as a power. Then evaluate the power.

a. $1.7 \times 1.7 \times 1.7$ **b.** $2 \times 2 \times 2 \times 2 \times 2$ **c.** 16×16

DISCUSSION GROUP TIPS

As you discuss this lesson with your partner or with your group, be sure to use the many new math terms precisely. Make notes to help you remember the meanings of new words and how they are used to describe mathematical topics.

MATH TERMS

A **numeric expression** is a mathematical phrase that uses numbers.

Examples of numerical expressions are $2 + 3$, $35 \div 7$, and 6^2.

You **evaluate** a numeric expression by performing any indicated operation in the expression.

3. a. Find 1^{17}.
b. Explain how you can find any power of 1.

4. a. Find 0^{31}.
b. Explain how you can find any power of 0.

5. a. Find 89^{1}.
b. Explain how you can find the first power of any number.

6. Make use of structure. Complete the following pattern:

$$2^4 = 16$$
$$2^3 = 8$$
$$2^2 = 4$$
$$2^1 = 2$$
$$2^0 = \underline{\quad}$$

You can use logic to complete the above pattern and will learn more about the numbers with an exponent of zero in later math classes. For now, remember that the zero power of any number is 1.

$$8^0 = 1 \qquad 37^0 = 1 \qquad (9.264)^0 = 1$$

You can use exponents to write the prime factorization of a number with repeated prime factors. For example:

$$28 = 2 \times 2 \times 7 = 2^2 \times 7$$

7. Describe why the prime factorization of a number is sometimes written with exponents. Use an example in your answer.

8. Model with mathematics. Use exponents to write the prime factorization of each number.
a. 72   **b.** 144   **c.** 800

My Notes

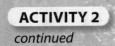

My Notes

Check Your Understanding

9. Evaluate each expression.
   a. 2^4
   b. 5^3
   c. 8.3^2
   d. 1^9
   e. 13^1
   f. 56.8^0
   g. 10^5
   h. 100^2
   i. 0^{12}
   j. eleven squared
   k. one and three-tenths cubed
   l. seven squared times two cubed
   m. three to the fifth power
   n. four squared cubed

10. Write the prime factorization of each number, using exponents as needed.
    a. 20
    b. 54
    c. 45
    d. 225
    e. 98
    f. 729

LESSON 2-2 PRACTICE

11. Evaluate each expression.
    a. 3^4
    b. 7^3
    c. 3.8^2
    d. 1^7
    e. 31^1
    f. 86.5^0
    g. fifteen squared
    h. four to the fourth power

12. Write the prime factorization of each number.
    a. 40
    b. 63
    c. 120

13. a. Find 10^1.
    b. Find 10^2.
    c. Find 10^3.
    d. **Make use of structure.** Describe a method you can use to find any power of 10 easily.

14. **Model with mathematics.** Write 64 in exponential form three different ways.

15. a. Write a possible explanation for why 5^2 is read "five *squared*."
    b. Write a possible explanation for why 5^3 is read "five *cubed*."

16. **Make use of structure.** Evaluate 11^2, 111^2, and $1,111^2$. Then predict the value of $11,111^2$. Explain how you made your prediction.

ACTIVITY 2 PRACTICE
Write your answers on notebook paper. Show your work.

Lesson 2-1

1. Which of the numbers below is NOT a prime number?
   A. 13   **B.** 37
   C. 39   **D.** 47

2. Which is the prime factorization of 81?
   A. 1×81 **B.** 3×27
   C. 9×9 **D.** $3 \times 3 \times 3 \times 3$

3. Explain the difference between a prime number and a composite number. Include examples in your explanation.

4. List the prime numbers between 80 and 90.

5. List the composite numbers between 39 and 50.

6. To check whether 59 is prime, Claudia divided 59 by every odd number from 3 to 29. All of the quotients had a remainder.
   a. Why did she test with only odd numbers?
   b. To be sure that 59 is prime, does she need to continue to divide 59 by odd numbers from 31 to 57? Why or why not?

7. A certain natural number is not divisible by 7. Can it be divisible by 14? Why or why not?

8. Determine the prime factorization of each number.
   a. 30   **b.** 33
   c. 52   **d.** 72
   e. 65   **f.** 76

9. Is the number 147 prime or composite? Explain how you know.

10. Is $2 \times 3 \times 4$ the prime factorization of 24? Explain your reasoning.

11. List all of the numbers from 1 to 100 that have 13 as a factor.

12. Desmond has 169 square bricks that he is arranging in rows to make a patio. Every row must have the same number of bricks.
    a. How many bricks are in each row?
    b. Describe the shape of the patio. Explain your reasoning.

13. **a.** Find the prime factorization of 132.
    b. Explain how you found the prime factorization.

14. **a.** Find the prime factorization of 180.
    b. Explain why every natural number with a zero in the ones place is a composite number.

15. Jason said that any number that has 1 as a factor must be a composite number? Do you agree? Explain your reasoning.

16. Express each number as a sum of two prime numbers.
    a. 10   **b.** 22
    c. 30   **d.** 50

17. Express each number as a difference of two prime numbers.
    a. 2   **b.** 8
    c. 14   **d.** 16

Lesson 2-2

18. Evaluate each expression.
   a. 3^3 b. 9^2
   c. 1.6^2 d. 26^1
   e. 1^{15} f. 22.91^0
   g. 0^{25} h. 10^7
   i. two and two-tenths squared
   j. four to the fourth power
   k. seven cubed
   l. three cubed squared

19. Write the prime factorization of each number. Use exponents if needed.
   a. 32   b. 38
   c. 175   d. 120
   e. 108   f. 121

20. Write 81 in exponential form two different ways.

21. a. Write 25 in exponential form.
   b. Identify the base in the expression that you wrote and explain what it means.
   c. Identify the exponent in the expression that you wrote and explain what it means.

22. There were two bacteria in a dish at the beginning of an experiment. Every 15 minutes, the number of bacteria in the dish doubled. Write in exponential form the number of bacteria in the dish two hours after the experiment began.

23. Which of the given numbers equals $2^5 \times 3^2$?
   A. 90   B. 192
   C. 240   D. 288

24. Which expression equals 5^0?
   A. 0^5 B. 1^5
   C. 5^1 D. 0^1

25. How many factors does the number $2^2 \times 3^2$ have?
   A. 4   B. 6
   C. 9   D. 36

26. Which equation is true?
   A. $1^6 = 6^1$ B. $2^3 = 3^2$
   C. $2^4 = 4^2$ D. $3^4 = 4^3$

27. Each room in a library has 3^4 bookshelves. Each shelf holds 2^7 books.
   a. Write an expression for the number of books that are shelved in each room.
   b. How many rooms do you need to hold $2^7 \times 3^6$ books?

MATHEMATICAL PRACTICES
Construct Viable Arguments

28. A sixth grade math student made this conjecture: Every prime number can be expressed as the product of two prime numbers. Do you agree with the conjecture? Why or why not?

Greatest Common Factor and Least Common Multiple ACTIVITY 3

Parties and Pups
Lesson 3-1 Greatest Common Factor

Learning Targets:
- Find all the factors of a whole number.
- Find the greatest common factor of two whole numbers.

> **SUGGESTED LEARNING STRATEGIES:** Think-Pair-Share, Paraphrasing, Discussion Groups, Create Representations

Sheila is planning a surprise birthday party for her little sister. She makes a list of all the necessary party items. One of the first items on the list is balloons.

Sheila buys 24 purple balloons and 36 red balloons. For party decorations, she will make balloon arrangements. Each arrangement has will have the same number of purple balloons and the same number of red balloons. What is the greatest number of arrangements she can make?

You can use the *greatest common factor (GCF)* to solve problems like the balloon problem. One way to find the GCF is to use prime factorizations.

Example A
Find the GCF of 24 and 36.

Step 1: Write the prime factorization of each number.
$$24 = 2 \times 2 \times 2 \times 3$$
$$36 = 2 \times 2 \times 3 \times 3$$

Step 2: Look for common factors (factors that are the same in both lists).
$$24 = \boxed{2} \times \boxed{2} \times 2 \times \boxed{3}$$
$$36 = \boxed{2} \times \boxed{2} \times 3 \times \boxed{3}$$

Step 3: Find the product of the common factors.
$$2 \times 2 \times 3 = 12$$

Solution: The GCF of 24 and 36 is 12. This means that 12 is the *greatest* number that is a factor of both 24 and 36.

Try These A
Find the greatest common factor of each set of numbers.

a. 18, 24   **b.** 12, 20   **c.** 11, 16

d. 28, 42   **e.** 15, 25, 40   **f.** 16, 24, 48

MATH TERMS

The **greatest common factor (GCF)** for a set of two or more whole numbers is the largest number that is a factor of all the numbers in the set.

MATH TIP

When finding the GCF using prime factorization, it is usually easier to spot the common factors by listing them all, rather than by using exponents:

$2 \times 2 \times 2 \times 3$ rather than $2^3 \times 3$

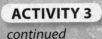

1. You determined in Example A that the greatest number of arrangements that Sheila can make is 12.
   a. How many purple balloons will there be in each arrangement?
   b. How many red balloons will there be in each arrangement?

2. The are 60 girls and 48 boys in the school chorus. They are seated in rows in the auditorium, with the same number of students in each row. Each row has only girls or only boys. What is the greatest number of students who could be in each row?

Another way to find the GCF is to use common factors.

> **MATH TIP**
>
> Use the pattern shown below to check that you have listed all the factors of a number:
>
> **24: 1, 2, 3, 4, 6, 8, 12, 24**
>
> $1 \times 24 = 24$ $\quad$ $2 \times 12 = 24$
>
> $3 \times 8 = 24$ $\quad$ $4 \times 6 = 24$
>
> Sometimes there may be a single number in the middle:
>
> **16: 1, 2, 4, 8, 16**
>
> $1 \times 16 = 16$ $\quad$ $2 \times 8 = 16$
>
> $\qquad 4 \times 4 = 16$

Example B

Find the GCF of 24 and 40.

Step 1: List all the factors (not just the prime factors) of each number.
$\qquad$ 24: 1, 2, 3, 4, 6, 8, 12, 24
$\qquad$ 40: 1, 2, 4, 5, 8, 10, 20, 40

Step 2: List the common factors.
$\qquad$ The common factors are 1, 2, 4, and 8.

Step 3: Choose the greatest factor from the list of common factors. This is the greatest common factor.

Solution: The GCF is 8.

Try These B

List the factors of each number. Then find the greatest common factor for each set of numbers.
a. 18, 24
b. 12, 20
c. 16, 21

3. **Attend to precision.** Of the 108 students in the school chorus, 48 are sopranos, 24 are altos, and 36 are tenors. What is the greatest number of groups that can be formed with the same number of each type of voice in each group?

My Notes

Check Your Understanding

4. Find the greatest common factor of each set of numbers.
   a. 28, 40   b. 40, 48   c. 63, 135
   d. 26, 39, 78   e. 12, 18, 26   f. 54, 72, 90

5. The are 72 girls and 60 boys waiting to audition for the school play. They are seated in rows the auditorium, with the same number of students in each row. Each row has only girls or only boys.
   a. How many rows of girls will there be?
   b. How many rows of boys will there be?

6. Of the 108 students in the school band, 48 are in the woodwind section, 24 are in the percussion section, and 36 are in the brass section. How many woodwind players, percussion players, and brass players will there be in each group?

7. Describe how to find the GCF of three numbers. Use an example with your explanation.

LESSON 3-1 PRACTICE

8. The youth orchestra has 18 violinists and 24 flutists. The music director wants to place these 42 musicians in rows with only violinists or flutists in each row. Each row must have the same number of musicians. What is the greatest number of musicians the director can place in each row?

9. **Model with mathematics.** The Venn diagram at the right shows a way to find the greatest common factor of 42 and 60.

   Draw a Venn diagram to find the GCF of 154 and 210. Explain how your diagram shows the GCF.

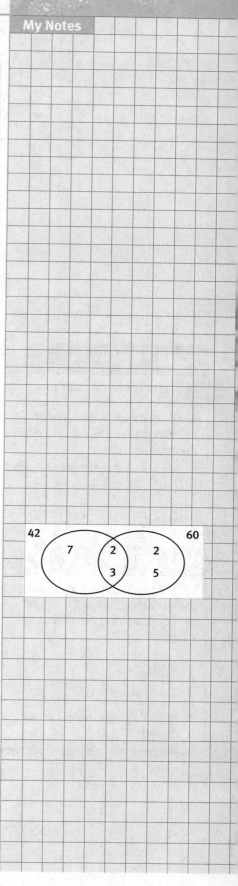

10. **Attend to precision.** A carpenter has three pieces of wood measuring 210 cm, 245 cm, and 315 cm in length. She wants to cut them into shorter pieces that are all the same length, and with no wood left over.
    a. What is the greatest possible length of each shorter piece?
    b. How many shorter pieces will there be altogether?

11. The greatest common factor of 24 and another number is 6.
    a. Find two possible values of the other number.
    b. Describe the process you used to find the other number.

12. Ingrid has 48 roses, 32 daisies, and 24 tulips.
    a. How many floral bouquets can she make if each bouquet must have the same number of each flower and every flower is used?
    b. How many of each type of flower will there be in each bouquet?

My Notes

Learning Targets:
- Find multiples of a whole number.
- Find the least common multiple of two or more whole numbers.

SUGGESTED LEARNING STRATEGIES: Interactive Word Wall, Paraphrasing, Discussion Groups, Create Representations

Sheila decides to purchase hot dogs to serve at her sister's birthday party. Hot dogs come in packages of 10 and hot dog buns come in packages of 8.

1. It is hard for Sheila to decide how many packages of hot dogs and how many packages of buns to buy. Explain why this may be a hard decision for Sheila.

Sheila's first thought is to buy 3 packages of hot dogs and 4 packages of buns.

2. Will she end up with the same number of hot dogs and buns? Explain.

To solve this problem, Sheila can find the *least common multiple (LCM)* of 8 and 10. The LCM will help her to determine the *least* number of packages of hot dogs and buns that she must buy in order to have the same number of each.

MATH TERMS

The **least common multiple (LCM)** for a set of two or more whole numbers is the smallest number that is a multiple of all the numbers in the set.

MATH TIP

To find the multiples of a number, multiply the number by whole numbers starting with 1. For example:

$5 \times 1 = 5$
$5 \times 2 = 10$
$5 \times 3 = 15$ and so on.

The first three multiples of 5 are 5, 10, and 15.

Example A

Find the least common multiple of 8 and 10. Use your answer to determine the least number of packages of hot dogs and buns Sheila can buy to have the same number of hot dogs and buns.

Step 1: List multiples of 8 and 10.

8: 8, 16, 24, 32, 40, 48, 56, 64, 72, 80
10: 10, 20, 30, 40, 50, 60, 70, 80, 90

Step 2: Identify the smallest multiple that is in both lists.

The least common multiple of 8 and 10 is 40, so Sheila needs to determine how many packages of hot dogs will give her exactly 40 hot dogs and how many packages of buns will give her exactly 40 buns.

Step 3: Use the least common multiple, 40, to solve the problem.

There are 10 hot dogs to a package, and $10 \times 4 = 40$.
There are 8 buns to a package, and $8 \times 5 = 40$.

Solution: 4 packages of hot dogs and 5 packages of buns

Try These A
Use multiples to find the LCM of each set of numbers.

a. 6, 8   **b.** 5, 10   **c.** 9, 12

3. **Reason abstractly.** What is the next equal number of hot dogs and buns Sheila could buy after 40 to end up with the same number of hot dogs and buns? Explain.

You can also find the least common multiple of two or more numbers using prime factorizations.

Example B
Find the LCM of 12 and 30.

Step 1: List the prime factorizations of the numbers.

$$12: 2 \times 2 \times 3$$
$$30: 2 \times 3 \times 5$$

Step 2: Find the product of the common factors in both lists.

$$12 = \boxed{2} \times 2 \times \cancel{3}$$
$$30 = \boxed{2} \times \cancel{3} \times 5$$

The common factors are 2 and 3, and their product is $2 \times 3 = \mathbf{6}$.

Step 3: Multiply the product of the common factors, 6, by the factors that are not common, 2 and 5.

$$\mathbf{6} \times 2 \times 5 = 60$$

Solution: The least common multiple of 12 and 30 is 60.

Try These B
Use prime factorizations to find the LCM of each set of numbers.

a. 12, 20   **b.** 24, 30   **c.** 15, 25

4. **Construct viable arguments.** Which is greater, the least common multiple of two numbers or their greatest common factor? Explain your reasoning. As you explain your reasoning, remember to use complete sentences, including transitions and words such as *and, or, since, for example, therefore,* and *because of*. Also, remember to provide a concluding statement in your explanation.

My Notes

Check Your Understanding

5. Find the least common multiple of each set of numbers using the prime factorization method.

a. 8, 12   b. 10, 15   c. 10, 20
d. 6, 9   e. 14, 21   f. 9, 12
g. 3, 4, 6   h. 2, 4, 10   i. 4, 15, 30

6. Construct viable arguments. This is part of Marcia's homework. Is she finding the GCF or LCM? Explain your choice.

$$72 = 9 \times 8 = 2 \times 2 \times 2 \times 3 \times 3$$
$$48 = 6 \times 8 = 2 \times 2 \times 2 \times 2 \times 3$$

The common factors are 2, 2, 2, and 3.

The answer is 24.

LESSON 3-2 PRACTICE

7. Three dogs barked at exactly 11 P.M. Thereafter, Fritzie barked every 4 minutes, Spike barked every 5 minutes, and Dixie barked every 3 minutes. What was the next time when the dogs barked at the same time?

8. Ben's car gets 24 miles to each gallon of gasoline. Tina's car gets 20 miles to the gallon of gasoline. While driving from Hartdale to Lawton, they each used the same number of gallons of gas. What is the least number of miles that could be the distance between Hartdale and Lawton?

9. Make sense of problems. The Venn diagram shows the prime factors of 30 and 42. Explain how you can use the diagram to find the LCM of 30 and 42.

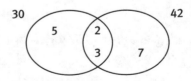

10. Of the methods you have learned for finding the least common multiple, which do you think is the most useful? Explain your reasoning.

11. What is the LCM of the two numbers $2^6 \times 3^4 \times 5$ and $2^5 \times 3^7 \times 5$? Write the solution using exponents.

ACTIVITY 3 PRACTICE
Write your answers on notebook paper.
Show your work.

Lesson 3-1

1. What is the greatest common factor of 36 and 60?
   - **A.** 3
   - **B.** 4
   - **C.** 6
   - **D.** 12

2. Which number is NOT a common factor of 32 and 48?
   - **A.** 2
   - **B.** 4
   - **C.** 3
   - **D.** 8

3. The factors of a number are given below:

   1, 2, 4, 5, 8, 10, 16, 20, 40, 80

   What is the number?

4. The factors of two numbers are given below:

   Number 1: 1, 3, 5, 7, 15, 21, 35, 105

   Number 2: 1, 3, 7, 21, 49, 147

   What is the greatest common factor of the numbers?

5. Find the greatest common factor of each set of numbers using either the listing method or the prime factorization method.
   - **a.** 12, 14
   - **b.** 9, 27
   - **c.** 18, 32
   - **d.** 15, 35
   - **e.** 24, 60
   - **f.** 70, 90
   - **g.** 13, 21
   - **h.** 28, 42
   - **i.** 28, 35, 63
   - **j.** 12, 16, 21
   - **k.** 24, 56, 64
   - **l.** 24, 51, 66

6. **a.** Find two numbers that have a greatest common factor of 13.
   b. Explain how you found the two numbers.

7. Rory has 18 granola bars and 12 apples to package for snack bags. He wants each bag to contain the same number of granola bars and the same number of apples.
   a. What is the maximum number of bags he can make?
   b. How many granola bars and how many apples will each bag contain?

8. A courtyard has three walls with widths measuring 27 feet, 18 feet, and 30 feet. The builder plans to lay square tiles at the base of each wall. The dimensions of the tiles must be such that a whole number of them will exactly fit the width of each wall. If all tiles must be the same size what are the greatest dimensions each tile can have?

9. The 30 sixth graders, 70 seventh graders, and 45 eighth graders at science camp are being formed into teams. Each team must have the same numbers of sixth, seventh, and eight graders, and every camper must be on a team.
   a. How many teams will there be?
   b. How many campers from each grade will be on each team?

10. Peggy has three ribbons. The blue ribbon measures 96 inches, the green one 84 inches, and the yellow one 120 inches. She wants to cut them into shorter pieces all of the same length, with no ribbon left over.
    a. What is the greatest possible length of each shorter piece?
    b. What is the total number of shorter pieces she can cut?
    c. How many green pieces will there be?

Lesson 3-2

11. What is the least common multiple of 12 and 24?

A. 4   **B.** 12

C. 24   **D.** 60

12. Which number is NOT a common multiple of 4 and 6?

A. 8   **B.** 24

C. 12   **D.** 60

13. The factors of two numbers are given below:

Number 1: 1, 2, 3, 6, 9, 18

Number 2: 1, 2, 3, 4, 6, 12

What is the least common multiple of the numbers?

14. Find the least common multiple of each set of numbers using either the prime factorization method or the listing method.

a. 4, 8   **b.** 9, 12

c. 3, 5   **d.** 1, 29

e. 2, 4, 6   **f.** 2, 5, 6

g. 8, 12, 36   **h.** 4, 6, 18

15. A warehouse has boxes that are 18 inches tall and other boxes that are 30 inches tall.

a. If 18-inch boxes are stacked next to 30-inch boxes, what is the lowest height at which the two stacks will be the same height?

b. How many boxes will there be in each stack?

16. Pens come in packages of 6. Pencils come in packages of 8.

a. What is the smallest number of packages of pens and of pencils you need to buy in order to have the same number of pens and pencils?

b. How many pens and how many pencils will you have?

17. Baxter waters the lawn every 3 days and mows it every 7 days. He both watered and mowed the lawn on July 2. When will he next water and mow on the same day?

18. A restaurant manager buys eggs in 18-egg cartons and muffins in packages of 20 muffins.

a. What is the smallest number of egg cartons and muffin packages the manager must buy to have the same number of eggs and muffins?

b. How many eggs would the manager have, and how many muffins?

19. Pat and Fran are quality control specialists in a light bulb factory. Pat inspects every 20 cartons of bulbs for breakage. Fran inspects every 36 cartons for incorrect labeling. If they start at the same time, which carton will be the first that both of them inspect?

MATHEMATICAL PRACTICES
Make Sense of Problems

20. a. Find the greatest common factor and least common multiple of each pair of numbers in the table.

Numbers	GCF	LCM
8, 10		
9, 12		
12, 18		
5, 9		

b. For each row in the table, compare the product of the original numbers with the product GCF × LCM. Then make a conjecture about the relationship between the product of two given numbers and the product of the greatest common factor and the least common multiple of those numbers.

c. Use your conjecture to solve this problem: The GCF of two numbers is 5. The LCM is 60. One of the numbers is 20. What is the other number? Explain how you found the answer.

Write your answers on notebook paper. Show your work.

1. Ninety-one students signed up for the skating club. Coach Link wants to form teams with the same number of members on each team, but says that is impossible: the only teams he can make are 91 teams of 1 or 1 team of 91. Is Coach Link correct? Explain why or why not.

2. Coach Link's assistant is trying to figure out how to organize the 35 boys and 56 girls who signed up for the skating club in groups. To do so, she needs to find the greatest common factor and least common multiple of 35 and 56.
   a. Explain two ways she can find the GCF.
   b. Explain two ways she can find the LCM.

3. This year, there are 12 boys and 18 girls in the ski club. Coach Link wants to form teams with the same number of girls and the same number of boys on each team.
   a. What is the greatest number of teams that can be formed? Explain how you found the answer.
   b. How many boys and how many girls will be on each team?

4. There were 1,260 contestants at the State Ski and Skate meet.
   a. Without using a calculator, determine whether 1,260 is divisible by each number. Explain how you found your answers.

Number to Check	Divisible? (yes or no)	Explanation
2		
3		
4		
5		
6		
9		
10		

   b. Write the prime factorization of 1,260, using exponents if needed.

Scoring Guide	Exemplary	Proficient	Emerging	Incomplete
	The solution demonstrates these characteristics:			
Mathematics Knowledge and Thinking (Items 1, 2a-b, 3a-b, 4a-b)	• Clear and accurate understanding of finding the LCF and GCM of a pair of numbers. • Clear and accurate understanding of the rules of divisibility and factorization.	• Correctly finding the GCF and LCM of a pair of numbers. • Correct application of the rules of divisibility and factoring a number.	• Finding factors and multiples of a pair of numbers, but not necessarily the GCF and LCM. • Use of some of the rules of divisibility and partial factoring of a number.	• Incorrect or incomplete determination of factors and multiples. • Use of few or none of the rules of divisibility; no factoring of numbers.
Problem Solving (Items 3a-b)	• An appropriate and efficient strategy that results in a correct answer.	• A strategy that may include unnecessary steps that result in a correct answer.	• A strategy that results in some incorrect answers.	• No clear strategy when solving problems.
Mathematical Modeling / Representations (Item 4b)	• Clear and accurate understanding of representing a number with its prime factorization.	• Some difficulty in writing the prime factorization of a number.	• Errors in writing the prime factorization of a number.	• Inaccurate or incomplete prime factorization of a number.
Reasoning and Communication (Items 1, 2a-b, 3a, 4a)	• Precise use of appropriate math terms and language when explaining GCF, LCM, and divisibility.	• Adequate explanation of GCF, LCM, and divisibility.	• A misleading or confusing explanation of GCF, LCM, and divisibility.	• Incomplete or inaccurate explanation of GCF, LCM, and divisibility.

Fractions and Mixed Numbers

The Choice Is Yours

Lesson 4-1 Meaning of Fractions

Learning Targets:

- Given a proper fraction, find equivalent fractions.
- Express proper fractions in simplest form.
- Locate proper fractions on a number line.

SUGGESTED LEARNING STRATEGIES: Interactive Word Wall, Create Representations, Critique Reasoning, Use Manipulatives

During physical education class, Ms. Pitts let the students vote on what game to play: $\frac{1}{3}$ of the students chose volleyball, $\frac{2}{6}$ chose basketball, and $\frac{3}{9}$ chose dodge ball. Which sport received the most votes?

To help you determine which fraction of the votes is largest, you can use fraction strips. Since the fractions have denominators of 3, 6, and 9, cut out the strips showing thirds, sixths, and ninths.

1. **Use tools strategically.** Use fraction strips to compare the fractions $\frac{1}{3}$, $\frac{2}{6}$, and $\frac{3}{9}$. What do you notice about these fractions?

Fractions that name the same part of the whole are called *equivalent fractions*. One way to determine equivalent fractions is to use the ***Property of One***. To find an equivalent fraction, multiply or divide the numerator and denominator of a fraction by the same number.

$$\frac{3}{4} \cdot \frac{2}{2} = \frac{6}{8} \qquad \frac{3}{4} \cdot \frac{3}{3} = \frac{9}{12} \qquad \frac{3}{4} \cdot \frac{4}{4} = \frac{12}{16}$$

The fractions $\frac{3}{4}$, $\frac{6}{8}$, $\frac{9}{12}$, and $\frac{12}{16}$ are equivalent fractions.

2. Why do you think multiplying by a fraction such as $\frac{2}{2}$ or $\frac{5}{5}$ is called using the Property of One?

3. Shade the figures to show that $\frac{3}{4}$, $\frac{6}{8}$, and $\frac{9}{12}$ are equivalent fractions.

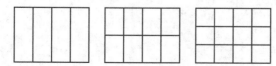

You can use the Property of One with multiplication to find equivalent fractions.

My Notes

MATH TERMS

The **Property of One** states that when a given number is multiplied by 1, the product is the given number. For example, $6 \times 1 = 6$.

Recall that a fraction with the same numerator and denominator is equal to 1. So, multiplying a given number by a fraction equal to 1 is similar to multiplying by 1.

MATH TERMS

A **proper fraction** is a fraction with a numerator that is less than the denominator.

$\frac{5}{8}$ is a proper fraction because $5 < 8$. A proper fraction has a value less than 1.

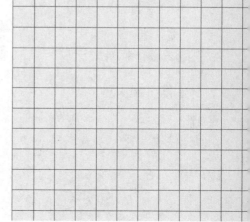

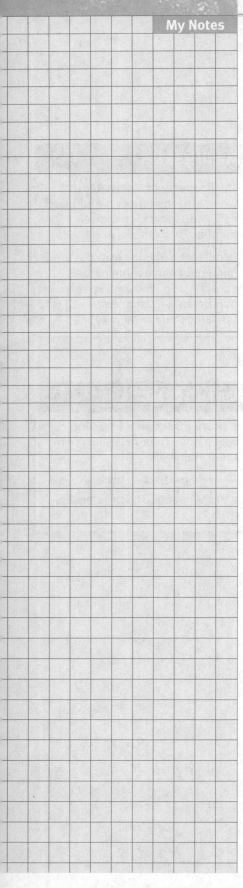

My Notes

Example A

Complete: $\frac{2}{5} = \frac{?}{15}$

Step 1: Think: To change the denominator 5 to 15, multiply by 3.
$$5 \times 3 = 15$$

Step 2: Use the Property of One and multiply the numerator and denominator of $\frac{2}{5}$ by 3.
$$\frac{2}{5} = \frac{2 \times 3}{5 \times 3} = \frac{6}{15}$$

Solution: $\frac{2}{5} = \frac{6}{15}$

Try These A

Complete.

a. $\frac{1}{2} = \frac{?}{8}$ b. $\frac{3}{5} = \frac{12}{?}$ c. $\frac{5}{6} = \frac{?}{30}$

You can use the Property of One with division to find equivalent fractions.

Example B

Complete: $\frac{16}{24} = \frac{2}{?}$

Step 1: Think: To change 16 to 2, divide by 8.
$$16 \div 8 = 2$$

Step 2: Use the Property of One and divide the numerator and denominator of $\frac{16}{24}$ by 8.
$$\frac{16}{24} = \frac{16 \div 8}{24 \div 8} = \frac{2}{3}$$

Solution: $\frac{16}{24} = \frac{2}{3}$

Try These B

Complete.

a. $\frac{6}{9} = \frac{?}{3}$ b. $\frac{6}{36} = \frac{1}{?}$ c. $\frac{6}{21} = \frac{?}{7}$

A fraction is in **simplest form** when the only factor that the numerator and denominator have in common is 1.

$\frac{5}{12}$ is in simplest form because 1 is the only common factor of 5 and 12.

$\frac{14}{28}$ is NOT in simplest form because 1, 2, and 7 are common factors of 14 and 28.

4. Is $\frac{25}{30}$ in simplest form? Explain your reasoning.

Example C

Physical education class lasts $\frac{24}{30}$ of an hour. Write $\frac{24}{30}$ in simplest form.

Step 1: Find the common factors of 24 and 30.

24: **1**, **2**, **3**, 4, **6**, 8, 12, 24

30: **1**, **2**, **3**, 5, **6**, 10, 15, 30

Step 2: Divide the numerator and denominator by a common factor.
$$\frac{24}{30} = \frac{24 \div 2}{30 \div 2} = \frac{12}{15}$$

Step 3: Continue dividing until the fraction is in simplest form.
$$\frac{12}{15} = \frac{12 \div 3}{15 \div 3} = \frac{4}{5}$$

Solution: $\frac{24}{30}$ in simplest form is $\frac{4}{5}$.

Try These C

Determine the simplest form of each fraction.

a. $\frac{16}{32}$ **b.** $\frac{15}{18}$ **c.** $\frac{8}{12}$ **d.** $\frac{18}{24}$

Notice in Example C that two division steps were used to convert $\frac{24}{30}$ to its simplest form. You can also find the simplest form of a fraction in just one division step by dividing by the greatest common factor.

5. What is the GCF of 24 and 30?

6. Complete Step 2 of Example C by dividing by the GCF.

$$\frac{24}{30} = \frac{24 \div \rule{1cm}{0.4pt}}{30 \div \rule{1cm}{0.4pt}} = \rule{2cm}{0.4pt}$$

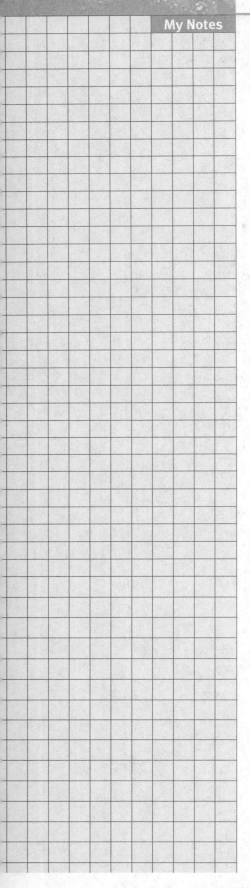

My Notes

Each student in the physical education class set a goal of how many chin-ups they want to be able to do by year's end. The table below shows the goals set by four students.

Name	Goal
Carrie	20
Franco	31
Destiny	10
Vince	25

The physical education teacher hung a large number line in the gym where students mark the progress they make toward reaching their goals. This line runs from 0 to 1, where 1 represents the goal of each student.

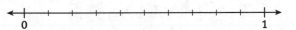

7. The number of chin-ups each student can do at the beginning of the year is shown below.

   Carrie, 16   Franco, 17   Destiny, 7   Vince, 23

   Write fractions to represent how far the students are toward reaching their goals.

   Carrie: Franco: Destiny: Vince:

8. Draw a point on the number line to indicate Destiny's progress and write "D" over the point. Explain how you determined where to place this point.

9. Explain how equivalent fractions can be used to decide where to put the point showing Carrie's progress and write "C" over it.

10. **Construct viable arguments.** Explain how estimation can be used to determine where to mark Franco's and Vince's progress. Add points for the progress of each boy and write "F" and "V" over them.

Check Your Understanding

11. Determine the equivalent fraction.

   a. $\frac{10}{15} = \frac{?}{3}$ **b.** $\frac{3}{4} = \frac{21}{?}$ **c.** $\frac{?}{8} = \frac{35}{40}$

12. Write each fraction in simplest form.

   a. $\frac{18}{90}$ **b.** $\frac{28}{42}$ **c.** $\frac{16}{40}$

13. Draw points on the number line to represent each fraction. Write the appropriate letter over each point.

0   1

   a. $\frac{2}{5}$ **b.** $\frac{9}{10}$ **c.** $\frac{6}{25}$ **d.** $\frac{19}{40}$

LESSON 4-1 PRACTICE

Write each fraction in simplest form.

14. $\frac{4}{24}$ **15.** $\frac{10}{18}$ **16.** $\frac{24}{30}$

17. Write three fractions equivalent to $\frac{9}{15}$.

18. Is $\frac{27}{51} = \frac{18}{34}$? Explain your reasoning.

19. Explain how fraction strips can be used to find five fractions equal to $\frac{3}{6}$. List these equivalent fractions.

20. Arthur answered 85 out of 95 questions correctly on his math exam. Miguel answered 64 out of 76 questions correctly on his history exam. Which student received the higher score? Explain your reasoning.

21. Construct viable arguments. The Property of One permits you to multiply or divide the numerator and denominator of a fraction by the same number without changing the value of the fraction. Is there a Property of One for addition? Support your answer using examples.

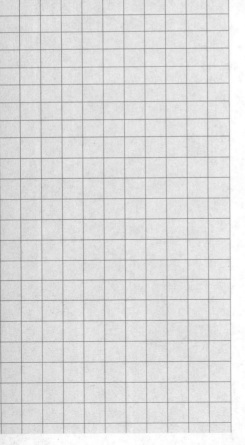

My Notes

ACADEMIC VOCABULARY

To *simulate* means to use an experiment to model a situation that can be represented with numbers such as votes in an election.

Learning Targets:

- Interpret statements of inequality of proper fractions in terms of a number line and in terms of real-world contexts.
- Compare proper fractions.
- Order a set of proper fractions.

SUGGESTED LEARNING STRATEGIES: Interactive Word Wall, Sharing and Responding, Create Representations, Look for a Pattern, Create a Plan, Identify a Subtask

Every West Middle School homeroom elects a student council representative at the beginning of each school year. Since Mr. Fare's homeroom students do not know each other yet, he has asked interested students to volunteer. Andy, Betty, Chenetta, and Deon decide to volunteer.

To *simulate* the election, each of the 23 students in Mr. Fare's homeroom will roll a number cube to vote. A roll of 1 is a vote for Andy, 2 is a vote for Betty, 3 is a vote for Chenetta, and 4 is a vote for Deon. If 5 or 6 is rolled, the student rolls again until either a 1, 2, 3, or 4 is rolled.

1. Simulate the election in your group.
   a. Take turns rolling a number cube until you have a total of 23 votes. Organize your data in the table below.

Andy (1)	Betty (2)	Chenetta (3)	Deon (4)	Total Votes

   b. Whom did your group elect as the homeroom representative?

2. List the names of the candidates by the number of votes received from greatest to least. Next to each name, write the number of votes the candidate received.

3. Find the fraction of the total number of votes each candidate received. Write the fractions in order from greatest to least.

My Notes

4. In the actual election in Mr. Fare's homeroom, Andy received $\frac{5}{23}$ of the total votes. Betty received $\frac{7}{23}$ of the total, Chenetta received $\frac{8}{23}$ of the total, and Deon received $\frac{3}{23}$ of the total. Which candidate was elected? Explain how you know.

The 300 students at West Middle School held a traditional election for student council officers. Eden, Frank, Gabrielle, and Hernando ran for president. Eden received $\frac{4}{15}$ of the votes. Frank received $\frac{3}{10}$, Gabrielle received $\frac{1}{30}$, and Hernando received $\frac{2}{5}$.

5. Why is it more difficult to decide who won this election than it was for the election in Item 1?

To make it easier to compare the results from this election, you can rewrite these fractions as equivalent fractions with a common denominator.

6. What is the least common denominator of the fractions of votes received in the West Middle School election?

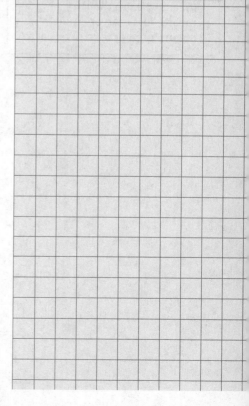

MATH TIP

The Least Common Denominator (LCD) is the smallest number that can be used as the denominator of two or more fractions. It is always the Least Common Multiple (LCM) for a set of denominators.

7. Write the fractions of votes from the West Middle School election as equivalent fractions using this least common denominator.

Eden: $\frac{4}{15} =$ Frank: $\frac{3}{10} =$

Gabrielle: $\frac{1}{30} =$ Hernando: $\frac{2}{5} =$

8. **Reason quantitatively.** Write the fractions in order from least to greatest. Explain your reasoning.

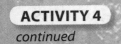
My Notes

MATH TIP

You do not have to find the LCD to write equivalent fractions. You can always use the product of the denominators as a common denominator.

READING MATH

The symbols $<$, $>$, $\leq$ and $\geq$ are *inequality symbols*.
$<$ means "less than"
$>$ means "greater than"
$\leq$ means "less than or equal to"
$\geq$ means "greater than or equal to"

9. **Construct viable arguments.** Nathaniel ordered the fractions in Item 7 from least to greatest after finding equivalent fractions with denominators of 300. Do you think Nathaniel's method is less difficult or more difficult than the method you used to order the fractions? Explain.

10. List the candidates in order from first place to fourth place.

Example A

Find common denominators to compare $\frac{4}{9}$ and $\frac{7}{18}$. Use inequality symbols to write the comparison.

		Using the LCD	**Using the Product of the Denominators**
Step 1:	Find a common denominator.	18	$9 \times 18 = 162$
Step 2:	Write equivalent fractions.	$\frac{4}{9} = \frac{8}{18}$ $\frac{7}{18} = \frac{7}{18}$	$\frac{4}{9} = \frac{72}{162}$ $\frac{7}{18} = \frac{63}{162}$
Step 3:	Compare the fractions with the common denominator.	$\frac{8}{18} > \frac{7}{18}$	$\frac{72}{162} > \frac{63}{162}$

Step 4: Substitute original fractions in the Step 3 inequalities.

LCD denominators:
$\frac{8}{18} > \frac{7}{18}$ and $\frac{8}{18} = \frac{4}{9}$,

so substitute $\frac{4}{9}$ for $\frac{8}{18}$ to get $\frac{4}{9} > \frac{7}{18}$.

Product of the denominators:
Since $\frac{72}{162} > \frac{63}{162}$ and $\frac{72}{162} = \frac{4}{9}$ and $\frac{63}{162} = \frac{7}{18}$,

substitute $\frac{4}{9}$ for $\frac{72}{162}$ and $\frac{7}{18}$ for $\frac{63}{162}$ to get $\frac{4}{9} > \frac{7}{18}$.

Solution: $\frac{4}{9} > \frac{7}{18}$

Try These A

Use common denominators to compare the fractions. Write $<$, $=$, or $>$ in the circle.

a. $\frac{2}{5} \bigcirc \frac{1}{3}$ b. $\frac{7}{9} \bigcirc \frac{5}{6}$ c. $\frac{5}{6} \bigcirc \frac{3}{4}$

Lesson 4-2
Comparing and Ordering Fractions

You can also compare fractions using cross products.

Example B

Compare $\frac{4}{9}$ and $\frac{5}{11}$ using cross products. Use inequality symbols to write the comparison.

To compare two fractions using cross products, multiply the numerator of one fraction by the denominator of the other fraction. Then compare the products.

$$\frac{4}{9} \diagup\!\!\!\diagdown \frac{5}{11}$$

$$4 \times 11 = \qquad 5 \times 9 =$$

$$44 < 45, \text{ so } \frac{4}{9} < \frac{5}{11}$$

Solution: $\frac{4}{9} < \frac{5}{11}$

Try These B

Use cross products to compare the fractions. Write an inequality symbol in the circle.

a. $\frac{2}{9} \bigcirc \frac{3}{7}$ b. $\frac{5}{9} \bigcirc \frac{7}{13}$ c. $\frac{11}{15} \bigcirc \frac{5}{7}$

As president of the student council, Hernando wants to speak with all the student groups about their concerns. The guidance counselor gave Hernando the following data:

- $\frac{8}{15}$ of the students take part in music.
- $\frac{1}{6}$ of the students are in art club.
- $\frac{16}{33}$ of the students participate in sports.
- $\frac{4}{9}$ of the students are in academic clubs.

Hernando decides to speak first with the groups that have the most participants. To do so he must order these fractions. He knows that a common denominator for them would be very large, so he asks his math teacher, Ms. Germain, if there is an easier way to order the fractions.

11. **Model with mathematics.** Ms. Germain decides to explain the concept using easier fractions. She first asks Hernando to represent each of these unit fractions in different ways to compare them.

    a. Shade each rectangle below to show the fraction.

    $\frac{1}{3}$ ┌─────────────────────┐

    $\frac{1}{4}$ ┌─────────────────────┐

    $\frac{1}{2}$ ┌─────────────────────┐

    $\frac{1}{5}$ ┌─────────────────────┐

ACTIVITY 4
continued

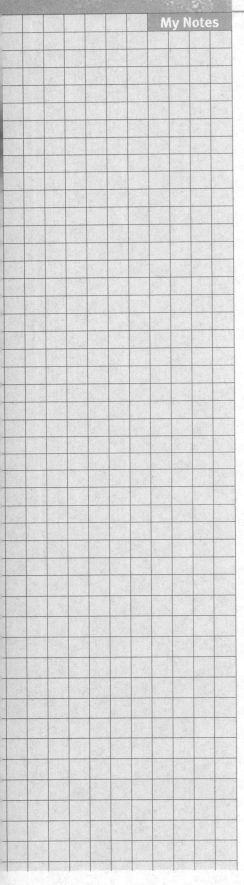

My Notes

b. Graph each fraction on the number lines below.

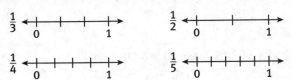

c. Use the representations you created in Parts a and b to order the fractions $\frac{1}{3}$, $\frac{1}{4}$, $\frac{1}{2}$, and $\frac{1}{5}$ from greatest to least. Explain how the representations helped you.

d. Each of the four fractions you just ordered has the same numerator. Explain how to use numerators to order fractions.

e. Order the fractions $\frac{4}{5}$, $\frac{4}{11}$, $\frac{4}{7}$, and $\frac{4}{25}$ from greatest to least.

12. The fractions Hernando wants to order have neither a common numerator nor a common denominator. He already knows it would be hard to find a common denominator.

a. What number could Hernando use as a common *numerator* of the fractions $\frac{8}{15}$, $\frac{1}{6}$, $\frac{16}{33}$, and $\frac{4}{9}$? Explain.

b. Rewrite each of the fractions in Part a as an equivalent fraction with the common numerator you found.

c. Use inequality symbols to write the fractions in Part a from least to greatest.

d. If two numbers are graphed on a number line, how can you tell which number is greater?

e. Graph the fractions in Part a on the number line below.

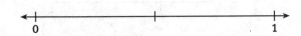

f. In what order will Hernando talk with the student groups?

Check Your Understanding

13. Compare the fractions. Use <, =, or >.

    a. $\dfrac{9}{16} \bigcirc \dfrac{5}{8}$ **b.** $\dfrac{3}{10} \bigcirc \dfrac{4}{15}$ **c.** $\dfrac{5}{21} \bigcirc \dfrac{3}{14}$

14. Model with mathematics. Draw and shade rectangles to model each fraction. Then order the fractions from greatest to least.

    $\dfrac{3}{4}$

    $\dfrac{1}{2}$

    $\dfrac{7}{8}$

15. What is the difference between an LCD and an LCM?

LESSON 4-2 PRACTICE

16. A jar is filled with 70 cubes. There are 15 red cubes, 9 green cubes, 21 yellow cubes, 20 purple cubes, and 5 orange cubes. Write the fraction of the total represented by each color and order them from least to greatest.

17. SB Middle School is holding a mock election for president. Candidate 1 receives $\dfrac{10}{50}$ of the votes. Candidate 2 receives $\dfrac{9}{25}$ of the votes. Candidate 3 receives $\dfrac{4}{10}$ of the votes. Candidate 4 receives $\dfrac{5}{125}$ of the votes. List the candidates in order from least to greatest number of votes.

18. After planting, a plant grew $\dfrac{3}{11}$ inch the first week, $\dfrac{6}{7}$ inch the second week, and $\dfrac{12}{13}$ inch the third week. In which week did the plant grow the most?

19. Reason quantitatively. Students voted for their favorite after-school activity. The table shows the fraction voting for each activity. Use mental math to order the activities from most popular to least popular. Explain your reasoning.

Computer Games	Read	Watch TV	Play Sports
$\dfrac{1}{2}$	$\dfrac{1}{12}$	$\dfrac{1}{6}$	$\dfrac{1}{4}$

My Notes

MATH TERMS

An **improper fraction** is a fraction with a numerator that is greater than the denominator.
$\frac{9}{5}$ is an improper fraction because $9 > 5$.
An improper fraction has a value greater than 1.

Learning Targets:

● Locate mixed numbers on a number line.
● Convert an improper fraction to a whole number or mixed number.
● Convert a whole number or mixed number to an improper fraction.

SUGGESTED LEARNING STRATEGIES: Interactive Word Wall, Summarizing Visualization, Simplify the Problem, Create Representations

Members of the Science Club are studying fossils. Fossils are the remains of animals and plants that lived long ago. The shells of ancient sea creatures called ammonites are among the most common fossils. Ammonites have spiral-shaped shells as shown in the picture to the left. They have been found in a wide variety of colors and range in width from a fraction of an inch to more than 6 feet.

Measurements in feet and inches are often expressed as **mixed numbers.** A mixed number is the sum of a whole number and a proper fraction. The number $1\frac{3}{4}$ is an example of a mixed number; it is the sum of 1 and $\frac{3}{4}$:

$$1\frac{3}{4} = 1 + \frac{3}{4}.$$

Fraction strips can be used to represent mixed numbers.

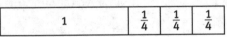

| 1 | $\frac{1}{4}$ | $\frac{1}{4}$ | $\frac{1}{4}$ |

1. **Attend to precision.** Kelly laid a length of string across the widest part of an ammonite. Then she measured the length of the string.

How wide is the ammonite? Write your answer as a mixed number.

2. How many $\frac{1}{2}$ inches are in $2\frac{1}{2}$ inches? Count the number of $\frac{1}{2}$-inch intervals on the ruler and write your answer as an *improper fraction.*

3. You can also use models to represent mixed numbers and improper fractions. Name the shaded parts of this model two ways.

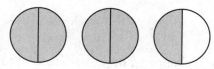

mixed number: _____   improper fraction: _____

My Notes

MATH TIP

A **number sentence** is an equation or inequality expressed using numbers and symbols. Number sentences can be true or false.

$12 + 3 = 15$	True
$9 - 4 = 1$	False
$2 + 7 \leq 9$	True
$13 > 13$	False

4. Both the mixed number and the improper fraction in Item 3 describe the same number. Write a **_number sentence_** that shows that the mixed number and the improper fraction are equal.

5. Another ammonite had a width of $3\frac{1}{4}$ inches.

   a. Shade the circles to represent the width.

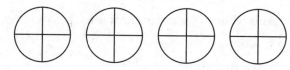

   b. Write $3\frac{1}{4}$ as a sum of whole numbers and a fraction.

$$3\frac{1}{4} = 1 + \underline{} + \underline{} + \frac{1}{4}$$

$$= \frac{4}{4} + \underline{} + \underline{} + \frac{1}{4}$$

$$= \frac{}{4}$$

6. Rewrite $3\frac{1}{4}$ as an improper fraction.

Drawing a model and division are two methods for changing an improper fraction to a mixed number.

7. a. Color the model below to show $\frac{9}{4}$.

   b. Write $\frac{9}{4}$ as a mixed number.

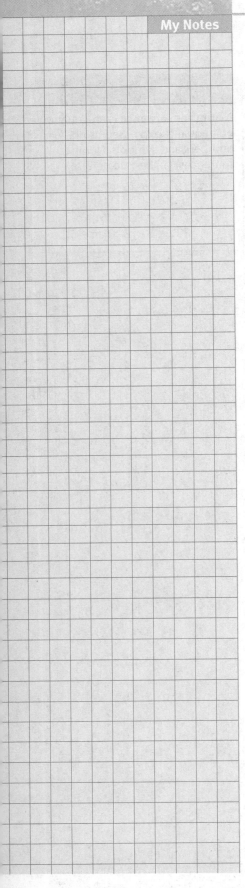

My Notes

c. Reason abstractly. How does the model in Part a help you write the mixed number in Part b?

You can use division to change an improper fraction to a mixed number since the fraction bar indicates division.

$\frac{a}{b}$ represents the same number as $a \div b$, where $b \neq 0$.

$$\frac{2}{5} = 2 \div 5 \qquad \frac{6}{3} = 6 \div 3 \qquad \frac{27}{15} = 27 \div 15$$

Example A

Rewrite $\frac{14}{4}$ as a mixed number in simplest form by dividing. Express the remainder as a fraction.

Step 1: Set up the division.
$$\frac{14}{4} = 14 \div 4 = 4\overline{)14}$$

Step 2: Divide.
$$\begin{array}{r} 3 \\ 4\overline{)14} \\ \underline{12} \\ 2 \end{array} \leftarrow \text{The remainder is 2.}$$

Step 3: Write the remainder over the divisor and simplify, if possible.
$$\frac{2}{4} = \frac{1}{2}$$

Step 4: Use the quotient and the remainder to form a mixed number.
$$3 + \frac{1}{2} = 3\frac{1}{2}$$

Solution: $\frac{14}{4} = 3\frac{1}{2}$

Try These A

Write each improper fraction as a mixed number in simplest form.

a. $\frac{11}{3}$ b. $\frac{15}{7}$ c. $\frac{16}{6}$

Check Your Understanding

8. Write each mixed number as an improper fraction.

 a. $4\frac{1}{5}$ **b.** $3\frac{2}{7}$ **c.** $7\frac{2}{3}$

 d. $2\frac{3}{4}$ **e.** $1\frac{1}{6}$ **f.** $9\frac{1}{2}$

9. Write each improper fraction as a mixed number in simplest form.

 a. $\frac{8}{3}$ **b.** $\frac{3}{2}$ **c.** $\frac{17}{5}$

 d. $\frac{10}{9}$ **e.** $\frac{18}{4}$ **f.** $\frac{15}{6}$

10. Explain how you can find the number of sevenths in $5\frac{3}{7}$.

11. Draw a model representing $\frac{7}{3} = 2\frac{1}{3}$.

LESSON 4-3 PRACTICE

12. Write each mixed number as an improper fraction.

 a. $4\frac{4}{5}$ **b.** $3\frac{5}{7}$ **c.** $7\frac{1}{7}$

13. Write each improper fraction as a mixed number in simplest form.

 a. $\frac{8}{3}$ **b.** $\frac{3}{2}$ **c.** $\frac{17}{5}$

14. The largest ammonite ever found measured $8\frac{1}{2}$ feet in diameter. Write the width in feet as an improper fraction.

15. The largest ammonite weighs $3\frac{1}{2}$ tons. Write $3\frac{1}{2}$ as an improper fraction three different ways.

16. Convert $11\frac{28}{6}$ to an improper fraction and a mixed number, both in simplest form.

17. Describe an improper fraction that simplifies to a whole number.

18. **Reason abstractly.** Can any fraction be written as a mixed number? Explain, giving examples to illustrate your answer.

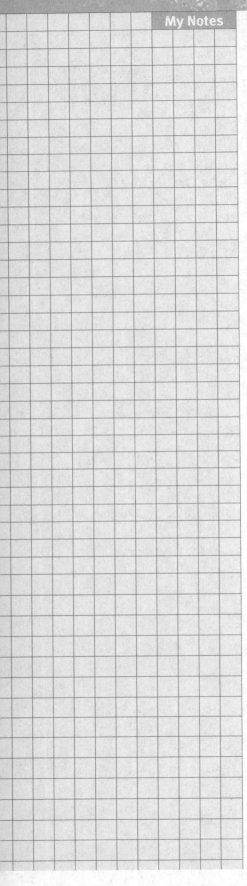

My Notes

Learning Targets:

● Interpret statements of inequality of mixed numbers in terms of a number line and in terms of real-world contexts.

● Compare mixed numbers.

● Order a set of mixed numbers or fractions.

SUGGESTED LEARNING STRATEGIES: Summarizing, Visualization, Sharing and Responding, Simplify the Problem

Five students are growing sunflowers in the school garden. The table below shows the height of the tallest sunflower each student has grown.

Andy	Bianca	Cody	Deronda	Elyse
$4\frac{1}{4}$ ft	$4\frac{3}{4}$ ft	$\frac{37}{8}$ ft	$5\frac{1}{2}$ ft	$4\frac{7}{8}$ ft

1. **Make use of structure.** Write an inequality using $<$ or $>$ to compare the sunflower heights for the students listed. Explain how you determined which of the heights is greater.
   a. Elyse and Deronda

   b. Andy and Bianca

   c. Bianca, Cody, and Elyse

2. Place the flower heights on the number line below. Write the first letter of each student's name over the appropriate point.

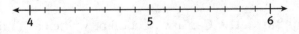

3. When two numbers are plotted on a number line, how can you tell which number is greater?

Check Your Understanding

4. Compare the numbers. Use <, =, or >.

   a. $3\frac{1}{10} \bigcirc 2\frac{9}{10}$ b. $5\frac{2}{7} \bigcirc 5\frac{5}{7}$ c. $1\frac{8}{12} \bigcirc 1\frac{6}{9}$

   d. $2\frac{1}{3} \bigcirc 2\frac{1}{2}$ e. $6\frac{3}{4} \bigcirc 6\frac{8}{10}$ f. $1\frac{7}{12} \bigcirc \frac{3}{2}$

   g. $7\frac{1}{3} \bigcirc 7\frac{2}{7}$ h. $\frac{41}{8} \bigcirc \frac{31}{6}$ i. $2\frac{16}{20} \bigcirc 2\frac{12}{15}$

5. **Make use of structure.** Explain how you can compare the given types of numbers.

   a. two mixed numbers with different whole-number parts
   b. two improper fractions
   c. one mixed number and one improper fraction
   d. two mixed numbers with equal whole number parts

LESSON 4-4 PRACTICE

6. The table gives the heights of five of the tallest players ever to play professional basketball. Order the players from tallest to least tall.

Name	Height (m)
Manute Bol	$2\frac{3}{10}$
Randy Breuer	$2\frac{21}{100}$
Yao Ming	$2\frac{7}{25}$
Chuck Nevitt	$2\frac{13}{50}$
Ralph Sampson	$2\frac{6}{25}$

7. **Use appropriate tools strategically.** Draw a number line like the one below. Plot points A–E. Write the letter above the point.

   A. $2\frac{7}{12}$ **B.** $2\frac{5}{6}$ **C.** $2\frac{2}{3}$ **D.** $2\frac{3}{4}$ **E.** $2\frac{1}{2}$

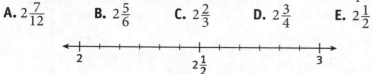

ACTIVITY 4 PRACTICE
Write your answers on notebook paper.
Show your work.

Lesson 4-1

1. Write each fraction in simplest form.
   a. $\frac{16}{80}$ b. $\frac{36}{96}$ c. $\frac{34}{51}$

2. Which of the following fractions is NOT equivalent to $\frac{36}{54}$?
   A. $\frac{12}{18}$ B. $\frac{8}{12}$
   C. $\frac{24}{30}$ D. $\frac{48}{72}$

3. This number line goes from 0 to 1 and is subdivided into tenths. Describe where you would locate the point for $\frac{15}{25}$.

Lesson 4-2

4. Which of the following inequalities is true?
   A. $\frac{3}{4} < \frac{5}{9}$ B. $\frac{17}{20} > \frac{4}{5}$
   C. $\frac{5}{6} < \frac{11}{14}$ D. $\frac{7}{12} > \frac{16}{25}$

5. There are 60 marbles in a bag. One-fourth of the marbles are red, $\frac{2}{5}$ of the marbles are blue, $\frac{1}{12}$ of the marbles are green, and $\frac{4}{15}$ of the marbles are yellow. List the fractions from greatest to least. Explain how you determined your list.

6. Last month Ellen grew $\frac{7}{8}$ inch, Kelvin grew $\frac{9}{16}$ inch, and Grady grew $\frac{3}{4}$ inch. Which student grew the least?

Lesson 4-3

Write each mixed number as an improper fraction.

7. $5\frac{1}{5}$ 8. $4\frac{2}{7}$ 9. $1\frac{1}{8}$

10. $6\frac{4}{9}$ 11. $1\frac{5}{12}$ 12. $7\frac{2}{3}$

Write each improper fraction as a mixed number in simplest form.

13. $\frac{4}{3}$ 14. $\frac{19}{4}$ 15. $\frac{18}{8}$

16. $\frac{25}{15}$ 17. $\frac{12}{11}$ 18. $\frac{12}{9}$

19. Convert $8\frac{9}{6}$ to an improper fraction and a mixed number, both in simplest form.

20. Write $6\frac{7}{8}$ as an improper fraction three different ways.

21. Explain how you can find the number of ninths in $2\frac{5}{9}$.

Lesson 4-4

22. This number line goes from 3 to 4 and is subdivided into twelfths. Describe where you would locate the point for $3\frac{5}{6}$.

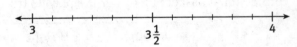

Compare each pair of numbers. Use <, =, or >.

23. $4\frac{3}{10} \bigcirc 3\frac{9}{10}$ 24. $1\frac{8}{12} \bigcirc 1\frac{12}{18}$

25. $5\frac{1}{2} \bigcirc 5\frac{1}{3}$ 26. $1\frac{5}{12} \bigcirc \frac{3}{2}$

27. $7\frac{3}{7} \bigcirc 7\frac{1}{2}$ 28. $\frac{51}{8} \bigcirc \frac{41}{6}$

MATHEMATICAL PRACTICES
Make Use of Structure

29. Explain how you can compare two different mixed numbers that have the same whole number part.

Multiplying Fractions and Mixed Numbers

Skateboarding Fun!

Lesson 5-1 Multiplying by Fractions

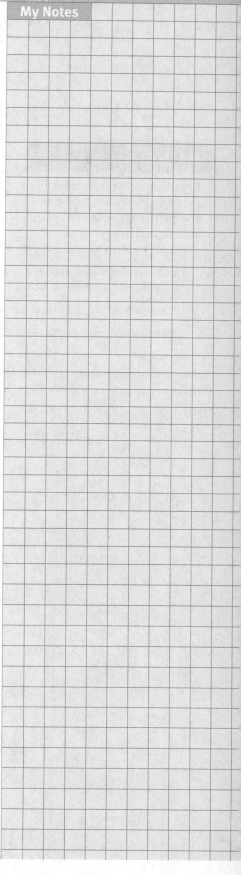

Learning Targets:

- Multiply a whole number by a fraction less than 1.
- Multiply two fractions less than 1.
- Estimate the product of a fraction and a whole number.

> **SUGGESTED LEARNING STRATEGIES:** Paraphrasing, Visualization, Sharing and Responding, Note Taking, Create Representations, Identify a Subtask

At Jefferson Middle School, two-thirds of the students are in the After-School Program. Of the students in the program, two-fifths are skateboarders. To find the fraction of the entire student body that are both in the After-School Program and skateboarders, you need to find the product $\frac{2}{5} \times \frac{2}{3}$. You can use a grid to model the product.

Model with mathematics. The grid represents the whole number 1. The first fraction is $\frac{2}{5}$, so divide the length of the rectangle into five equal columns and shade two of the columns. The second fraction is $\frac{2}{3}$, so divide the height of the rectangle into three equal rows and shade two of the rows.

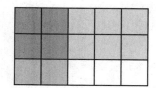

1. The portion of the grid where the two shadings overlap represents the product $\frac{2}{5} \times \frac{2}{3}$.
   a. How many squares are in the entire rectangle?
   b. How many squares show overlapping shading?
   c. What is the product $\frac{2}{5} \times \frac{2}{3}$?

You can also use an algorithm to find the product $\frac{2}{5} \times \frac{2}{3}$.

2. What is the product of the numerators?

3. What is the product of the denominators?

4. Compare your answers to Items 2 and 3 with your answer for Item 1c. Then write an algorithm for finding the product of two fractions in the My Notes section to the right.

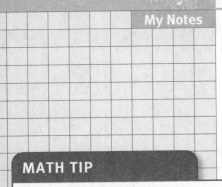

My Notes

Sometimes, the product of two fractions can be simplified.

5. Multiply and write the product in simplest form.

   a. $\frac{3}{4} \times \frac{1}{3}$ b. $\frac{3}{8} \times \frac{4}{9}$ c. $\frac{2}{5} \times \frac{4}{7}$

6. Explain why the product is always less than 1 when you multiply a fraction by another fraction.

MATH TIP

To estimate products of fractions, round each fraction to the nearest one-half or whole to help you make an estimate.

A fraction such as $\frac{7}{8}$ is close to 1 because the numerator and denominator are close in value.

A fraction such as $\frac{7}{12}$ is close to $\frac{1}{2}$ because the numerator is about half of the denominator.

When you added and subtracted fractions, you estimated the sums and differences so you could be sure your answers were reasonable. You can also estimate the products of fractions, and of fractions and whole numbers.

7. Estimate the product $\frac{5}{11} \times \frac{8}{9}$ to the nearest half. Explain how you made your estimate.

8. Estimate the product $\frac{4}{9} \times 15$. Explain how you made your estimate.

When the numerator of one fraction and the denominator of the other fraction being multiplied have common factors, you can simplify before multiplying.

Example A

At Northside Middle School, $\frac{8}{21}$ of the students participate in the After-School Program. Of those in the program, $\frac{7}{12}$ are skateboarders. What fraction of the entire student body are skateboarders?

Step 1: Determine the operation to solve.

Multiply: $\frac{8}{21} \times \frac{7}{12}$

Step 2: Look for common factors in the numerator and the denominator. 8 and 12 are divisible by 4; 7 and 21 are divisible by 7.

$$\frac{8}{21} \times \frac{7}{12}$$

Step 3: Divide 8 and 12 by 4. Cross out 8 and 4 and write the quotients, 2 and 3. Divide 7 and 21 by 7. Cross out 7 and 21 and write the quotients, 1 and 3.

$$\frac{^2\cancel{8}}{\cancel{21}_3} \times \frac{^1\cancel{7}}{\cancel{12}_3}$$

Step 4: After simplifying, multiply the numerators and multiply the denominators.

$$\frac{2}{3} \times \frac{1}{3} = \frac{2 \times 1}{3 \times 3} = \frac{2}{9}$$

Solution: $\frac{2}{9}$ of the students are skateboarders.

Try These A

Determine the product in simplest form by dividing by common factors and then multiplying.

a. $\frac{3}{4} \times \frac{1}{3}$ **b.** $\frac{3}{8} \times \frac{4}{9}$ **c.** $\frac{2}{5} \times \frac{4}{7}$

When multiplying a fraction by a whole number, first write the whole number as a fraction. Then use the algorithm for multiplying two fractions.

9. Estimate the product $\frac{7}{8} \times 24$.

10. Rewrite $\frac{7}{8} \times 24$ with both factors as fractions.

11. Multiply. Simplify first if possible. $\frac{7}{8} \times 24 = ?$

12. Is your answer reasonable? Explain.

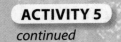

My Notes

Check Your Understanding

13. Determine each product in simplest form.

a. $\frac{1}{2} \times \frac{1}{4}$ b. $\frac{4}{5} \times \frac{1}{4}$ c. $\frac{4}{7} \times \frac{7}{8}$

d. $\frac{8}{15} \times \frac{3}{4}$ e. $\frac{9}{20} \times \frac{2}{3}$ f. $\frac{8}{9} \times \frac{5}{11}$

g. $\frac{4}{5} \times 20$ h. $\frac{2}{11} \times 77$ i. $\frac{3}{5} \times 24$

14. Model with mathematics.

a. Draw a rectangle like the one shown. Shade it to find $\frac{2}{3} \times \frac{3}{4}$

b. Explain how you would make a model to find $\frac{5}{8} \times \frac{7}{9}$

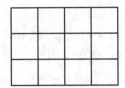

15. Explain how, without multiplying, you can determine whether to put < or > in the circle below.

$$\frac{2}{7} \times \frac{3}{10} \bigcirc \frac{2}{7}$$

LESSON 5-1 PRACTICE

16. Melissa is making a batch of cookies. The recipe calls for $\frac{2}{3}$ cup of chocolate. Melissa is making only one-fourth of a batch. How much chocolate will she need in order to make her cookies?

17. Yesterday the town of Harrington received $\frac{7}{8}$ inch of snow. Today the town received $\frac{2}{3}$ of yesterday's amount. How much snow fell in Harrington today?

18. Of the 245 shoppers at Shop 'n' Save yesterday, $\frac{2}{7}$ completed the customer survey. How many shoppers did NOT complete the survey?

19. Make sense of problems. Two fifteenths of the 630 students at Dillon Middle School are on a sports team. Of those on a sports team, $\frac{1}{4}$ play basketball. Three-sevenths of the basketball players are girls.

a. How many girls play on the Dillon basketball team?

b. How many boys play on the Dillon basketball team?

Learning Targets:

- Multiply mixed numbers by fractions, whole numbers, and other mixed numbers.
- Estimate products involving mixed numbers.

SUGGESTED LEARNING STRATEGIES: Paraphrasing, Visualization, Think-Pair-Share, Sharing and Responding, Identify a Subtask

The method for multiplying mixed numbers is similar to the method for multiplying fractions.

Example A

For his birthday, Buddy wants a skateboard $9\frac{3}{5}$ times the length of his $2\frac{1}{2}$-inch-long model skateboard. How long is the skateboard he wants?

Step 1: Determine the operation to use. Multiply: $9\frac{3}{5} \times 2\frac{1}{2}$

Step 2: Estimate the product to the nearest whole number. $10 \times 3 = 30$ inches

Step 3: Write the mixed numbers as improper fractions. $9\frac{3}{5} \times 2\frac{1}{2} = \frac{48}{5} \times \frac{5}{2}$

Step 4: Divide the numerators and denominators by any common factors. $= \frac{\overset{24}{\cancel{48}}}{\underset{1}{\cancel{5}}} \times \frac{\overset{1}{\cancel{5}}}{\underset{1}{\cancel{2}}}$

Step 5: Multiply. $= \frac{24}{1} \times \frac{1}{1} = 24$

Solution: The skateboard he wants is 24 inches long. The answer is reasonable because it is close to the estimate of 30 inches.

Try These A

Determine each product in simplest form.

a. $2\frac{3}{5} \times 1\frac{1}{2}$ **b.** $6\frac{3}{8} \times \frac{1}{4}$ **c.** $3\frac{2}{3} \times 33$

1. **Construct viable arguments.** If you multiply a number by a proper fraction, will the product be greater than or less than the number? Explain. Remember to provide a concluding statement in your written explanation.

2. If you multiply a number by an improper fraction, will the product be greater than or less than the number? Explain. Remember to provide a concluding statement in your written explanation.

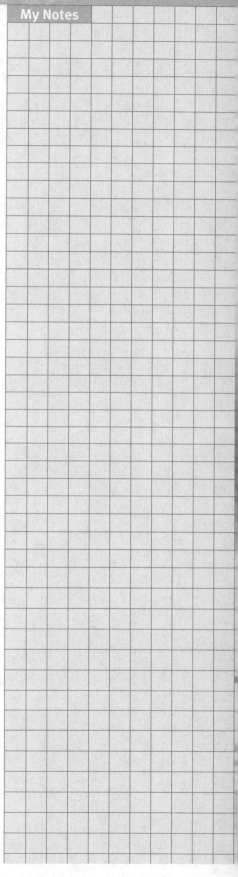

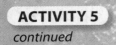

My Notes

Check Your Understanding

3. Determine each product in simplest form

   a. $3\frac{1}{8} \times 3\frac{1}{5}$ b. $2\frac{2}{7} \times 1\frac{1}{6}$ c. $3\frac{5}{6} \times 1\frac{5}{7}$

   d. $8\frac{1}{3} \times 6$ e. $1\frac{1}{6} \times \frac{2}{3}$ f. $1\frac{2}{3} \times 3\frac{2}{5}$

   g. $18 \times 4\frac{2}{3}$ h. $2\frac{5}{8} \times \frac{4}{7}$ i. $4\frac{2}{11} \times 1\frac{10}{23}$

4. Justify each step in the following problem.

   Step 1: $7 \times 3\frac{2}{7} = 7 \times \left(3 + \frac{2}{7}\right)$

   Step 2: $= (7 \times 3) + \left(7 \times \frac{2}{7}\right)$

   Step 3: $= 21 + 2$, or 23

LESSON 5-2 PRACTICE

5. Madeline is making a quilt. She found some pieces of fabric on sale that each measured $\frac{9}{10}$ of a yard. She is going to use $2\frac{1}{2}$ of the pieces for the quilt. What is the total length of the fabric she will use?

6. Meagan wants to make $2\frac{1}{3}$ batches of muffins. The recipe calls for $1\frac{1}{2}$ cups of sugar per batch. How much sugar will she need?

7. Max has a model of a sports car that is $2\frac{1}{5}$ inches long. He is making a larger model that will be $5\frac{1}{2}$ times the length of the smaller car. How long will the larger model be?

8. **Critique the reasoning of others.** Chase says that an easy way to multiply mixed numbers is simply to multiply the whole numbers, then multiply the fractions, and then add the two. Is he right? Include an example in your answer.

9. **Attend to precision.** Each day for 12 consecutive days, Ricardo jogged for $1\frac{2}{3}$ hours at an average rate of $6\frac{1}{4}$ miles per hour. Find the total distance that he jogged.

10. Stack A consists of three cartons, each $2\frac{2}{3}$ feet in height. Stack B consists of four cartons, each $1\frac{5}{6}$ feet in height.

    a. Which stack is taller?
    b. How many inches taller is it?

ACTIVITY 5 PRACTICE

Write your answers on notebook paper.
Show your work.

Express your answers in simplest form.

Lesson 5-1

1. Find the product: $\frac{5}{6} \times \frac{3}{10}$

  a. $\frac{1}{8}$ **b.** $\frac{2}{15}$

  c. $\frac{1}{2}$ **d.** $\frac{1}{4}$

2. Which is the most accurate statement about the product of a fraction and a whole number?
A. It is less than 1.
B. It is less than or equal to 1.
C. It is less than the whole number.
D. It is equal to or greater than the whole number.

3. Which is the best estimate of the product $\frac{17}{33} \times \frac{11}{20}$?
  A. $\frac{1}{4}$ **B.** $\frac{1}{2}$
  C. 1   **D.** 2

4. a. Copy the model below. Then shade it to find the product $\frac{3}{4} \times \frac{2}{5}$.

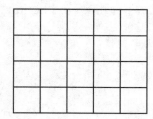

  b. Find the product $\frac{3}{4} \times \frac{2}{5}$ and express the answer in simplest form.

5. Three of the eight rows of a rectangular model are shaded. Five of the seven columns are shaded. What product can be found using the model?

6. The normal amount of rainfall for July in Apple Valley is $\frac{11}{24}$ feet. So far this July, only $\frac{3}{10}$ of the normal amount has fallen. Find the amount of rain that has fallen so far this month.

7. Complete: $\frac{3}{4} \times 20 = \frac{5}{6} \times ?$

8. A cookie recipe calls for $\frac{3}{4}$ tablespoon of salt. Hugo plans to make 10 batches of cookies. How much salt will he need?

9. Of the students in Marci's school, $\frac{5}{9}$ have a pet. Of the students who have a pet, $\frac{12}{25}$ have a dog. What fraction of the students in the school have a dog?

10. Each of the elephants in the Metro Zoo eats an average of 128 pounds of food per day. Each of the giraffes eats $\frac{7}{8}$ of the elephants' average. How many pounds of food does each giraffe eat per day?

11. Two-ninths of the 540 students at East Side Middle School are in the chorus. Three-fourths of the chorus members are girls. Two-fifths of the girls in the chorus are sopranos. What fraction of the students in the school are girl sopranos in the chorus?

12. The volume of a box is the product of its length, its width, and its height. What is the volume of a box that measures $\frac{8}{9}$ foot by $\frac{5}{12}$ foot by $\frac{3}{10}$ foot? Express your answer in cubic feet.

Remember to express your answers in simplest form.

Lesson 5-2

13. Find the product $1\frac{2}{3} \times 2\frac{1}{10}$.

    a. $2\frac{1}{15}$ b. $3\frac{3}{13}$

    c. $3\frac{1}{2}$ d. $3\frac{23}{30}$

14. Estimate the product by rounding to the nearest whole number: $8\frac{5}{12} \times 3\frac{6}{13}$.

    a. 24   b. 27
    c. 32   d. 36

15. Which is the most accurate statement about the product of a number and an improper fraction?
    A. It is less than 1.
    B. It is less than or equal to 1.
    C. It is greater than 1 but less than the number.
    D. It is greater than the number.

16. Explain why

    $12 \times \left(5 + \frac{4}{9}\right) = (12 \times 5) + \left(12 \times \frac{4}{9}\right)$

17. Colette is finding the product $\frac{41}{36} \times \frac{60}{19}$. Explain how she can divide out the common factors from the numerator and the denominator in one step.

18. Twelve square tiles, each measuring $5\frac{3}{8}$ inches on a side, are laid side by side. What is the total width of the tiles?

19. The following shows a student's calculation of the product $1\frac{1}{3} \times 1\frac{2}{3}$. Explain the error in the student's work.

    $$1\frac{1}{3} \times 1\frac{2}{3} = \frac{4}{3} \times \frac{5}{3}$$
    $$= \frac{20}{3}$$
    $$= 6\frac{1}{3}$$

20. The table shows the number of hours Monty spent doing homework last week.

Mon	Tue	Wed	Thu	Fri
$1\frac{1}{2}$	$\frac{3}{4}$	$2\frac{1}{4}$	$1\frac{5}{6}$	1

    This week Monty spent $1\frac{1}{2}$ times as much time doing homework as he did last week. How many hours did he spend this week?

21. On the first day of his backpacking trip, Andy left camp at 9:15 A.M. and arrived at his new camp at 4:45 P.M. His average rate of speed was $2\frac{1}{2}$ miles per hour. On the second day he left the new camp at 8:45 A.M. and arrived at his final camp at 3:30 P.M. His average rate of speed was 3 miles per hour. Find the total distance that he hiked over the two days.

MATHEMATICAL PRACTICES
Make Sense of Problems

22. Lainie earns $13.50 per hour as a grocery clerk. This week she worked $4\frac{1}{2}$ days for an average of $5\frac{1}{3}$ hours per day. Find her total earnings.

Dividing Fractions and Mixed Numbers

How Many Sandwiches?

Lesson 6-1 Dividing by Fractions

Learning Targets:

- Divide a whole number by a fraction less than 1.
- Divide a fraction by a whole number or fraction.
- Solve real-world problems by dividing such numbers.

SUGGESTED LEARNING STRATEGIES: Close Reading, Marking the Text, Predict and Confirm, Think Aloud, Create Representations, Identify a Subtask, Look for a Pattern

Brenna is in charge of ordering lunch for the student council members at Jackson Middle School. She buys a 6-foot-long sandwich at Significant Subs and slices it into $\frac{1}{2}$-foot sections.

1. **a.** Draw a pictorial model you can use to find the number of sections Brenna slices. Show the model divided into $\frac{1}{2}$-foot pieces.

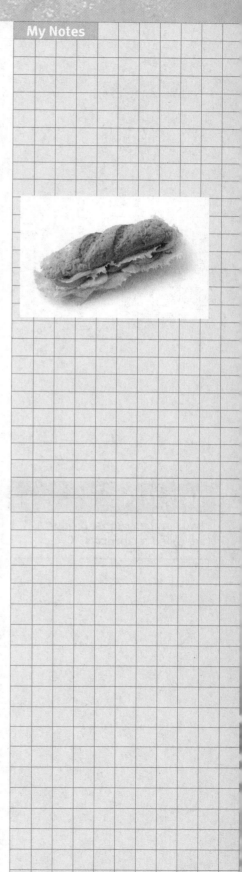

   b. $6 \div \frac{1}{2} =$ _____

For drinks, Brenna bought 4 quarts of milk. She figured that students would drink an average of $\frac{1}{3}$ quart apiece.

2. **a. Model with mathematics.** Draw a pictorial model you can use to find the number of servings of milk 4 quarts can provide. Show the model divided into $\frac{1}{3}$-quart sections.

   b. $4 \div \frac{1}{3} =$ _____

3. Look at the number sentences in Items 1b and 2b.
   a. Describe patterns that you see.

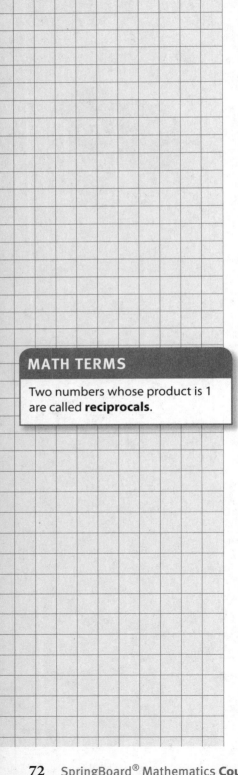

My Notes

b. **Reason abstractly.** Explain how you could have solved the problems without using the pictorial models.

The student council meeting lasted $\frac{5}{6}$ of an hour. The president decided that $\frac{1}{12}$ of an hour was to be allotted to discuss each item of business.

4. a. The model represents 1 hour. Shade the correct number of squares to represent $\frac{5}{6}$ of an hour, the length of the meeting.

b. How many $\frac{1}{12}$ hours are in $\frac{5}{6}$ of an hour?

c. **Make use of structure.** Use the pattern you found in Item 3 to find the answer to this division: $\frac{5}{6} \div \frac{1}{12} =$ _____

d. Does the pattern you described in Item 3 hold when you divide a fraction by another fraction? Explain.

The patterns you have investigated can be summarized in this algorithm:

• To divide by a fraction, *multiply* by the **reciprocal** of the fraction.

The reciprocal of a fraction is the fraction you obtain by interchanging the numerator and the denominator.

fraction: $\frac{3}{7}$ reciprocal: $\frac{7}{3}$

The product of a number and its reciprocal is always 1.

$$\frac{{}^{1}\cancel{3}}{\cancel{7}_{1}} \times \frac{{}^{1}\cancel{7}}{\cancel{3}_{1}} = 1$$

MATH TERMS

Two numbers whose product is 1 are called **reciprocals**.

5. Find the reciprocal of each number.

a. $\frac{4}{5}$ b. 6   c. $\frac{8}{5}$

My Notes

Example A

Divide: $\frac{3}{11} \div \frac{3}{8}$.

Step 1: Multiply by the reciprocal of the divisor.

Step 2: Simplify.

Step 3: Write the quotient in simplest form.

Solution: $\frac{3}{11} \div \frac{3}{8} = \frac{8}{11}$

$$\frac{3}{11} \div \frac{3}{8} = \frac{3}{11} \times \frac{8}{3}$$
$$= \frac{\overset{1}{\cancel{3}}}{11} \times \frac{8}{\underset{1}{\cancel{3}}}$$
$$= \frac{8}{11}$$

Try These A

Determine each quotient in simplest form.

a. $\frac{1}{13} \div \frac{1}{2}$ **b.** $\frac{7}{8} \div \frac{3}{4}$ **c.** $\frac{2}{5} \div \frac{7}{10}$

When you divide by a fraction, the dividend may be a whole number or a mixed number. When this happens, rewrite the dividend as an improper fraction. Then use the algorithm for dividing fractions.

Example B

Divide: $1\frac{2}{3} \div \frac{5}{6}$.

Step 1: Write the mixed number as an improper fraction.

Step 2: Multiply by the reciprocal of the divisor.

Step 3: Simplify.

Step 4: Write the quotient in simplest form.

Solution: $1\frac{2}{3} \div \frac{5}{6} = 2$

$$1\frac{2}{3} \div \frac{5}{6} = \frac{5}{3} \div \frac{5}{6}$$
$$= \frac{5}{3} \times \frac{6}{5}$$
$$= \frac{\overset{1}{\cancel{5}}}{3} \times \frac{6}{\underset{1}{\cancel{5}}}$$
$$= \frac{6}{3}, \text{ or } 2$$

Try These B

Determine each quotient in simplest form.

a. $2\frac{5}{6} \div \frac{5}{12}$ **b.** $4 \div \frac{2}{7}$ **c.** $4\frac{5}{8} \div \frac{5}{8}$

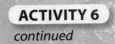

My Notes

6. Complete: The number of fourths in 20 equals the number of _____ in 10 which equals the number of fifths in _____.

7. Find the value of n: $\frac{4}{5} \div \frac{n}{6} = \frac{4}{5} \times \frac{n}{6}$

Check Your Understanding

8. Determine the reciprocal of the fraction.
   a. $\frac{5}{9}$
   b. $\frac{12}{11}$
   c. $\frac{1}{15}$

9. Determine each quotient in simplest form.
   a. $\frac{1}{2} \div \frac{1}{4}$
   b. $\frac{4}{5} \div \frac{2}{3}$
   c. $7 \div \frac{1}{4}$
   d. $\frac{5}{12} \div \frac{5}{6}$
   e. $3\frac{1}{3} \div \frac{3}{4}$
   f. $\frac{18}{25} \div \frac{3}{5}$
   g. $1 \div \frac{9}{13}$
   h. $1\frac{3}{5} \div \frac{5}{6}$
   i. $\frac{7}{8} \div \frac{7}{16}$

LESSON 6-1 PRACTICE

10. Hannah bought $9\frac{1}{2}$ pounds of ground beef to make hamburgers for a party. How many $\frac{1}{4}$-pound burgers can she make?

11. A bookshelf has 7 shelves, each measuring 4 feet 3 inches in length. The average width of a book is $\frac{3}{4}$ inch. How many books will the shelves hold?

12. A snail sets out on a $3\frac{3}{5}$-mile journey, traveling at a speed of $\frac{2}{65}$ miles per hour.
    a. How many hours will the journey take?
    b. How many days will the journey take?

13. **Make sense of problems.** A 4-foot-long submarine sandwich costs $24. A 6-inch submarine sandwich costs $3.95. How much money can you save by buying the 4-footer and slicing it into 6-inch sandwiches?

14. Jake has $3 in quarters in his pocket. Explain how to use reciprocals to find the number of quarters that he has.

15. **Reason abstractly.** State a simple rule you can use to find the quotient of two fractions that have the same denominator.

16. Write a problem that you can solve by finding the quotient $\frac{1}{2} \div \frac{2}{3}$.

17. The Baxter Freeway is 24 miles long. There is a telephone at the beginning, the end, and every $\frac{3}{4}$ mile along the freeway. How many telephones are there altogether?

Learning Targets:

- Divide a mixed number, whole number, or fraction by a mixed number.
- Estimate such quotients.
- Solve real-world problems by dividing such numbers.

> **SUGGESTED LEARNING STRATEGIES:** Marking the Text, Think Aloud, Sharing and Responding, Identify a Subtask

When you divide by a mixed number, rewrite the mixed number as an improper fraction. Then use the algorithm for dividing fractions.

Example A

The school day at Jackson Middle School is $7\frac{1}{2}$ hours long. It is divided into double periods, each lasting $1\frac{1}{4}$ hours. How many double periods are there in a day?

Step 1: Determine the operation:

Divide: $7\frac{1}{2} \div 1\frac{1}{4}$

Step 2: Estimate the number of double periods in a day.

Round $7\frac{1}{2}$ to 8 and $1\frac{1}{4}$ to 1: $8 \div 1 = 8$, so there are about 8 double periods.

Step 3: Write the mixed numbers as improper fractions. $\qquad 7\frac{1}{2} \div 1\frac{1}{4} = \frac{15}{2} \div \frac{5}{4}$

Step 4: Multiply by the reciprocal of the divisor. $\qquad = \frac{15}{2} \times \frac{4}{5}$

Step 5: Multiply. $\qquad = \frac{15}{2} \times \frac{4}{5}$

Solution: $\qquad = 6$

There are 6 double periods in a day. The answer is reasonable because it is close to the estimate.

Try These A

Divide. Write the quotient in simplest form.

a. $1\frac{2}{5} \div 1\frac{13}{15}$ **b.** $3\frac{3}{5} \div 2\frac{1}{4}$ **c.** $4\frac{1}{8} \div 1\frac{5}{6}$

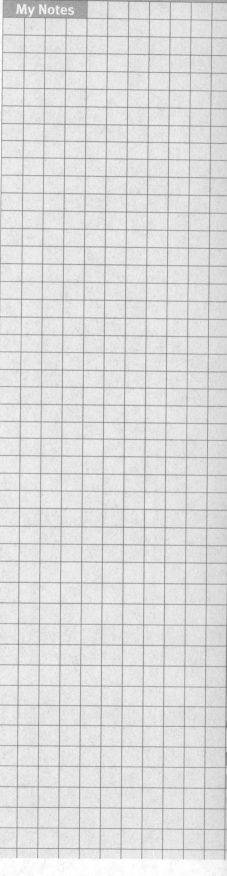
My Notes

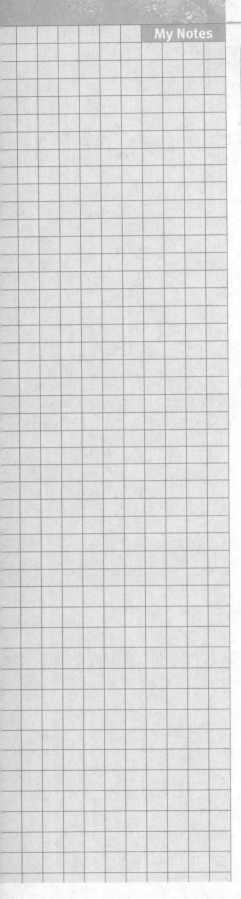

My Notes

Check Your Understanding

1. Give the reciprocal of the number.

   a. $2\frac{2}{3}$ b. $5\frac{5}{11}$ c. $9\frac{9}{10}$

2. Estimate the quotient.

   a. $14\frac{2}{5} \div 1\frac{3}{4}$ b. $3\frac{3}{7} \div 7\frac{1}{5}$ c. $12\frac{2}{11} \div 2\frac{6}{11}$

3. Divide.

   a. $1\frac{5}{7} \div 1\frac{3}{7}$ b. $5 \div 3\frac{3}{4}$ c. $1\frac{5}{6} \div 1\frac{2}{9}$

   d. $5\frac{1}{4} \div 4\frac{1}{5}$ e. $6\frac{2}{5} \div 1\frac{2}{5}$ f. $1 \div 3\frac{6}{7}$

   g. $8\frac{1}{8} \div 1\frac{5}{8}$ h. $3\frac{5}{8} \div 1\frac{1}{6}$ i. $6\frac{1}{2} \div 3\frac{3}{4}$

LESSON 6-2 PRACTICE

4. A candle burns for $3\frac{2}{15}$ hours. Estimate the number of candles you would need to give light for 24 hours.

5. A machine can make a box in $3\frac{17}{20}$ seconds. Estimate the number of boxes it can make in $33\frac{1}{2}$ seconds.

6. A recipe for onion soup calls for $1\frac{1}{4}$ cups of onions. Amy has 5 cups of onions.

   a. **Model with mathematics.** Draw a model you can use to find the number of batches of soup Amy can make.

   b. $5 \div 1\frac{1}{4} = ?$

7. Ted has 18 feet of lumber. How many $2\frac{1}{2}$-foot shelves can he make? Explain your answer.

8. Claire has 38 yards of material to make costumes for the school play. She needs $2\frac{3}{8}$ yards for each costume. How many costumes can she make?

9. Val talked for $3\frac{1}{2}$ hours on her cell phone this week. That is $1\frac{1}{2}$ times as long as she talked last week. How long did she talk last week?

10. a. $4\frac{2}{11} \times$ some number $= 6$. What is the number?

    b. **Reason quantitatively.** Explain how you found the number.

ACTIVITY 6 PRACTICE
Write your answers on notebook paper.
Show your work.

Express your answers in simplest form.

Lesson 6-1

1. Find the quotient $8 \div \frac{1}{5}$.

   A. $\frac{1}{40}$ **B.** $\frac{5}{8}$

   C. $\frac{8}{5}$ **D.** 40

2. What is the reciprocal of $\frac{7}{11}$?

   A. $1\frac{4}{7}$ **B.** 7

   C. 11   **D.** 77

3. a. Copy the model below. Then shade it to show the fraction $\frac{4}{5}$.

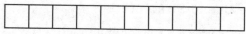

   b. Mark X's in the square to show the quotient $\frac{4}{5} \div \frac{1}{10}$.

   c. $\frac{4}{5} \div \frac{1}{10} = ?$

4. One event at a debate tournament lasted $2\frac{4}{5}$ hours. Each contestant spoke for $\frac{2}{15}$ of an hour. How many contestants were there?

5. Each side of Jose's patio is $21\frac{1}{4}$ feet long and is lined with bricks measuring $\frac{17}{24}$ of a foot in length. How many bricks line each side of the patio?

6. Use the algorithm for dividing by a fraction to show that when you divide a fraction by itself, the quotient is 1. Use an example to illustrate your answer.

7. Jonas's vacuum cleaner uses $\frac{5}{8}$ kilowatt of electricity per hour. His clothes dryer uses $4\frac{11}{16}$ kilowatts of electricity per hour. How many hours can he operate his vacuum cleaner on the same amount of energy it takes to power his clothes dryer for 1 hour?

8. Denise sells pizza for $0.89 a slice. Each slice of her pepperoni pizza is $\frac{1}{8}$ of a pizza. Each slice of her mushroom pizza is $\frac{1}{10}$ of a pizza. Today she sold all of the slices of 7 pepperoni pizzas and 6 mushroom pizzas. How much money did she make?

9. A turtle walking at an average speed of $\frac{3}{10}$ mile per hour takes $\frac{13}{20}$ hour to walk from its home to the seashore. How long will the journey take if the turtle doubles its average speed? Explain your reasoning.

Remember to express your answers in simplest form.

Lesson 6-2

10. What is the reciprocal of $2\frac{3}{8}$?

   A. $\frac{1}{2} \times \frac{8}{3}$ B. $\frac{8}{19}$

   C. $\frac{19}{8}$ D. $2\frac{8}{3}$

11. Estimate the quotient $24\frac{3}{7} \div 3\frac{7}{13}$ by rounding to the nearest whole number.

   A. 6   B. $6\frac{1}{4}$

   C. 8   D. $8\frac{1}{3}$

12. Divide: $1\frac{4}{5} \div 2\frac{1}{4}$.

   A. $\frac{20}{81}$ B. $\frac{4}{5}$

   C. $1\frac{1}{4}$ D. $4\frac{1}{20}$

13. In the country of Remish, 1 dollar is worth $1\frac{7}{20}$ rems. Find the value, in dollars, of $33\frac{3}{4}$ rems.

14. During the days leading up to her piano recital, Lana practiced an average of $1\frac{5}{12}$ hours per day. Her total practice time was $11\frac{1}{3}$ hours. How many days did she practice?

15. A rectangular garden has an area of $9\frac{5}{24}$ square yards. The garden is $2\frac{1}{6}$ yards wide. How long is it?

   (area of rectangle = length × width)

16. A shoot of bamboo, one of the world's fastest-growing plants, grew at a rate of $2\frac{3}{10}$ inches per hour. How long did it take for the shoot to grow $14\frac{3}{8}$ inches?

17. One rod equals $16\frac{1}{2}$ feet. The One Island East Centre Building in Hong Kong, China, is 979 feet tall. Find the height of the building in rods.

18. The seating area of a school bus is $35\frac{3}{4}$ feet long. Each row uses $3\frac{1}{4}$ feet of space. On the left side of the bus, 3 students sit in each row. On the right side, 2 students sit in each row. How many students can ride the bus?

MATHEMATICAL PRACTICES
Make Use of Structure

19. Explain each step of dividing $13\frac{1}{2}$ by $1\frac{1}{2}$:

   a. $13\frac{1}{2} \div 1\frac{1}{2} = \frac{27}{2} \div \frac{3}{2}$

   b. $\qquad = \frac{27}{2} \times \frac{2}{3}$

   c. $\qquad = \frac{\overset{9}{\cancel{27}}}{\cancel{2}} \times \frac{\overset{1}{\cancel{2}}}{\cancel{3}_{1}}$

   d. $\qquad = \frac{9}{1}$

   e. $\qquad = 9$

Multiplying and Dividing Fractions and Mixed Numbers

JUAN'S BOOKCASE

Write your answers on notebook paper. Show your work.

Juan plans to build a bookcase to store his paperback books, DVDs, and CDs. He has lumber that he will use for the sides and back of the bookcase. The bookcase will have five shelves, and each shelf will be $2\frac{1}{2}$ feet long.

1. Juan bought a piece of lumber that is 18 feet long.
   a. Does he have enough lumber to make the five shelves? If not, how much more does he need? If so, how much will be left over?
   b. Describe two ways you could find the answer to Part a.

2. DVD cases are $\frac{9}{16}$ inch wide.
   a. If Juan has 60 DVDs, how many of them will fit on one shelf?
   b. How wide would a DVD case have to be in order for 60 of them to fit on one shelf? Give the answer in feet.

3. Juan has 28 paperback books. Each book is $1\frac{1}{4}$ inches wide. Will all his books fit on one shelf? If not, how many will fit and how many will have to go on another shelf? If yes, how many more paperback books, if any, will fit on the same shelf? Explain.

4. Juan measured the location for the bookcase and realized that his shelves can be no more than $1\frac{3}{4}$ feet wide.
   a. What is the maximum number of shelves Juan could build for this new bookcase using the lumber he bought?
   b. How many DVD cases will he be able to store on each of the shorter shelves?
   c. How many paperback books will he be able to store on each of the shorter shelves?

5. Juan has a set of books called *Favorites of World Food*. The set is made up of this list of books, with the thickness of each book given:

   American Favorites: $\frac{5}{8}$ in. thick   Jamaican Favorites: $\frac{3}{8}$ in. thick

   Chinese Favorites: $\frac{6}{3}$ in. thick   Korean Favorites: $\frac{3}{4}$ in. thick

   Greek Favorites: $\frac{3}{5}$ in. thick   Mexican Favorites: $\frac{5}{2}$ in. thick

   Italian Favorites: $\frac{7}{4}$ in. thick

   Juan wants to place these books on a shelf in order from the thinnest book to the thickest. In what order should he place the books?

Scoring Guide	Exemplary	Proficient	Emerging	Incomplete
	The solution demonstrates these characteristics:			
Mathematics Knowledge and Thinking (Items 1a, 2a-b, 3, 4a-c)	• Clear and accurate understanding of multiplying and dividing mixed numbers and fractions.	• Correct multiplication and division of mixed numbers and fractions.	• Errors in multiplying and dividing mixed numbers and fractions.	• Incorrect or incomplete multiplication and division of mixed numbers and fractions.
Problem Solving (Items 1a, 2a-b, 3, 4a-c)	• An appropriate and efficient strategy that results in a correct answer.	• A strategy that may include unnecessary steps that result in a correct answer.	• A strategy that results in some incorrect answers.	• No clear strategy when solving problems.
Mathematical Modeling / Representations (Items 1a, 2a-b, 3, 4a-c)	• Clear and accurate representation of a problem situation as a multiplication or division expression.	• Some difficulty in representing a problem situation as a multiplication or division expression.	• Errors in representing a problem situation as a multiplication or division expression.	• Little or no understanding of representing a problem situation as a multiplication or division expression.
Reasoning and Communication (Items 1a-b, 2a-b, 3, 4a-c)	• Precise use of appropriate math terms and language when explaining a solution method. • A precise and accurate relating of a mathematical answer to a real-world situation.	• An adequate explanation of a solution method. • A relating of a mathematical answer to a real-world situation.	• A misleading or confusing explanation of a solution method. • Difficulty in the relating of a mathematical answer to a real-world situation.	• An incomplete or inaccurate explanation of a solution method • Little understanding of relating a mathematical answer to a real-world situation.

Integers

Unit Overview

In this unit, you will study negative numbers, and you will learn to add, subtract, multiply and divide them. You will graph positive and negative numbers on number lines and on the coordinate plane.

Key Terms

As you study this unit, add these and other terms to your math notebook. Include in your notes your prior knowledge of each word, as well as your experiences in using the word in different mathematical examples. If needed, ask for help in pronouncing new words and add information on pronunciation to your math notebook. It is important that you learn new terms and use them correctly in your class discussions and in your problem solutions.

Academic Vocabulary
- elevation

Math Terms
- absolute value
- integer
- opposite
- additive inverse
- coordinate plane
- origin
- quadrants
- ordered pair
- reflection

ESSENTIAL QUESTIONS

? How can integers be represented visually and how can operations with integers be represented with models?

? How are positive and negative numbers used in real-world situations?

EMBEDDED ASSESSMENTS

These assessments, following activities 8 and 10, will give you an opportunity to demonstrate your understanding of operations with integers to solve mathematical and real-world problems.

Embedded Assessment 1:

The Number Line and Adding and Subtracting Integers   p.107

Embedded Assessment 2:

Coordinate Plane and Multiplying and Dividing Integers   p.127

1. Plot the numbers on a number line. Label each number.

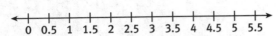

   a. 4

   b. $1\frac{1}{2}$

   c. 2.4

2. Create a visual representation to illustrate each of the following.

   a. the number of pieces of fruit in a basket if there are 3 apples, 2 pears and 4 oranges in the basket

   b. having 6 pencils and giving your friend 2 of them

3. Put the following numbers in order from smallest to largest

   a. $140 + 38 + 36 - 85$

   b. $2 \times 21 \times 3$

   c. $2048 \div 16$

   d. $150 - 67 + 53 - 9$

4. The numbers 3 and 10 are on a number line.

   a. Use a model to explain how to find the distance between the numbers.

   b. Explain in words how to find the distance between 3 and 10 on the number line.

5. Plot the following points on the coordinate plane. Label each point.

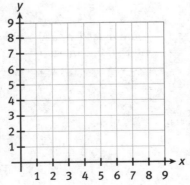

   a. $A(1, 4)$ **b.** $B(5, 3)$

   c. $C(6, 6)$ **d.** $D(0, 2)$

   e. $E(7, 0)$

6. Tell the coordinates of the points on the graph.

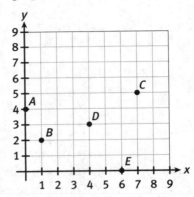

7. Olivia is getting ready to host a party.

   a. She bought 13 boxes of cookies and each box has 24 cookies in it. How many cookies does she have?

   b. She bought 3 packages of invitation and each pack had 15 invitations in it. After she mailed the invitations she had 7 invitations left. How many invitations did she send?

8. There are 265 sixth grade students at Rocky River Middle School. Each student participates in exactly one sport. 53 students play tennis, 84 play basketball, 53 play lacrosse, and the rest of the students participate in track.

   a. Explain in words one way to find the number of students who participate in track.

   b. Give a visual representation of a different way to find the number of students who participate in track.

Introduction to Integers
Get the Point?
Lesson 7-1 Integers and the Number Line

Lesson Targets:

- Use integers to represent quantities in real-world contexts.
- Position and identify integers on a number line.
- Find the opposite of an integer.
- Find the absolute value of an integer.
- Classify whole numbers, integers, and positive rational numbers.

> **SUGGESTED LEARNING STRATEGIES:** Marking the Text, Summarizing, Note Taking, Create Representations, Discussion Groups

Ms. Martinez has a point system in her classroom. Students earn points for participation, homework, teamwork, and so forth. However, students lose points for inappropriate behavior or not completing assignments. At the end of each term, students in the group with the most points receive a book or a DVD. She assigns a letter to each student for tracking his or her total points. One student is letter *A*, the next is *B*, and so on.

1. This table shows each student's total points at the end of the week. Your teacher will assign you a letter.

A	B	C	D	E	F	G	H	I	J	K	L
−3	3	8	−1	0	−5	−6	10	7	−4	1	2

M	N	O	P	Q	R	S	T	U	V	W	X
−3	−2	12	1	−7	2	−1	6	−4	−1	9	3

a. Write the total points and the letter assigned to you on a sticky note and post it on the class number line.

b. Copy the letters from the class number line to this one.

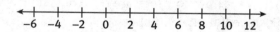

c. What do the numbers to the right of zero on the number line represent?

d. What do the numbers to the left of zero represent?

e. Explain how you knew where to place your number on the number line.

My Notes

f. Student *E* was in class for only 2 days during the week. On the first day, *E* was awarded points. On the second day, *E* lost points. Explain how *E*'s score can be zero.

> **WRITING MATH**
>
> Positive integers are written with or without a plus sign. For example, +2 and 2 indicate the same number. Negative integers are written with a negative sign. For example, −2.

The number lines below give visual representations of integers. Notice that zero is the only integer that is neither positive nor negative. **Integers** are the natural numbers (1, 2, 3, . . .), their opposites, and zero. The opposite of 0 is 0.

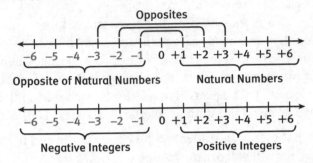

> **WRITING MATH**
>
> To indicate the opposite of a number, place a negative sign in front of the number. The opposite of 4 is −4. The opposite of −4 is −(−4) = 4.

2. Ms. Martinez uses negative numbers to represent points lost by students. Work with your group to name at least three other uses for negative numbers in real life. As you discuss the uses, ask your group members for clarification of any terms you do not understand.

> **MATH TERMS**
>
> The symbol ℤ is often used to represent the set of integers. This is because in German, the word *Zahl* means "number."

Numbers may belong to more than one category or set.
- All whole numbers are also integers.
- All whole numbers are also positive rational numbers.
- Some integers are positive rational numbers.
- Some positive rational numbers are integers.

3. **Model with mathematics.** Place the following on the Venn diagram below to show how they are related: Whole Numbers; Integers; Positive Rational Numbers.

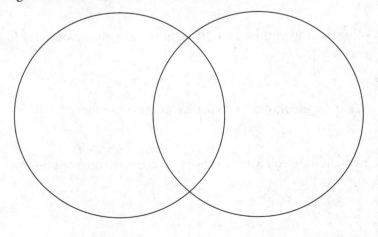

Numbers that are the same distance from zero but are on different sides of zero on a number line are **opposites**.

4. Recall that the table shows each student's total points at the end of the week.

A	B	C	D	E	F	G	H	I	J	K	L
−3	3	8	−1	0	−5	−6	10	7	−4	1	2

M	N	O	P	Q	R	S	T	U	V	W	X
−3	−2	12	1	−7	2	−1	6	−4	−1	9	3

Find three pairs of students with scores that are opposites. Explain your reasoning.

5. Look at the points for Students *A* and *B*.
   a. How many points does *A* need to *earn* to have a total of 0? Explain.

   b. How many points does *B* need to *lose* to have a total of 0? Explain.

   c. What do you notice about both student *A*'s and student *B*'s point distance from zero?

The **absolute value** of a number is the distance of the number from zero on a number line. Absolute value is always positive, because distance is always positive. The symbol for absolute value is a vertical bar on each side of a number. For example, $|3| = 3$ and $|−3| = 3$.

6. Why is distance always positive? Use an example in your explanation.

READING MATH

Read $|6| = 6$ as the absolute value of 6 is 6. Read $|−6| = 6$ as the absolute value of negative 6 is 6.

7. From the ground floor of the school, Ms. Martinez goes down 1 flight of stairs to get to the basement.
   a. Write an integer to represent the situation.
   b. What is the opposite of the situation above? What integer represents this situation?

   c. Explain what 0 represents in this situation.
   d. Explain what the absolute value | 1 | represents in this situation.

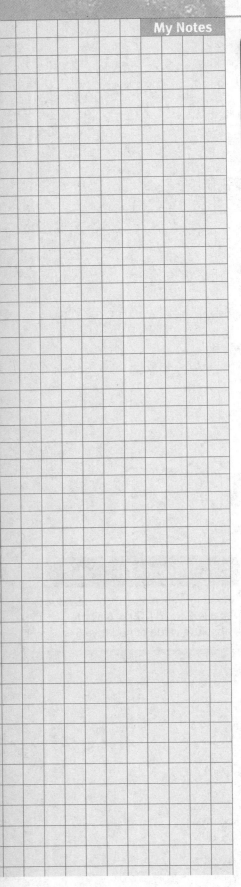

My Notes

Check Your Understanding

8. The football team loses 5 yards on first down.
   a. Write an integer to represent this situation.
   b. Write an integer to represent the opposite of the situation in part a.
   c. What does 0 mean in this situation?

9. Write the opposite of each integer.
   a. 9   b. 0   c. −12

10. Write each absolute value.
    a. $|10|$ b. $|-8|$ c. $|0|$

11. **Reason quantitatively.** What values can x have if $|x| = 8$?

LESSON 7-1 PRACTICE

For Items 12–14, locate each integer on a number line.

12. −4   13. 7   14. −9

For Items 15–17, identify the integer for each point.

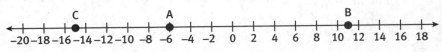

15. *A*   16. *B*   17. *C*

For Items 18–20, write the opposite of each integer.

18. 23   19. −41   20. −78

For Items 21–23, write an integer to represent each situation. Explain the opposite of the situation and write an integer to represent the opposite. Then explain what 0 means in each situation.

21. temperature of 7 degrees below 0

22. a gain of 3 pounds

23. a withdrawal of $15

For Items 24–26, write each absolute value.

24. $|9|$ 25. $|-3|$ 26. $|-46|$

27. **Model with mathematics.** The lowest elevation of Death Valley is about −282 feet. Find the absolute value of the lowest elevation of Death Valley. Explain what this absolute value means.

28. **Make sense of problems.** The height of an iceberg above the water is 38 meters. The bottom of the iceberg is 21 meters below sea level. Write integers to represent the height and depth of the iceberg. Explain what 0 means in the situation.

29. The counting, or natural, numbers are 1, 2, 3,... How could you add counting numbers to the Venn diagram on page 84?

Lesson Targets:

- Compare and order integers.
- Interpret statements of inequality of integers in terms of a number line and of real-world contexts.
- Distinguish comparisons of absolute value from statements about the order of integers.

> **SUGGESTED LEARNING STRATEGIES:** Marking the Text, Summarizing, Create Representations, Sharing and Responding, Use Manipulatives

Ms. Martinez sometimes assigns students to cooperative learning groups. She assigns each group member a role based on his or her total points. The roles are reporter (lowest total), recorder (next to lowest total), facilitator (next to highest total), and timekeeper (highest total).

1. Use the number lines to plot each student's total for Groups 1 through 4. For Groups 5 and 6, create your own number lines. Then order the points for the members in each group from lowest to highest and determine who will have each role in the group.

My Notes

MATH TIP

Numbers increase from left to right on a number line.

a. Group 1:

A	B	C	D
−3	3	8	−1

$$\begin{array}{ccccccc} \mid & \mid & \mid & \mid & \mid & \mid & \mid \\ -4 & -2 & 0 & 2 & 4 & 6 & 8 \end{array}$$

b. Group 2:

E	F	G	H
0	−5	−6	10

$$\begin{array}{ccccccccc} \mid & \mid & \mid & \mid & \mid & \mid & \mid & \mid & \mid \\ -6 & -4 & -2 & 0 & 2 & 4 & 6 & 8 & 10 \end{array}$$

c. Group 3:

I	J	K	L
7	−4	1	2

$$\begin{array}{ccccccccc} \mid & \mid & \mid & \mid & \mid & \mid & \mid & \mid \end{array}$$

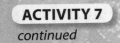

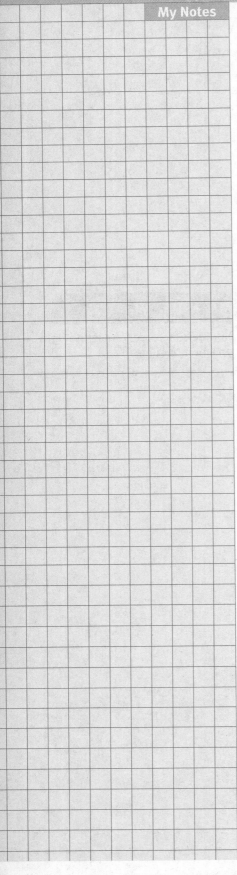

d. Group 4:

M	N	O	P
−3	−2	12	1

e. Group 5:

Q	R	S	T
−7	2	−1	6

f. Group 6:

U	V	W	X
−4	−1	9	3

2. a. Student *T* has 4 points and Student *X* has 3 points. Who has more points? Explain.

b. Student *S* has −1 point and Student *P* has 1 point. Who has more points? Explain.

c. Student *U* has −4 points and Student *N* has −2 points. Who has more points? Explain.

d. Complete using > or <.

4 ◯ 3   −1 ◯ 1   −4 ◯ −2

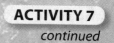

3. Student *F* has −5 points and Student *R* has 2 points. Explain how to determine which student has the greater number of points.

You used a number line to compare and order integers. You can also use absolute value to compare and order integers.

Example

Compare −98 and −90.

Step 1: Find the absolute value of each integer.

$$|-98| = 98 \qquad |-90| = 90$$

Step 2: Compare the distances from 0.

−98 is farther left from 0 than −90, so −98 is less than −90.

Solution: −98 < −90

Try These

Use absolute value to compare. Write > or <.
a. −58 ◯ −63
b. −21 ◯ −19
c. −100 ◯ −110

4. The first week a student in Ms. Martinez's class had a total of −6 points. The second week the student had a total of −2 points. In which week did the student have the greater number of points? Explain your thinking.

5. Student *M* has a total of −3 points, Student *Q* has −7 points, Student *S* has −1 point, and Student *U* has −4 points. Explain how to use absolute value to order each student's points from least to greatest.

My Notes

My Notes

Check Your Understanding

6. Explain how to use a number line to order the integers −5, 6, and −2 from least to greatest.

7. Explain how to use absolute value to determine which integer is greater, −43 or −39.

LESSON 7-2 PRACTICE

For Items 8–16, compare each pair of integers. Write > or <.

8. 17 ◯ 20   **9.** 0 ◯ −5   **10.** 23 ◯ −46

11. −9 ◯ 3   **12.** −1 ◯ −16   **13.** −82 ◯ 0

14. −39 ◯ −90   **15.** −4 ◯ 4   **16.** −71 ◯ −28

For Items 17 and 18, use the number line to write the integers in order from least to greatest.

17. 4, −7, 3, −2, 0

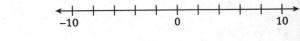

18. −5, 8, 2, −6, −9, 1

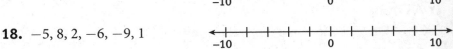

For Items 19–22, write the integers in order from least to greatest.

19. −8, 1, −11, 10   **20.** 3, −26, 0, −17, 15

21. 7, −8, 9, −16, −13   **22.** 48, −53, 32, −41, −35, 20

23. Critique the reasoning of others. Lexie says that −68 feet is a greater depth than −75 feet, since −68 > −75. Is Lexie correct? Explain why or why not.

24. Make sense of problems. In golf, the person with the lowest score wins the round. At the end of a golf round, Henry's score was 2 under par, Maria's score was 1 above par, Jorge's score was 3 under par, and Setsuko's score was 4 above par. Write each player's score as an integer. Then order the scores from least to greatest. Who won the round? Explain your reasoning.

25. Reason quantitatively. On Monday, the prices of four of Kyle's stocks fell. At market close, Stock A was −8 points from the opening price, Stock B was −3 points, Stock C was −12 points, and Stock D was −7 points. Which stock lost the greatest amount on Monday? Which stock lost the least amount? Explain your reasoning.

26. Consider the inequality −4 > −6. What does the inequality tell you about the relative positions of −4 and −6 on a horizontal number line?

ACTIVITY 7 PRACTICE
Write your answers on a separate piece of paper.
Show your work.

Lesson 7-1

1. Locate each integer on a number line.
   a. 3   **b.** −1
   c. −7   **d.** 8
   e. 12   **f.** −15

2. Identify the integer for each point.

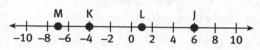

   a. *J*   **b.** *K*
   c. *L*   **d.** *M*

For Items 3–6, write an integer to represent each situation.

3. loss of 8 yards

4. change in score after an inning with no runs

5. depth of 15 meters below sea level

6. go up 4 flights of stairs

For Items 7–11, write an integer to represent each situation. Then tell what 0 means for the situation.

7. loss of 6 pounds

8. a withdrawal of $25

9. an elevation of 1,200 feet

10. a score of 2 under par

11. an elevator going down 7 floors

12. Write the opposite integer.
    a. 2   **b.** −13
    c. −68   **d.** 94
    e. 187   **f.** −275

13. What is the value of −(−8)? Explain your answer.

14. Write the answer for items a–b.
    a. Write an integer that represents the opposite of 15.
    b. Write an integer that represents the opposite of the opposite of 15.
    c. What is the result of finding the opposite of the opposite of a number?

15. Which integer is its own opposite? Explain your thinking.

For Items 16–19, explain the opposite of each situation. Then write an integer to represent the opposite.

16. a deposit of $20

17. 9 degrees below zero

18. a loss of 12 points

19. 35 feet above sea level

20. Write each absolute value.
    a. $|-14|$ **b.** $|0|$
    c. $|123|$ **d.** $|-80|$
    e. $|-204|$ **f.** $\left|1\frac{1}{2}\right|$

21. Which integer is neither positive nor negative?

22. Classify each number as a whole number, an integer, or a positive rational number. Use as many ways as possible.
    a. 8   **b.** −15
    c. 0   **d.** $\frac{3}{4}$

23. On first down, a football team moved −15 yards. Did the team gain or lose yards on the play? How many yards? Explain.

24. The base of a volcano is on the ocean floor 20,000 feet below sea level. Write an integer to represent the depth of the volcano in the ocean. Find the absolute value of the integer and explain what it means.

25. At dawn, the temperature on the mountain peak was 3 degrees below 0. Which integer below represents this temperature?
    A. −3°   **B.** 3°
    C. −15°   **D.** 15°

26. Sketch a Venn diagram showing the relationship between the sets of numbers.
    a. the positive integers and positive rational numbers
    b. the integers and the whole numbers

Lesson 7-2

For Items 27–37, Write > or < to compare the integers.

27. $6 \bigcirc -3$

28. $-1 \bigcirc 0$

29. $9 \bigcirc 7$

30. $-14 \bigcirc -2$

31. $-7 \bigcirc -5$

32. $12 \bigcirc 0$

33. $-4 \bigcirc -19$

34. $-28 \bigcirc 1$

35. $0 \bigcirc -8$

36. $-21 \bigcirc -17$

37. $-49 \bigcirc -50$

For Items 38–40, use the number line to write the integers in order from least to greatest.

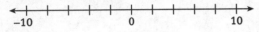

38. $6, -2, 4, -5$

39. $-4, -8, 3, 0, 7$

40. $10, -1, 5, -9, -6$

For Items 41–45, write the integers in order from least to greatest.

41. $-2, 8, -12, 3$

42. $10, -9, 14, -5, -1$

43. $-30, -25, 20, -50, 35$

44. $7, 14, -21, 35, -42$

45. $-40, -32, 8, -48, 24$

46. Which choice below shows the integers in order from least to greatest?
 A. $3, -3, -1, 1$
 B. $-1, -3, 1, 3$
 C. $-3, -1, 1, 3$
 D. $1, 3, -3, -1$

The table shows the high and low temperatures for 5 consecutive days in February at North Pole, Alaska. Use the table for Items 47–49.

	Mon	Tues	Wed	Thurs	Fri
High	1	−29	−27	5	7
Low	−13	−45	−54	−2	1

47. Order the high temperatures from warmest to coldest over this five-day period. Which day had the warmest high temperature?

48. Order the low temperatures from coldest to warmest over this five-day period. Which day had the coldest low temperature?

49. Is the order of days from warmest to coldest daily low temperatures the same as for the daily high temperatures? Explain.

50. Use the absolute value of the given integer to explain what each statement represents.
 a. The elevation of the cave is below −45 feet.
 b. The temperature is below −10 degrees.

51. A diver made two dives. The first dive was to a sunken ship located at a depth of −45 feet. The second dive was to a coral reef at a depth of −29 feet. Which was the deeper dive, to the sunken ship or to the coral reef?

52. Randy played four rounds of golf on his vacation. Randy's score for his first round was 6 above par, for his second round 1 above par, for his third round 2 under par, and for his last round 1 under par. Order his scores from least to greatest. Which round was Randy's best round?

53. Which integer is not between 2 and −18?
 A. −9
 B. 0
 C. 3
 D. −10

54. Consider the inequality $-8 < -2$. What does the inequality tell you about the relative positions of -8 and -2 on a horizontal number line?

MATHEMATICAL PRACTICES
Reason Abstractly and Quantitatively

55. What is the opposite of $|-6|$? Explain your reasoning.

Adding and Subtracting Integers

What's the Temperature?
Lesson 8-1 Using Models to Add Integers

Learning Targets:

- Using models, create several representations of a given integer.
- Using models, add any two integers with absolute value less than 10.

> **SUGGESTED LEARNING STRATEGIES:** Summarizing, Create Representations, Use Manipulatives

Students are tracking winter temperature changes throughout their state for a class science project. They will determine temperatures at different times as the temperature rises or falls. To find the temperatures, they will have to add integers. Models can be used to add integers, but first the students must create models to represent the integers.

Two ways to represent integers with models are on a number line or with counters.

Example A

Represent the number 4 using counters and on a number line.

Solution: Line up 4 positive counters to represent 4. $\oplus \oplus \oplus \oplus$
Place a dot at 4 on a number line.

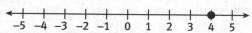

MATH TIP

A positive counter, $\oplus$, represents 1.
A negative counter, $\ominus$, represents -1.

Try These A

Represent each integer below using both a number line and counters. You may draw the counters or use counters from your teacher.

a. 7   **b.** -3

1. This morning, the temperature was 2°F at 6 A.M. The temperature rose 3°F by 7 A.M. What was the temperature at 7 A.M.?
   a. Use counters to represent the addends of the problem.

   b. Explain how these counters model $2 + 3 = 5$.

   c. Explain how the number line models $2 + 3 = 5$.

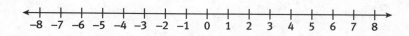

MATH TIP

To add using a number line, start at 0. Move the number of units represented by the first addend. From that point, move the number of units represented by the second addend. The final location is the sum.

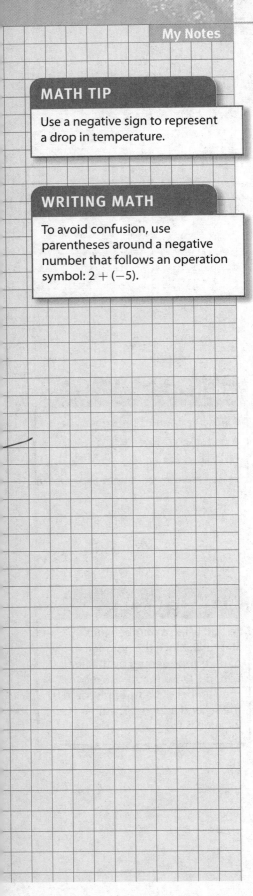

My Notes

MATH TIP

Use a negative sign to represent a drop in temperature.

WRITING MATH

To avoid confusion, use parentheses around a negative number that follows an operation symbol: $2 + (-5)$.

2. At a ski resort, the temperature is $-3°F$ at 9 P.M. The temperature drops $4°F$ by midnight. What is the temperature at midnight?
   a. Use counters to represent the problem.

   b. Explain how the counters model $-3 + (-4)$.

   c. Show and explain how to use a number line to model $-3 + (-4)$.

   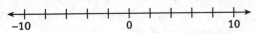

   d. Explain how both models can be used to find the temperature at midnight.

You used models to add integers with like signs. You can also use models to add integers with unlike signs.

3. What happens when you add an integer and its opposite? For example, what is $3 + (-3)$? Model this on the number line.

4. A number and its opposite are called **additive inverses**. Another name for a number and its opposite is a **zero pair**.
   a. Why do you think they are also called a **zero pair**?

   b. Which zero pair is modeled below using counters?

You can also use counters to add two integers with unlike signs.

Example B

Use counters to add $4 + (-5)$.

Step 1: Use counters to represent each integer.

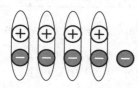

Step 2: Combine the counters to make zero pairs.

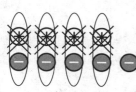

> **MATH TIP**
>
> Remember, zero pairs have a sum of zero ($-1 + 1 = 0$), so they are eliminated.

Step 3: Eliminate the zero pairs. Find the number of counters that remain.

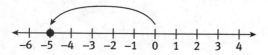 One negative counter remains.

Solution: $4 + (-5) = -1$

Try These B

Use counters to find each sum.

a. $-3 + 7$ **b.** $5 + (-2)$ **c.** $-6 + 1$

Number lines can be used to add two integers with unlike signs as well.

Example C

Use a number line to add $-5 + 3$.

Step 1: Start at 0 and move 5 units to the left to -5.

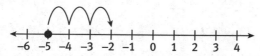

Step 2: To add 3, move 3 units to the right of -5.

> **MATH TIP**
>
> Remember, to add a positive integer move to the right on the number line. To add a negative integer, move to the left.

Step 3: The sum is the point where you land. The point is -2.

Solution: $-5 + 3 = -2$

My Notes

Try These C
Use a number line to find each sum.
a. $3 + (-8)$ **b.** $-4 + 6$ **c.** $(-5) + 1$

Check Your Understanding

5. Show how to use counters to find the sum of $3 + (-7)$. What is the sum?

6. Show how to add $-5 + 4$ using a number line. What is the sum?

LESSON 8-1 PRACTICE

Use counters or a number line to find each sum.

7. $2 + 7$

8. $-3 + (-1)$

Write an addition number sentence for the models shown.

9. ⊕ ⊕ ⊕ ⊕
   ⊖ ⊖ ⊖ ⊖

10. ⊖ ⊖
   ⊖ ⊖

11. ⊕ ⊕ ⊕
   ⊖ ⊖ ⊖ ⊖ ⊖

12. ⊕ ⊕ ⊕ ⊕ ⊕ ⊕
   ⊖ ⊖

Use counters to find each sum.

13. $1 + (-8)$

14. $-6 + 2$

15. $-3 + 9$

16. $7 + (-6)$

Use a number line to find each sum.

17. $8 + (-5)$

18. $4 + (-9)$

19. $-7 + 1$

20. $-2 + 8$

Use a model to add.

21. $-6 + 6$ **22.** $-5 + (-4)$ **23.** $-3 + 7$

24. $2 + (-2)$ **25.** $9 + (-5)$ **26.** $-8 + 4$

27. Construct viable arguments. Is adding two integers with the same sign on a number line the same as or different from adding two whole numbers on a number line? Support your answer.

28. Critique the reasoning of others. Matt used counters to add $-4 + 6$. He said that the sum is 10 since there are 10 counters in the model. Is he correct? Explain why or why not.

Learning Targets:
- Add two or more integers.
- Solve real-world problems by adding integers.

> **SUGGESTED LEARNING STRATEGIES:** Summarizing, Sharing and Responding, Look for a Pattern

You have used models to add integers. You can also use absolute value to add integers.

Rule for adding integers with the same sign:
- Find the sum of the absolute values of the addends.
- Use the same sign as the integers in the sum.

Example A
Add $-23 + (-9)$.

Step 1: Find the absolute value of each addend.
$$|-23| = 23 \qquad |-9| = 9$$

Step 2: Add the absolute values.
$$23 + 9 = 32$$

Step 3: Use the same sign as the integers in the sum.
$$-32$$

Solution: $-23 + (-9) = -32$

Try These A
Find each sum.
a. $-8 + (-7)$
b. $35 + 48$
c. $-42 + (-26)$

1. At the ski resort where the students are tracking temperatures, the low temperature on Monday is $-12°F$. Tuesday's low temperature is $15°F$ lower than on Monday.
   a. Write an addition expression to find the low temperature on Tuesday.

   b. What is the low temperature at the ski resort on Tuesday? Explain your reasoning.

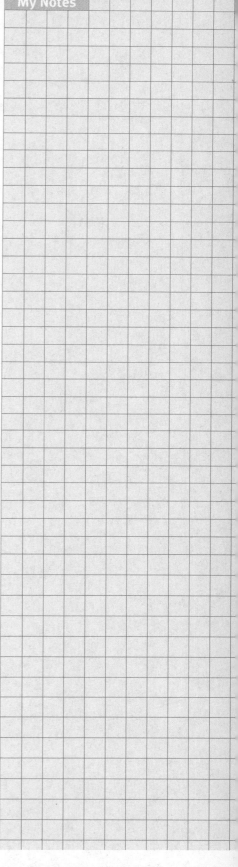

My Notes

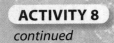

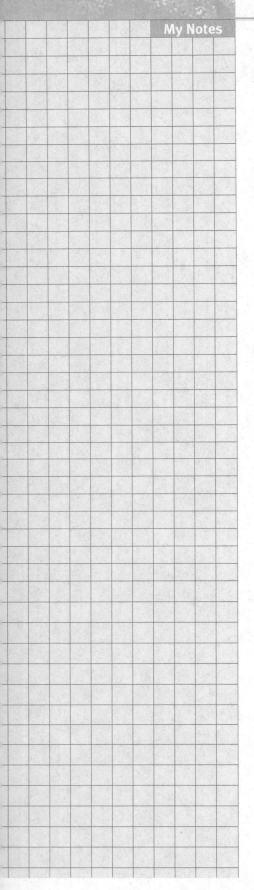

My Notes

You can also use absolute value to add integers with unlike signs.

Rules for Adding Integers with Unlike Signs:
- When adding integers with different signs, find the difference of the absolute values.
- Use the sign of the integer with the greater absolute value for the sum.

Example B

Add $31 + (-45)$.

Step 1: Find the absolute value of each addend.
$$|31| = 31 \qquad |-45| = 45$$

Step 2: Subtract the lesser absolute value from the greater absolute value.
$$45 - 31 = 14$$

Step 3: Use the sign of the integer with the greater absolute value.
$|-45| > |31|$, so the sum is negative.

Solution: $31 + (-45) = -14$

Try These B

Determine if the sum is positive or negative. Then find each sum.
a. $-16 + 4$
b. $23 + (-15)$
c. $-50 + 72$

2. At the ski resort, the high temperature on Thursday is $-7°$F. Friday's high temperature is $14°$F higher than on Thursday.
a. Write an addition expression to find the high temperature on Friday.

b. What is the high temperature at the ski resort on Friday? Explain.

3. At 8 A.M., the temperature at the peak on the mountain is $-24°$F. The temperature at mid-mountain is 8 degrees warmer than at the peak. The temperature at the base of the mountain is 11 degrees warmer than it is at mid-mountain. Explain how to find the temperature at the base of the mountain.

Lesson 8-2
Using Rules to Add Integers

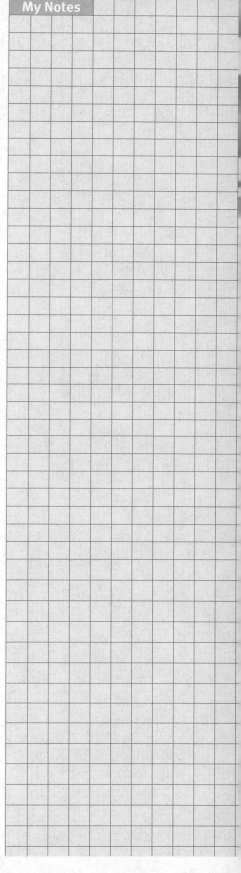

Check Your Understanding

4. Explain how to use absolute value to add $-17 + (-4)$.

5. Explain how to use absolute value to add $-8 + 12$.

LESSON 8-2 PRACTICE

For Items 6–9, determine if each sum is positive or negative.

6. $-10 + (-4)$ 7. $-51 + 25$

8. $16 + (-11)$ 9. $-32 + 39$

For Items 10–19, find the sum.

10. $-3 + 9$ 11. $-5 + (-7)$

12. $-14 + 6$ 13. $-32 + 39$

14. $16 + (-11)$ 15. $-16 + 24$

16. $-3 + (-29)$ 17. $48 + (-27)$

18. $58 + (-65)$ 19. $-72 + 41$

20. Is $-9 + 14$ the same as $-14 + 9$? Explain.

21. Is $-8 + 6$ the same as $6 + (-8)$? Explain.

22. One winter morning, the temperature fell below $-6°F$. What does this temperature mean?

23. At dawn the temperature was $-3°C$. By noon the temperature increased by $5°C$. What was the temperature at noon?

24. A submarine at a depth of -26 meters rises 8 meters. What is the elevation of the submarine after it rises?

25. A liquid solution at $53°C$ is cooled $60°C$. If the solution freezes at $0°C$, is the solution frozen? Explain your reasoning.

26. **Make sense of problems.** A football team gained 5 yards, lost 8 yards, lost another 2 yards, and then gained 45 yards. What were the total yards gained or lost? Explain your reasoning.

27. **Construct viable arguments.** When is the sum of two integers negative? When is the sum positive? Write a short note explaining your thinking.

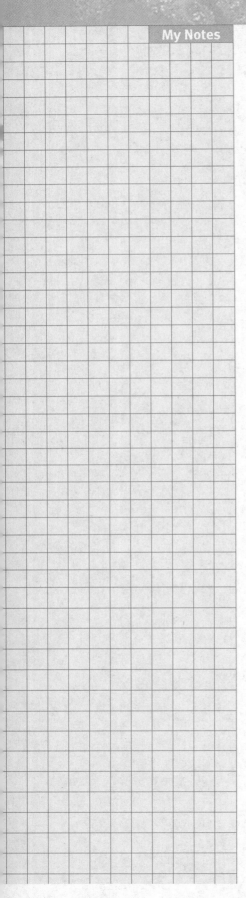

My Notes

Learning Targets:

- Use models to subtract one integer with absolute value less than 10 from another.
- Subtract integers.
- Solve real-world problems by subtracting integers.

> **SUGGESTED LEARNING STRATEGIES:** Summarizing, Sharing and Respondiing, Create Representations, Use Manipulatives

To track the winter temperatures, the students also have to subtract integers to find temperature differences. One way to subtract integers is to use models.

Example A

Use counters to subtract $-5 - (-3)$.

Step 1: Use counters to represent -5.
-5:

Step 2: Subtract 3 negative counters.

Step 3: The difference is the number of counters that remain.

Solution: $-5 - (-3) = -2$

Try These A

Use counters to find each difference. You may draw the counters or use counters from your teacher.

a. $-6 - (-1)$
b. $-4 - (-2)$
c. $-5 - (-5)$

1. **Make Use of Structure.** Consider the subtraction method used in Example A.

   a. You can use the method to subtract positive integers when the number being subtracted is less than the beginning number. Explain why.

   b. To subtract negative integers using the method in Example A, the number being subtracted must be greater than the beginning number. Explain why.

Zero pairs can be used to subtract other combinations of integers.

Example B

Use counters to subtract $6 - (-2)$.

Step 1: Start with 6 positive counters.

$\oplus \oplus \oplus \oplus \oplus \oplus$

Step 2: You need to subtract 2 negative counters. There are no negative counters in Step 1. So insert 2 zero pairs.

Step 3: Subtract the 2 negative counters.

Step 4: The difference is the number of counters that remain.

$\oplus \oplus \oplus \oplus \oplus \oplus \oplus \oplus$

Solution: $6 - (-2) = 8$

Try These B

Use counters to find each difference. You may draw the counters or use counters from your teacher. Check students' models.

a. $-2 - (-3)$　　**b.** $7 - (-1)$　　**c.** $-6 - (-4)$

2. Look at each subtraction sentence and its corresponding addition sentence.

Subtraction Sentence	Addition Sentence
$-5 - (-3) = -2$	$-5 + (+3) = -2$
$6 - (-2) = 8$	$6 - (+2) = 8$
$-8 - (+5) = -13$	$-8 + (-5) = -13$
$7 - (+4) = 3$	$7 + (-4) = 3$

a. How did the operation symbol change?

b. How did the sign of the integer being subtracted change?

c. What do you notice about the answer to each subtraction sentence and its corresponding addition sentence?

MATH TIP

Remember, zero pairs have a sum of zero $(-1 + 1 = 0)$, so adding a zero pair is like adding zero to an expression. It does not change the value of the expression.

CONNECT TO ENGLISH

Subtracting a negative number is somewhat similar to stating a double negative in English.

In English, the two negatives result in a positive to form an affirmative, or nonnegative, statement. Example: *I do not disagree.*

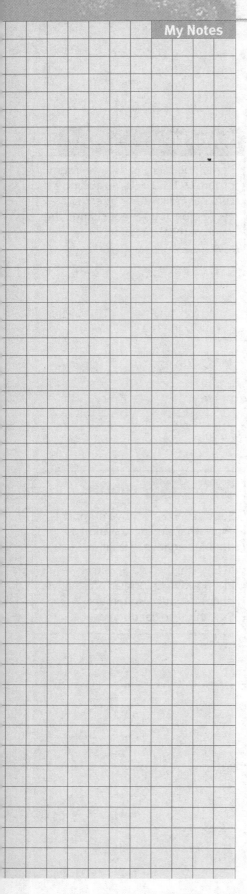

My Notes

3. Write a corresponding addition sentence for the following subtraction sentence.

$$-4 - (+6) = -10$$

You have used models to subtract integers. You have used addition to subtract integers.

Rule for Subtracting Integers: Change the subtraction sign to an addition sign and change the integer being subtracted to its opposite. Then use the rule for adding integers.

4. Use the rule for subtracting integers. Show your work.

  a. $-5 - 7$ **b.** $4 - (-9)$

  c. $-2 - (-4)$ **d.** $-8 - (-6)$

  e. $3 - (+8)$ **f.** $6 - (-2)$

  g. $-6 - (-6)$ **h.** $-3 - (-3)$

  i. $4 - (+9)$ **j.** $-5 - (+8)$

  k. $-3 - (+5)$ **l.** $7 - 9$

  m. $7 - (-2)$ **n.** $-6 - (+3)$

5. At the ski resort, the outside temperature is −7°F. The wind chill factor makes it feel like it is −12°F.

   a. Model with mathematics. Write an expression to model the difference between the actual temperature and what the temperature feels like with the wind chill.

   b. What is the difference between the actual temperature and what the temperature feels like with the wind chill?

6. At the state capital, the outside temperature is 18°F. The wind chill factor makes it feel like it is −3°F. What is the difference between the actual temperature and what the temperature feels like with the wind chill? Explain your reasoning.

7. The temperature at 6 A.M. was −15°F. At 6 P.M. the temperature was 20°F. What was the change in temperature?

8. a. Evaluate 8 − 3 and 3 − 8.

   b. Does reversing the order of the numbers in subtraction change the difference? Explain your thinking.

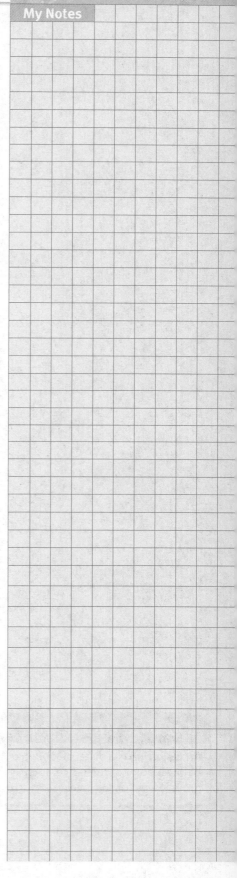

My Notes

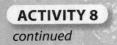

My Notes

Check Your Understanding

9. Show how to use counters to subtract $5 - (-7)$.

10. How is the expression $-8 - 2$ related to the expression $-8 + (-2)$?

11. Use the rules for subtracting integers to find each difference.
  a. $-2 - (-3)$ **b.** $1 - 6$

LESSON 8-3 PRACTICE

Write a subtraction number sentence for the models shown.

12.

13.

Use counters to find each difference.

14. $1 - (-8)$ **15.** $-6 - (-2)$

16. $-3 - 9$ **17.** $7 - (-6)$

Subtract.

18. $-4 - (-4)$ **19.** $5 - (-12)$

20. $-8 - (-17)$ **21.** $-10 - (-8)$

22. $34 - (-3)$ **23.** $9 - (-9)$

24. $-20 - (-4)$ **25.** $7 - 16$

26. Reason quantitatively. Is $5 - (-5)$ the same as $-5 - 5$? Explain your reasoning.

27. Make sense of problems. A diver jumps from a platform 16 feet above the water to a depth of 6 feet below the surface of the water. What is the distance he dives?

28. A skyscraper is 1,150 feet above ground level. It extends 35 feet below ground level. What is the total length of the skyscraper from top to bottom?

29. A submarine at an *elevation* of -48 meters descends 12 meters. What is its elevation after it descends?

30. From Monday to Tuesday, the temperature fell from 23°F to -6°F. How many degrees is this temperature change?

ACADEMIC VOCABULARY

An *elevation* is a distance above or below a point of reference, such as ground level or sea level.

ACTIVITY 8 PRACTICE

Write your answers on a separate piece of paper.
Show your work.

Lesson 8-1

1. Write an addition number sentence for the model shown.

   a.

   b.

2. Use counters to find each sum.
   a. $-8 + 2$
   b. $9 + (-7)$
   c. $-4 + (-6)$

3. Use a number line to find each sum.
   a. $6 + (-1)$
   b. $3 + (-7)$
   c. $-9 + 6$

4. Use models to add.
   a. $2 + (-5)$
   b. $-3 + (-4)$
   c. $-7 + 1$
   d. $-5 + 8$
   e. $9 + (-4)$

5. What is the sum of a number and its opposite? Use a model in your explanation.

Lesson 8-2

6. Determine if each sum will be positive or negative.
   a. $9 + (-1)$
   b. $-6 + 3$
   c. $5 + (-8)$
   d. $-3 + 7$

For Items 7–16, find each sum.

7. $-6 + 14$

8. $-3 + (-10)$

9. $12 + (-5)$

10. $-8 + (-4)$

11. $9 + (-11)$

12. $-24 + (-15)$

13. $-19 + 16$

14. $50 + (-21)$

15. $-46 + 32$

16. $6 + (-12)$
   a. -18 b. -6
   c. 6 d. 18

17. The Commutative Property of Addition says that the order of the addends does not change the sum. Is the Commutative Property true for integers? Explain your reasoning.

18. A scuba diver is swimming at an elevation of 52 feet below sea level. She sees a school of fish and rises 16 feet to watch the fish. What is her elevation now?

19. The temperature of some frozen chicken was $-18°C$. After thawing in the refrigerator overnight, the temperature of the chicken rose by $22°C$. What was the temperature of the chicken after thawing overnight?

20. At 6 A.M., the temperature was $-9°F$. By 11 A.M., the temperature had increased $34°F$. What was the temperature at 11 A.M.?

Lesson 8-3

21. Write a subtraction number sentence for the model shown.

a.

b.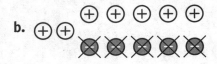

For Items 22–25, use counters to find each difference.

22. $3 - (-1)$

23. $-6 - (-4)$

24. $2 - 7$

25. $-4 - 3$

For Items 26–37, find each difference.

26. $9 - (-9)$

27. $-17 - 6$

28. $1 - 14$

29. $-24 - 11$

30. $-13 - (-8)$

31. $31 - (-10)$

32. $-8 - (-4)$

33. $-14 - (-20)$

34. $-10 - (-1)$

35. $-17 - (-6)$

36. $5 - 21$

37. $16 - (-16)$

38. $9 - 14 =$
   A. -23
   B. -5
   C. 5
   D. 23

39. The highest elevation in North America is Denali, in Alaska, with an elevation of 20,320 feet above sea level. The lowest elevation in North America is Death Valley, in California, with an elevation of 282 feet below sea level. What is the difference in the highest and lowest elevations in North America? Explain your reasoning.

40. The temperature was 12°C before the storm. During the storm, the temperature dropped 19°C. By the end of the storm, the temperature dropped another 7°C. What was the temperature at the end of the storm? Explain your reasoning.

41. Explain how to evaluate the following expression:

   $6 + (-3) - 9$.

42. Delia evaluated the expression $2 - (-7)$ and found a difference of -5. Is she correct? Explain why or why not.

43. Compare and contrast subtracting integers and subtracting whole numbers.

44. The rule for subtracting integers can be used to subtract whole numbers. Explain why.

MATHEMATICAL PRACTICES
Express Regularity in Repeated Reasoning

45. Explain how to use a number line to add and subtract integers. Use examples in your explanation.

Integer Sums and Differences
HOT AND COLD

Write your answers on notebook paper. Show your work.

Antonia's hobby is astronomy. She is learning about the surface temperatures of the planets in our solar system. She knows that the temperatures on a given planet can vary widely, just as Earth's temperatures do. She has compiled a table that gives average temperatures on each of the eight planets.

Planet	Temperature (°C)
Earth	20
Jupiter	−120
Mars	−20
Mercury	440
Neptune	−200
Saturn	−140
Uranus	−180
Venus	460

1. Which two temperatures are opposites? Explain your choice.

2. a. Order the temperatures from least to greatest. Explain how you determined the order.

   b. Draw a number line like the one below and place a dot at the location of each of the eight temperatures. Write the name of each planet above its temperature.

3. Find the difference between the temperatures of each pair of planets.

   a. Venus and Earth

   b. Mercury and Saturn

   c. the warmest planet and the coldest planet

   d. Mars and Uranus

4. a. The sum of the temperatures of Earth and Neptune is the same as the temperature of which planet?

   b. The sum of the temperatures of Jupiter and Mars is the same as the temperature of which planet?

   c. The sum of the temperatures of Jupiter, Saturn, and Neptune has the same absolute value as the temperature of which planet?

Scoring Guide	Exemplary	Proficient	Emerging	Incomplete
	The solution demonstrates these characteristics:			
Mathematics Knowledge and Thinking (Items 1, 2a, 3a-d, 4)	• A clear understanding of ordering integers, finding opposites, and absolute value. • An effective understanding of and accuracy in adding and subtracting integers.	• A functional understanding of ordering integers, finding opposites, and absolute value. • Addition and subtraction of integers that is usually correct.	• Partial understanding of integers and opposites; difficulty using absolute value. • Difficulty with addition and subtraction of integers.	• An inaccurate understanding of integers and opposites; no understanding of absolute value. • Inaccurate addition and subtraction of integers.
Problem Solving (Items 4a-c)	• An appropriate and efficient strategy that results in a correct answer.	• A strategy that may include unnecessary steps but results in a correct answer.	• A strategy that results in some incorrect answers.	• No clear strategy when solving problems.
Mathematical Modeling / Representations (Items 2a-b, 3a-d, 4a-c)	• Clear and accurate ordering and graphing of integers on a number line. • Clear and accurate rewriting of problems as addition and subtraction expressions that can be solved.	• Graphing of integers on a number line with little difficulty. • Some difficulty in rewriting addition and subtraction of integer problems as expressions, but can get the correct answer.	• Partially accurate graphing of integers on a number line. • Difficulty in writing expressions leading to errors in solving addition and subtraction of integer problems.	• Inaccurate graphing of integers on a number line. • No understanding of addition and subtraction of integers.
Reasoning and Communication (Items 1a, 4a-c)	• Precise use of appropriate math terms and language to explain opposites of integers and ordering of integers. • Relating a mathematical result to a table of data accurately and easily.	• An adequate explanation of opposites of integers and ordering of integers. • Relating a mathematical result to a table of data with little difficulty.	• A misleading or confusing explanation of opposites of integers and ordering of integers. • Poor understanding of relating a mathematical result to a table of data.	• An incomplete or inaccurate description of opposites of integers and ordering of integers. • No understanding of how a mathematical result might relate to a table of data.

The Coordinate Plane
Map It Out!
Lesson 9-1 Integers in the Coordinate Plane

Learning Targets:

- Graph and identify ordered pairs of rational numbers.
- Understand and use terms such as *origin, quadrant, x-axis, y-axis, first coordinate,* and *second coordinate* associated with graphing on the coordinate plane.

> **SUGGESTED LEARNING STRATEGIES:** Summarizing, Note Taking, Sharing and Responding, Create Representations

Student volunteers at the zoo are making a new map of the zoo grounds with additional information about the exhibits. They decide to use a coordinate plane to design the map since it is a quick way to locate points.

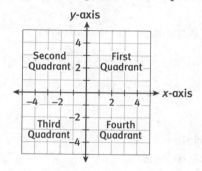

CONNECT TO HISTORY

The coordinate plane is also called a Cartesian coordinate plane. It is named after Rene Descartes, a 17th century French philosopher and mathematician who first used a coordinate plane.

A **coordinate plane**, or **grid,** is formed by a horizontal number line, called the **x-axis,** and a vertical number line, called the **y-axis.** The two axes intersect at right angles at a point called the **origin**. The axes divide the coordinate plane into four sections called **quadrants**.

You can locate any point in the coordinate plane using a pair of numbers called an **ordered pair**.

> The *first coordinate* in an ordered pair is the **x-coordinate.** It tells how far to move on the *x*-axis from the origin.

> The *second coordinate* is the **y-coordinate**. It tells how far to move on the *y*-axis from the origin.

To graph a point in the coordinate plane, start at the origin and go right (+) or left (−) along the *x*-axis by the number of units given by the first coordinate. From that point, go up (+) or down (−) by the number of units given by the second coordinate.

MATH TIP

You can identify the quadrant in which a point is located by looking at the signs of the coordinates.

Quadrant I: (+,+)
Quadrant II: (−,+)
Quadrant III: (−,−)
Quadrant IV: (+,−)

MATH TIP

Remember that the second coordinate in an ordered pair is the *y*-coordinate by remembering that *y* comes after *x* in the alphabet.

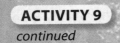

My Notes

Example

Graph and label the point *J* (−4, −2) on the coordinate plane.

Step 1: Start at the origin and go left 4 units.

Step 2: Move down 2 units. Draw and label the point.

Solution: The grid shows point *J* graphed at (−4, −2).

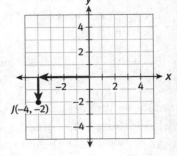

Try These

Graph and label each point on the grid above.

a. *K*(3, 4)   **b.** *L*(−1, 3)   **c.** *M*(2, −4)

The student volunteers have started a map. The origin represents the education center at the zoo. Each point on the grid shows the location of a different exhibit.

Sometimes, a decimal, a fraction, or a mixed number is used to name a point on a grid.

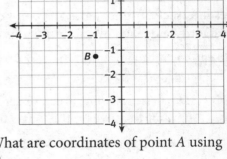

1. Point *A* shows the location of the African Plains exhibit. The *x*-coordinate of point *A* is halfway between 3 and 4. What are coordinates of point *A* using decimals? How do you know?

2. Point *B* shows the location of the Bat Exhibit. The *y*-coordinate of point *B* is one quarter of the way from −1 to −2. What are the coordinates of point *B* using mixed numbers? How do you know?

3. The coordinates of the petting zoo are (−3, 2.75). Which letter names the location of the petting zoo?

My Notes

Check Your Understanding

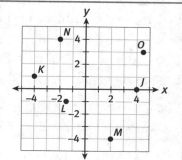

4. Explain how to use the first coordinate and the second coordinate of the ordered pair $P(7, -2)$ to graph the point in the coordinate plane. Then plot the point on a coordinate plane.

5. Write the ordered pair for each point.
   a. J b. K c. L
   d. M e. N f. O

LESSON 9-1 PRACTICE

6. Graph and label each point on a coordinate plane.
   a. $A(6, 3)$ b. $B(2, -7)$ c. $C(8.5, -4)$
   d. $D(-5, -3)$ e. $E\left(-1\frac{1}{2}, 6\right)$ f. $F(-3, 4)$

7. **Attend to precision.** Write the ordered pair for each point graphed on the coordinate grid below.
   a. P b. Q c. R
   d. S e. T f. U

8. Graph the following points on a coordinate grid: $X(0, 4)$, $Y(0, 0)$, and $Z(4, 0)$. Then draw line segments XY, YZ, and XZ. Name the type of figure that you have drawn.

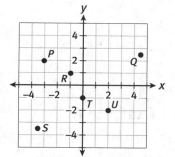

9. Graph the following points on a coordinate grid: $A(0, 0)$, $B(0, 3)$, $C(4.5)$, and $D(4.5, 0)$. Then draw line segments AB, BC, CD, and DA. Name the type of figure that you have drawn.

10. A point is located in the second quadrant of the coordinate plane. What can you conclude about the signs of the coordinates of the point?

11. A point is located in the third quadrant of the coordinate plane. What can you conclude about the signs of the coordinates of the point?

My Notes

Learning Targets:
- Find the distance between points in the coordinate plane with the same first coordinate or the same second coordinate.
- Solve real-world and mathematical problems by graphing points in the coordinate plane and finding the distances between them.
- Find the reflection of a point over one or both axes.

SUGGESTED LEARNING STRATEGIES: Summarizing, Note Taking, Sharing and Responding, Create Representations, Discussion Groups

Ryan has a map of the zoo. He has just gone through the Bird exhibit and wants to go to the Reptile house next. Each unit on the map represents 10 yards.

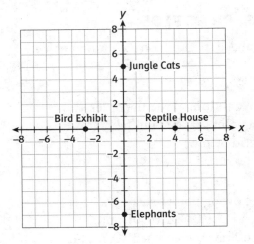

Example A
How far must Ryan go to get from the Bird exhibit to the Reptile house?

Step 1: Count the number of units between 0 and the Bird exhibit.
There are 3 units.

Step 2: Count the number of units between 0 and Reptile house.
There are 4 units.

Step 3: Find the sum of these two distances.
$3 + 4 = 7$

Solution: Ryan must go 7 units. Since 1 unit = 10 yards, he must go 7×10 yards, or 70 yards.

Example B

How far apart are the Jungle cats and the Elephants?

Step 1: Write the coordinates for each exhibit.

Jungle cats: $(0, 5)$ Elephants: $(0, -7)$

Step 2: Since both exhibits are on the y-axis. Find the difference of the y-coordinates.

$$5 - (-7) = 5 + (7) = 12$$

Solution: The distance between the Jungle cats and the Elephants is 12 units, or 120 yd.

Try These A–B

Find the distance between each pair of points.

a. $(0, 3)$ and $(0,12)$
b. $(-1, 0)$ and $(6, 0)$
c. $(-8, 0)$ and $(-2, 0)$

1. Students plan to list the distances between some of the exhibits on the back of the map. Each unit on the map shown represents 1 yard.

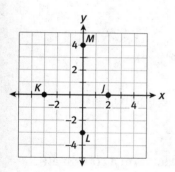

a. How far apart are Exhibits J and K? Explain.

b. How far apart are Exhibits L and M? Explain.

> **MATH TIP**
>
> If Step 2 in Example B showed the subtraction of the y-coordinates as $-7 - 5 = -7 + (-5)$, the result would be -12. However, distance cannot be negative. To avoid negative results when finding distances, find the absolute value of the difference of the coordinates:
>
> $$|-7 - 5| = |-7 + (-5)|$$
> $$= |-12|$$
> $$= 12$$

You can use distance on a coordinate grid to find the **reflection** of a point. The reflection of a given point across the x-axis or y-axis is another point that is the same distance from the axis as the given point.

My Notes

Designers are using a coordinate grid, as shown, to draw the new Native American exhibit. The exhibit will be in the shape of a rectangle. Each corner will have a totem pole. The designers have drawn points *T* and *P* where two of the totem poles will be located.

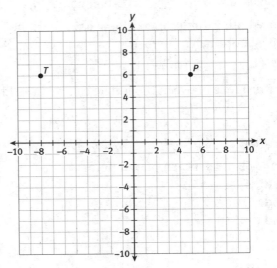

2. a. What is the distance from point *P* to the *x*-axis directly below point *P*? Explain.

b. Point *Q* will be the reflection of point *P* across the *x*-axis. What will be the coordinates of point *Q*? Explain.

c. Point *S* will be the reflection of point *T* across the *x*-axis. What are the coordinates of point *S*?

3. Work with your group to create a simple exhibit on a coordinate grid. Prepare a brief report to share with your class describing the location of objects on your map making sure to include terms such as point, distance, and reflection. As needed, refer to the Glossary to review translations of key terms.

GROUP DISCUSSION TIPS

Be sure to use appropriate vocabulary, both real-world and mathematical, to describe your exhibit. Refer to the Word Wall as needed to help you to choose words for your description. Assign each group member a role in creating the exhibit and make sure to set a reasonable time frame for completing the exhibit.

Check Your Understanding

4. Explain how to find the distance between the points −2 and −5 on a number line.

5. Point *C* has coordinates (1, 3) and Point *D* has coordinates (1, −4).
  a. Graph the points on a coordinate plane.
  b. Explain how to find the distance between the points using their ordered pairs.

My Notes

LESSON 9-2 PRACTICE

6. Find the distance between each pair of points on a number line.
   a. 4 and 7
   b. −5 and 1
   c. −6 and 8
   d. −3 and −11

Use the coordinate plane at the right for items 7–10. Find the distance between each pair of points.

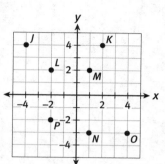

7. *J* and *K*

8. *L* and *M*

9. *N* and *O*

10. Which point is the reflection of point *L* across the *x*-axis?

Use the coordinate plane at the right for Items 11–14. Find the distance between each pair of points.

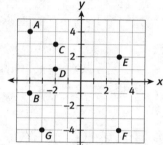

11. *A* and *B*

12. *C* and *D*

13. *E* and *F*

14. Which point is the reflection of point *F* across the *y*-axis?

15. Make sense of problems. Kurt used a coordinate plane to make a map of his neighborhood. Each unit on the map is 1 block.

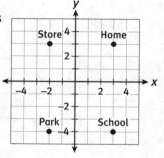

   a. How many blocks is Kurt's school from home?
   b. How far is the school from the park?
   c. If Kurt begins at his house, goes to the store and then to the park, how far will he travel? Explain your reasoning.

16. Reason abstractly. The point (−3, 8) is reflected over the *x*-axis. What is the distance between the point and its reflection? Explain your thinking.

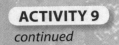
ACTIVITY 9 PRACTICE

Write your answers on a separate piece of paper.
Show your work.

Lesson 9-1

1. Graph and label each point on a coordinate plane.
   a. $A(1, 7)$ **b.** $B(0, -5)$
   c. $C(-4, 6)$ **d.** $D(-8\frac{1}{4}, -3)$
   e. $E(9, 0)$ **f.** $F(6.5, -2)$

2. Write the ordered pair for each point.

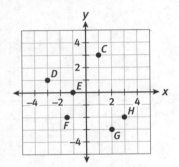

   a. C **b.** D **c.** E
   d. F **e.** G **f.** H

3. If the first coordinate in an ordered pair is 0, where does the point lie? If the second coordinate in an ordered pair is 0, where does the point lie? How do you know?

4. The coordinates of point H are $(12, -15)$. In which quadrant is point H located?
   A. First   **B.** Second
   C. Third   **D.** Fourth

5. David graphed the point $(6\frac{1}{2}, -9\frac{3}{4})$ on a coordinate grid. In which quadrant is the point? He then decided to graph a point that had coordinates opposite those of the first point. In which quadrant did he graph this point?

6. Do the points $(-4, 6)$ and $(6, -4)$ describe the same location? Explain your thinking.

7. Which point is common to both axes?

Lesson 9-2

Use the coordinate plane for Items 8–16.
The coordinate plane shows the locations of some classmates' homes. Each unit on the grid represents 1 block.

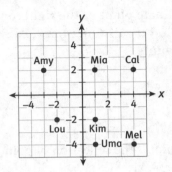

8. How far does Cal live from Mel?

9. How far does Mia live from Amy?

10. How far apart do Amy and Cal live?

11. How far apart do Mia and Uma live?

12. Does Kim live closer to Lou or to Uma? Explain.

13. Does Mia live closer to Amy or to Cal? Explain.

14. Whose house is a reflection of Mia's house across the x-axis? Explain.

15. Is Cal's house a reflection of Amy's house across the y-axis? Explain.

16. Starting at her house, Lou walks to see each of her classmates in the following order: Kim, Uma, Mel, Cal, Mia, and Amy. How far does Lou walk to reach Amy's house? Explain your thinking.

MATHEMATICAL PRACTICES
Make Use of Structure

17. Explain how to find the distance between the points $(28, -17)$ and $(-15, -17)$ on a coordinate plane.

Multiplying and Dividing Integers
Temperature Ups and Downs
Lesson 10-1 Multiplying Integers

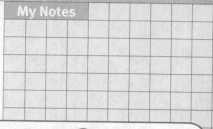

Learning Targets:

- Multiply integers.
- Solve real-world problems by multiplying integers.

> **SUGGESTED LEARNING STRATEGIES:** Marking the Text, Visualization, Predict and Confirm, Create Representations, Look for a Pattern

In science class, Mariah is learning about temperature. Mariah has decided to use the Celsius scale to investigate the three states of water.

- When the temperature of water is below 0°C, it is a solid called ice.
- From 0°C to 100°C, it is a liquid called *water*.
- Above 100°C, it is a gas called *steam*.

Mariah starts with a container of water with a temperature of 0°. That is the temperature at which ice changes to water. To study changes in the water's state, she increases the temperature at a constant rate for 10 minutes until it begins to steam.

1. What is the increase in temperature?

2. What is the rate at which the temperature increased? Write the answer in degrees per minute.

3. Would it be more appropriate to represent this rate of increase as a positive integer or as a negative integer? Explain your reasoning.

Mariah drew this number line to represent the minute-by-minute changes in temperature:

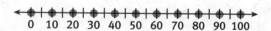

```
0   10  20  30  40  50  60  70  80  90 100
```

4. Let 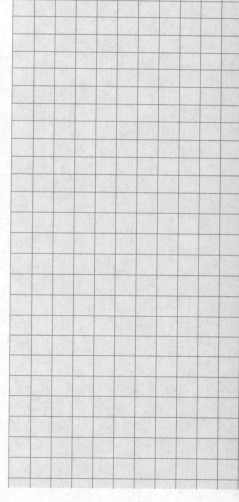 represent the rate you found in Item 2. Use △+△ to represent the total change in temperature.

CONNECT **TO** **SCIENCE**

Substances can exist in three different forms:
- solid,
- liquid, and
- gas.

Each form is called a *state*. Heating and cooling causes a substance to change from one state to another. Heating causes ice, the solid form of water, to become water, the liquid form, and finally to become steam, the gas form.

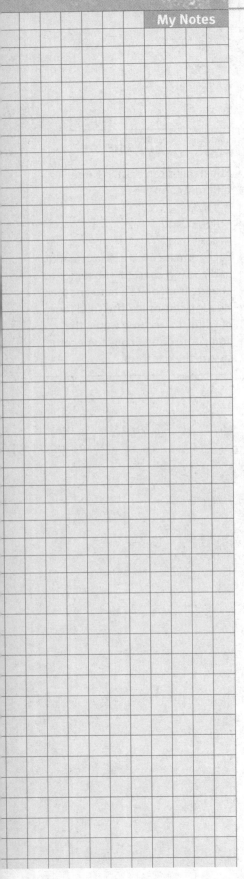

My Notes

Next, Mariah places the container in the laboratory freezer. Over the next 20 minutes, she lowers the temperature at a steady rate until the water begins to freeze.

5. What is the rate of decrease in temperature? Write the answer in degrees per minute.

6. Would it be more appropriate to represent this rate of decrease as a positive integer or a negative integer? Explain your reasoning.

7. Mark the number line to represent the minute-by-minute changes in temperature:

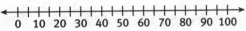

0 10 20 30 40 50 60 70 80 90 100

8. Let ▽ represent the rate that you found in Item 5. Use ▽ to represent the total change in temperature.

In Items 4 and 8, you used triangles to represent multiplication.

△+ represents a temperature increase of 10 degrees.

▽ represents a temperature decrease of 5 degrees.

So, 10 △+ = +100 and 20 ▽ = −100.

9. a. If ⊟ represents −8, what does ⊟ ⊟ ⊟ ⊟ ⊟ represent?

   b. If ⊟ represents −5, what does ⊟ ⊟ ⊟ represent?

   c. If ⊞ represents +3, what does ⊞ ⊞ ⊞ ⊞ represent?

   d. If ⊞ represents +9, what does ⊞ ⊞ ⊞ ⊞ ⊞ ⊞ represent?

Lesson 10-1
Multiplying Integers

ACTIVITY 10
continued

10. Write the number sentence represented by each diagram. Each counter stands for 10 or −10. The first one has been done for you.

a.  $2 \times 40 = 80$

b.

c.

d.

e.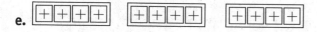

f.

11. Use $\boxed{+}$ and $\boxed{-}$ to represent each number sentence.
   a. $2 \times 50 = 100$

   b. $3 \times (-30) = -90$

12. Look at your results for Items 10 and 11. Answer the following questions:
   a. What was the sign of the product when you multiplied two positive integers?

   b. What was the sign of the product when you multiplied a positive integer and a negative integer?

   c. Use these observations to write rules to find the sign of the product of integers.

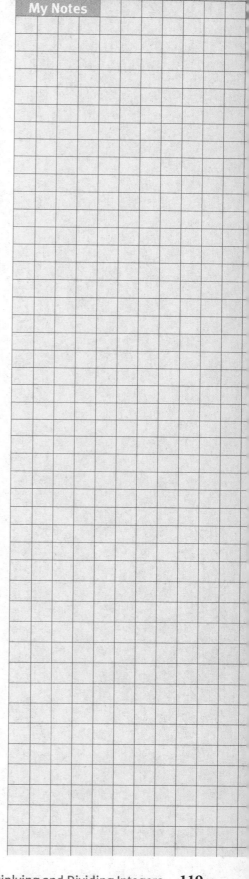

My Notes

ACTIVITY 10
continued

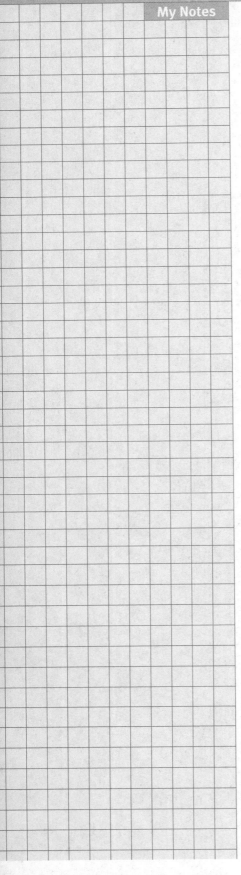

My Notes

13. You can use patterns to find the sign of the product of two negative integers.

   a. Fill in ONLY the first four squares in the table below.

×	3	2	1	0	−1	−2	−3
−3							

   b. **Make use of structure.** Describe the pattern in the four squares you filled in.

   c. Fill in the last three squares by continuing this pattern.
   d. Use the same procedure you used in parts a–c to complete the multiplication tables below.

×	3	2	1	0	−1	−2	−3
−5							

×	3	2	1	0	−1	−2	−3
−8							

×	3	2	1	0	−1	−2	−3
−11							

   e. Use your results in parts a and d to write a rule to find the sign of the product of two negative integers.

14. Complete the table at the right showing the sign of the product of integers. Write a positive sign or negative sign in each box.

×	positive	negative
positive		
negative		

15. **Make use of structure.** In parts a–c, state whether the product is positive or negative.
   a. the product of two negative integers
   b. the product of three negative integers
   c. the product of four negative integers
   d. State a rule for finding the sign of the product of an even number of negative integers.
   e. State a rule for finding the sign of the product of an odd number of negative integers.

Check Your Understanding

16. Find each product.
    a. 3(−9)   **b.** 7 · 6
    c. −10(−2)   **d.** 5(−8)

17. Complete.
    a. 3 × (−4) = −3 × _____   **b.** 2 × 5 = −2 × _____
    c. −6 × 7 = 6 × _____   **d.** −9 × (−9) = 9 × _____

18. Copy the number line below and use it to show the product of 2 and (−4).

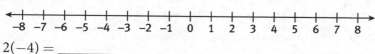

    2(−4) = _____

19. Which property justifies this equation? −5 × 12 = 12 × −5?

LESSON 10-1 PRACTICE

20. At 4 P.M. the temperature in Clarksville was 0°C. Over the next 8 hours the temperature fell at a rate of 3 degrees per hour.
    a. Write the rate that the temperature fell as an integer.
    b. Determine the temperature at midnight.

21. **a.** Blake borrowed $25 from his brother. Write an integer to express the $25 that Blake owes his brother.
    b. Blake borrowed $25 from his brother a total of 7 times. Write an integer that represents the amount that Blake owes his brother.

22. Find the 11th number in the pattern below:

    0, −7, −14, −21,…

23. A submarine on the surface of the ocean descended at a rate of 7 feet per second for 2 minutes. Then it ascended at a rate of 4 feet per second for 3 minutes, Finally, it descended at a rate of 9 feet per second for 5 minutes. What was the final elevation of the submarine? (The elevation of the ocean surface is 0 feet.)

My Notes

Learning Targets:

- Divide integers.
- Solve real-world problems by dividing integers.

> **SUGGESTED LEARNING STRATEGIES:** Marking the Text, Visualization, Predict and Confirm, Look for a Pattern

The low temperatures in Bismarck, North Dakota, during five days in January are given in the table. The local TV weather reporter wants to announce the mean low temperature for the week. To do this, the reporter will need to divide negative integers.

Day	Temperature (°F)
Monday	−7
Tuesday	−9
Wednesday	3
Thursday	5
Friday	−2

1. Use what you know about multiplying integers to draw a diagram using ⊞ and ⊟ for each problem. Give the answer. The first one has been done for you.

   a. $12 \div 2 = 6$ ⊞⊞⊞⊞⊞⊞   ⊞⊞⊞⊞⊞⊞

   b. $20 \div 4 = $ _____

   c. $-12 \div 4 = $ _____

   d. $-14 \div 7 = $ _____

2. **Make use of structure.** The equation $4 \cdot 7 = 28$ shows that the numbers 4, 7, and 28 are related by multiplication. Write two equations to show that 4, 7, and 28 are related by division.

3. **Make use of structure.** Use the fact $(-5)(-9) = 45$ to write two equations showing that −5, −9, and 45 are related by division.

4. **Make use of structure.** Use the fact $6(-3) = -18$ to write two equations showing that 6, −3, and −18 are related by division.

5. Use your results from Items 3 and 4 to complete these statements:
   a. When a positive integer is divided by a negative integer, the quotient is _____.
   b. When a negative integer is divided by a positive integer, the quotient is _____.
   c. When a negative integer is divided by a negative integer, the quotient is _____.
   d. The quotient of two integers with the same sign is _____.
   e. The quotient of two integers with different signs is _____.

6. Complete the table at the right to show the sign of the quotient of two integers. Write a positive sign or negative sign in each box.

÷	positive	negative
positive		
negative		

7. Compare the rules you determined for finding the sign of the product of two integers with the rules you determined for finding the sign of the quotient of two integers.

8. a. Use the table on the preceding page to find the sum of the low temperatures in Bismarck for the five given days.

   b. What was the mean low temperature in Bismarck for the five days?

   c. Draw a diagram showing how you can use ⌐+⌐ and ⌐−⌐ to find the mean temperature.

MATH TIP

To find the mean, find the average of the data items by taking the sum of the data values and dividing by the total number of data items.

9. Use the fact that multiplication and division are inverse operations to explain why the expression $6 \div 0$ has no answer.

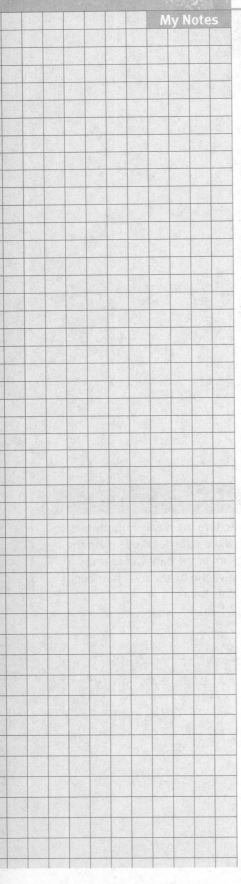

My Notes

Check Your Understanding

10. Find each quotient.

   a. $-15 \div 3$ **b.** $24 \div (-6)$ **c.** $30 \div 15$

   d. $-25 \div (-5)$ **e.** $36 \div (-9)$ **f.** $-50 \div (-25)$

   g. $\dfrac{-42}{6}$ **h.** $\dfrac{-56}{-7}$ **i.** $\dfrac{40}{-8}$

11. Multiplication and division are inverse operations. Use inverse operations to determine each missing number.

   a. $15 \times \underline{\hspace{1cm}} = -75$ **b.** $-12 \times \underline{\hspace{1cm}} = 156$

   c. $20 \times \underline{\hspace{1cm}} = 260$ **d.** $-18 \times \underline{\hspace{1cm}} = -126$

   e. $-23 \times \underline{\hspace{1cm}} = 207$ **f.** $-16 \times \underline{\hspace{1cm}} = -256$

LESSON 10-2 PRACTICE

12. The low temperatures in the town of Rigby for 5 consecutive days were $-12°F$, $-17°F$, $-11°F$, $-12°F$, and $-18°F$. What was the mean low temperature for the 5 days?

13. During the 7 minutes previous to landing, an airplane decreased in elevation by $-3{,}192$ feet. Determine the mean elevation change per minute.

14. Biff's Bakery had a slow year. Biff recorded the store's loss as $-\$10{,}308$ for the year. How would Biff record the store's mean monthly loss?

15. Evaluate each expression.

   a. $-2 \times 9 \div (-6)$ **b.** $40 \div (-10) \div 2$

   c. $-54 \div (-6) \div (-3)$ **d.** $\dfrac{4 \times (-15)}{-2 \times (-6)}$

16. Use $<$, $=$, or $>$ to complete each statement.

   a. $3 \times (-9) \bigcirc 50 \div (-2)$

   b. $-46 \div 2 \bigcirc 13 \times (-2)$

   c. $-5 \times (-6) \bigcirc -96 \div (-3)$

   d. $-2 \times (-3) \times (-4) \bigcirc -96 \div (-2) \div (-2)$

ACTIVITY 10 PRACTICE

Write your answers on notebook paper.
Show your work.

Lesson 10-1

1. Find: $-20(-4)$
   A. -80 **B.** -5
   C. 5 **D.** 80

2. Which is the most accurate statement about the sign of the product of a positive integer and a negative integer?
   A. It is positive.
   B. It is negative.
   C. It depends on the sign of the first of the two numbers.
   D. It cannot be predicted without knowing the integers.

3. Find the numerator of the fraction: $\frac{?}{5} = -10$
   A. -50 **B.** -2
   C. 2 **D.** 50

For Items 4–13, find each product.

4. $2 \times (-9)$

5. $-3 \times (-3)$

6. 8×6

7. -12×6

8. $-10 \times (-11)$

9. $7 \times (-7)$

10. $-1 \times (-1)$

11. $-1 \times (-1) \times (-1) \times (-1)$

12. $(-1)^7$

13. $-15(0)$

For Items 14–17, use $<$ or $>$ to complete each statement.

14. $-2(-5)$ ◯ 3×3

15. $-8(3)$ ◯ $5(-5)$

16. $10(-6)$ ◯ $-10(-6)$

17. $-3(12)$ ◯ $7(-5)$

18. A dolphin swimming in the ocean dove deeper, at a rate of -3 feet per second. Find the change in the dolphin's elevation one minute later.

19. **a.** The lowest temperature ever recorded in Michigan was 3 times the lowest temperature ever recorded in Georgia, which was $-17°F$. What was Michigan's lowest temperature?
    b. The highest temperature ever recorded in Oregon was -7 times the lowest temperature ever recorded in Georgia. What was Oregon's highest temperature?

20. Name the number property illustrated by this equation:
    $$-2(-3 + 7) = -2(-3) + (-2)(7)$$

21. Complete:
    a. $7 \times (-8) = -7 \times$ _____
    b. $-5 \times (3) = 5 \times$ _____
    c. $9 \times 2 = -9 \times$ _____

22. In golf, *par* is is the expected number of strokes needed to complete a course. Numbers of strokes greater than par (over par) are indicated with positive integers. Numbers of strokes less than par (under par) are indicated with negative integers. Clyde scored 6 under par each day of a 4-day tournament. Find his final score for the entire tournament.

Lesson 10-2

23. Find: $12 \div (-2)$
   A. -24 **B.** -6
   C. 6 **D.** 24

24. Which answer best explains why the following numerical relationship is true?

$$2 \times (-6) = -12, \text{ so } \frac{-12}{-6} = 2$$

   A. the Distributive Property
   B. the Associative Property
   C. the Commutative Property of Multiplication
   D. the inverse relationship between multiplication and division

25. Complete: $-6 \times \underline{\hspace{2em}} = 12$
   A. -72 **B.** -2
   C. 2 **D.** 72

For Items 26–34, find each quotient.

26. $8 \div (-4)$

27. $14 \div 2$

28. $-28 \div (-7)$

29. $-35 \div 5$

30. $\dfrac{-1}{-1}$

31. $\dfrac{0}{-12}$

32. $\dfrac{1}{-1}$

33. $60 \div (-4) \div 3$

34. $-80 \div (-2) \div 5 \div (-4)$

35. Which of the following expressions is not equivalent to the others?
   A. $\dfrac{-24}{3}$

   B. $\dfrac{24}{-3}$

   C. $-\dfrac{24}{3}$

   D. $-\dfrac{24}{-3}$

36. The temperature in Allenville fell from 25°F to -23°F in 8 minutes.
   a. Write a numerical expression you can evaluate to find the average change in temperature per minute.
   b. Find the mean change in temperature per minute.

37. The numbers below record the number of feet a hot-air balloon rose and fell each minute during a 6-minute period.

$$+410, +350, -570, +190, -470, -600$$

   a. Find the balloon's final position in relation to its original position.
   b. Find the balloon's mean change in position per minute.

38. Casey's bank statement records money taken from his checking account as a negative transaction and money added to his account as a positive transaction.

Date	Amount ($)
3/12	+60.00
3/15	−95.00
3/16	−34.00
3/20	−128.00
3/26	+75.00
3/29	−16.00

   a. Find the net change in the amount Casey had in his account during the period shown.
   b. Find the mean change per transaction for the same period.

MATHEMATICAL PRACTICES
Look For and Make Use of Structure

39. The product of two integers is positive. Is the quotient of those same integers positive, negative, or impossible to predict? Explain your reasoning

Write your answers on notebook paper. Show your work.

Pioneer School is holding a Scavenger Hunt. Teams are given clues that will lead them to places where prizes have been buried. You are the leader of your team.

The tract of farmland for the scavenger hunt measures 200 yards in each direction and has been marked with coordinate grid lines every 10 yards.

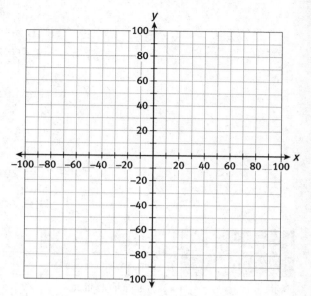

- The x-axis runs east-west.
- The y-axis runs north-south.

1. CLUE 1: Start at the origin. Go to $(-10, 30)$. Find Prize 1 at the point that is a reflection of $(-10, 30)$ over the x-axis.
   a. Give the coordinates of Prize 1 and explain how you found these coordinates.
   b. In which quadrant is Prize 1 located? Explain how you could determine this using only the coordinates of the point.

2. CLUE 2: Start at $(-60, 70)$. Go to $(-10, 70)$, keeping track of the distance walked between the two points. Continue by walking this same distance in the same direction.
   There you will find Prize 2.
   a. In which quadrant and what are the coordinates of Prize 2?
   b. Explain how you determined which quadrant Prize 2 was in using only the coordinate grid.
   c. What is the distance from the starting point to Prize 2?

3. CLUE 3: Start at the origin. Walk 20 yards south and 60 yards east. Divide the first coordinate of your present location by -3 to determine the first coordinate of Prize 3. Multiply the second coordinate of your present location by -3 to find the second coordinate of Prize 3.

   What are the coordinates of Prize 3 and in which quadrant is it located?

4. CLUE 4: Find Prize 4 at the point that is a reflection of Prize 3's location over the y-axis. Give the coordinates of Prize 4.

5. When you reach the spot for Prize #4, you have to dig 4 inches down 7 times. Write a number sentence to represent this situation and determine how far down you have to dig to find the prize.

6. The last clue tells you to run up the hill. You run at 3 feet per second and reach the top of the hill in 32 seconds. Write a number sentence to represent this situation and determine the distance you ran.

7. Explain how the signs of your answers to Items 5 and 6 make sense for the situation that they describe.

Scoring Guide	Exemplary	Proficient	Emerging	Incomplete
	The solution demonstrates:			
Mathematics Knowledge and Thinking (Items 1a, 2a, c, 3, 4, 5, 6)	• A clear understanding of ordered pairs of integers, and reflections and distance in the coordinate plane. • Effective understanding of and accuracy in multiplying and dividing integers.	• A functional understanding of ordered pairs of integers, and reflections and distance in the coordinate plane. • Multiplication and division of integers that is usually correct.	• Partial understanding of ordered pairs of integers, and reflections and distance in the coordinate plane. • Difficulty with multiplication and division of integers.	• An inaccurate understanding of ordered pairs of integers, and reflections and distance in the coordinate plane. • Inaccurate multiplication and division of integers.
Problem Solving (Items 2c, 5, 6)	• An appropriate and efficient strategy that results in a correct answer.	• A strategy that may include unnecessary steps but results in a correct answer.	• A strategy that results in some incorrect answers.	• No clear strategy when solving problems.
Mathematical Modeling/ Representations (Items 1a, 2a, c, 3, 4, 5, 6)	• Clear and accurate graphing and reflecting of points in the coordinate plane. • Clear and accurate writing and solving of problems with integer multiplication and division.	• Graphing and reflecting points on a coordinate plane with little difficulty. • Some difficulty in writing integer multiplication and division problems but with correct answers.	• Partially accurate graphing and inaccurate reflection of points on a coordinate plane. • Difficulty in writing expressions leading to errors in solving problems.	• Inaccurate graphing of ordered pairs of integers on a number line. • No understanding of multiplication and division of integers.
Reasoning and Communication (Items 1a-b, 2a-b, 5-7)	• Precise use of appropriate math terms and language to explain signs of integers and quadrants.	• An adequate explanation of signs of integers and quadrants in the coordinate plane.	• A misleading or confusing explanation of signs of integers and quadrants.	• An incomplete or inaccurate description of signs of integers and quadrants in the coordinate plane.

Expressions and Equations

Unit Overview
In this unit you will use variables to write expressions and equations. You will solve and graph equations and inequalities.

Key Terms
As you study this unit, add these and other terms to your math notebook. Include in your notes your prior knowledge of each word, as well as your experiences in using the word in different mathematical examples. If needed, ask for help in pronouncing new words and add information on pronunciation to your math notebook. It is important that you learn new terms and use them correctly in your class discussions and in your problem solutions.

Academic Vocabulary
- compare
- contrast

Math Terms
- numerical expression
- order of operations
- variable
- coefficient
- algebraic expression
- term
- unit rate
- mathematical property
- equation
- solution
- inverse operations
- inequality
- rate of change
- ordered pair
- independent variable
- dependent variable

ESSENTIAL QUESTIONS

? Why are tables, graphs, and equations useful for representing relationships?

? How can you use equations to solve real-world problems?

EMBEDDED ASSESSMENTS

These assessments, following activities 12 and 16, will give you an opportunity to demonstrate how you can write, graph, and solve equations and inequalities to solve mathematical and real-world problems.

Embedded Assessment 1:

Order of Operations and Expressions   p. 157

Embedded Assessment 2:

Expressions and Equations   p. 211

Write your answers on notebook paper.
Show your work.

1. Copy and complete the table.

Input	3	7	11	14	17	21
Output	0		8			

   Write the rule you used.

2. Copy and complete the table.

Input	Output
3	18
7	
9	
11	
20	120
35	

   Write the rule you used.

3. Make a grid like the one below. Then plot each point on it.

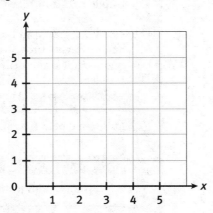

   a. (0, 2) **b.** (2, 1)
   c. (1, 3) **d.** (4, 4)
   e. (5, 0)

For Items 4–6, evaluate each expression for $n = 7$.

4. $n + 9$

5. $(n - 3) \div 4$

6. $\dfrac{35}{n}$

7. Tell how to undo each operation and explain why it works.
   a. adding 28
   b. dividing by 17

8. Write the reciprocal of each number.
   a. 7
   b. $\dfrac{1}{2}$
   c. $\dfrac{2}{5}$
   d. $\dfrac{4}{3}$
   e. Explain how a number and its reciprocal are related.

Expressions
A Fairly Ordered Operation
Lesson 11-1 Order of Operations

Learning Targets:

- Use the order of operations to simplify expressions involving addition, subtraction, multiplication, and division.
- Use the order of operations to simplify expressions involving whole number exponents and parentheses.

> **SUGGESTED LEARNING STRATEGIES:** Paraphrasing, Simplify the Problem, Critique Reasoning

Ayana and Zachary Wilson are going to the Pace County Fair.

1. Ayana loves to make lists of things to do to prepare for an activity. She made the following list for the morning of the fair.

To Do	Order
Take a shower	
Eat breakfast	
Get dressed	
Buy tickets for the fair	
Put on shoes	
Put on socks	
Ride to fair	
Get money from piggy bank	

a. Order the steps as you think Ayana will complete them.

b. Explain why the order of Ayana's steps is important.

At the fair, general admission is $8.00 per person. Tickets for rides and games must be bought separately. Food and drinks are purchased at the concession stands. A ride ticket costs $3.00.

2. Ayana plans to buy tickets for five rides. She wrote the expression $8 + 5 \cdot 3$ to represent the cost of her rides and admission to the fair. Zachary intends to go on 8 rides in the morning and on 5 rides in the afternoon. He also wrote the expression $8 + 5 \cdot 3$ to represent the total cost of the rides he wants to go on.

a. How much does Ayana expect to pay for admission to the fair and the rides she wants to go on?

b. How much does Zachary expect to pay for the total cost of his rides, not including his admission cost?

> **MATH TERMS**
>
> A **numerical expression** is a mathematical phrase that uses numbers or numbers with operations. For example: 6 or $4 + 3$.

My Notes

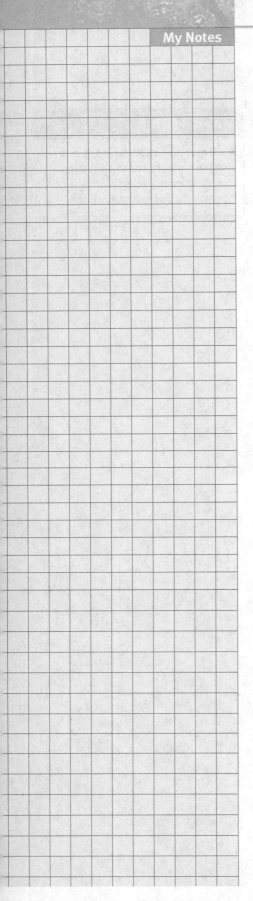

In solving math problems, there would be many miscalculations if one math problem could have two or more answers. To prevent this from occurring, mathematicians have agreed that when evaluating an expression containing both addition and multiplication, multiplication should be performed first.

3. The expression $8 + 5 \cdot 3$ does not accurately represent both Ayana's and Zachary's costs. Explain why.

When evaluating a numerical expression with addition and subtraction, the operations should be performed in the order they appear from left to right.

4. Make sense of problems. Ayana has $100 saved. Her dad gave her $5. She took $60 to the fair and left the $5 home. She wrote the expression $100 - 60 + 5$ to represent the amount she has left at home. Is this expression correct? Explain.

5. Construct viable arguments. Zachary has $100 saved. He takes $60 of it for rides, food, and admission to the fair and $5 of it for a souvenir. He wrote the expression $100 - 60 + 5$ to represent the amount of money he will have left after the fair. Does this expression correctly represent the amount he will have left? Explain.

6. Ayana and Zachary took some snacks to the fair. Ayana took a box of six granola bars and divided them evenly into three snack bags. She took three more boxes of six granola bars and shared them evenly into the same three snack bags. Zachary wrote the expression $6 \div 3 \times 4$ to represent the number of granola bars in each bag. Evaluate Zachary's expression. Does his expression work? Explain why your answer makes sense for this situation.

To simplify a numerical expression containing addition, subtraction, multiplication, and division, follow these rules:

Step 1: Multiplication and division are performed from left to right.

Step 2: Addition and subtraction are performed from left to right.

Example A

Simplify each of the following expressions.

a. $4 \cdot 5 \div 2$ Multiplication comes first when moving from
$(4 \cdot 5) \div 2$ left to right.
$20 \div 2 = 10$

b. $4 + 5 \cdot 2$ Multiplication is done before addition.
$4 + (5 \cdot 2)$
$4 + 10 = 14$

c. $4 + 5 - 2 \cdot 3$ Multiplication is done before addition or
$4 + 5 - (2 \cdot 3)$ subtraction.
$(4 + 5) - 6$ Addition and subtraction are done from left
$9 - 6 = 3$ to right.

Try These A

Simplify each of the following expressions.

a. $3 \cdot 6 + 7 = 25$
b. $3 + 6 \cdot 7 = 45$
c. $3 + 6 - 2 \cdot 2 = 5$
d. $3 + 6 - 7 = 2$

7. When Ayana and Zachary got to the fair, they played a game of darts. The target had three rings labeled 3, 3^2, and 3^3. Zachary threw two darts at the target, which both landed in the 3^2 circle.

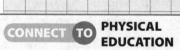

CONNECT TO **PHYSICAL EDUCATION**

Darts is a throwing game. Players throw darts at a circular target known as a dartboard.

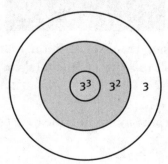

a. Ayana expressed Zachary's score as $3^2 + 3^2$. According to Ayana's expression, what is Zachary's score?

b. Zachary expressed his own score as $2 \cdot 3^2$. Could he evaluate his expression to give the same score as generated by Ayana's expression? Explain how he could, or why it is not possible.

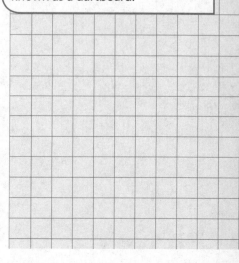

My Notes

When an expression involves exponents, it should be evaluated before doing addition, subtraction, multiplication, or division.

8. Simplify each expression.
   a. $2^4 \cdot 3^2$
   b. $19 + 32 \div 2^3$
   c. $9 \cdot (2 + 3)^2 - 14$

When an expression involves grouping symbols, such as parentheses or brackets, the operations inside the grouping symbols should be evaluated first.

9. **Make use of structure.** Add parentheses to the expression $8 + 5 \cdot 3$, so the expression will give the cost of buying 8 rides in the morning and 5 rides in the afternoon at $3.00 per ride. Explain your reasoning.

MATH TERMS

The **order of operations** is as follows:

- Do calculations inside grouping symbols first, beginning with the innermost set.
- Evaluate expressions with exponents.
- Do multiplication and division from left to right.
- Do addition and subtraction from left to right.

10. The Wilsons stop at a restaurant on the way home from the fair. They order one hamburger value meal, four apples, two juices, and two pizza value meals.

SNACKS
Pizza $3.00
Salad $5.00
Juice $2.00
Apples $2.00
Yogurt $2.50
Homemade Soup $4.00

VALUE MEALS
Pizza, Yogurt, Juice $6.00
Hamburger, Soup, Juice $8.00

   a. Write an expression that uses addition, multiplication, and a set of grouping symbols to represent the total cost of the meal.

   $$3 + 5 + 2 \cdot 2 + 2.5 + 4 + 6 + 8$$

   b. Evaluate your expression to find the total cost of the meal.

Example B

Simplify the expression.

$3(6 + 4) \div 5$	Operations inside grouping symbols are done first.
$3(10) \div 5$	Multiplication comes next when moving from left
$30 \div 5$	to right.
6	

Try These B

Evaluate each expression.

a. $(2 + 3)^2 \cdot 4$

b. $4 \cdot 25 \div (25 \div 5 \cdot 4)$

c. $8 + 6 \cdot 2 - 3$

d. $5 - 2^2 \div 4$

Check Your Understanding

Simplify each expression.

11. $18 - 12 \div 2 \cdot 3$ **12.** $9 \cdot 4 + 8 \div 2$

13. $2(8 + 2) \div 4$ **14.** $(1 + 3)^2 \cdot 5$

15. $4 \cdot 42 \div (56 \div 8 \cdot 3)$ **16.** $4 \cdot 2^2 + 1$

Insert parentheses when needed to make each number sentence true.

17. $11 + 8 \cdot 4 = 43$

18. $5 \cdot 2 + 3 = 25$

19. $16 \cdot 4 - 4 \cdot 4 = 0$

LESSON 11-1 PRACTICE

Simplify each expression.

20. $24 - 8 \div 2 = 20$ **21.** $7 \cdot 3 + 10 \div 5$

22. $6(5 + 3) \div 12 = 4$ **23.** $(2 + 4)^2 \div 3$

24. $8 \cdot 18 \div (16 \div 8 \cdot 3) = 24$ **25.** $5 \cdot 3^2 - 30$

Make sense of problems. Insert parentheses when needed to make each number sentence true.

26. $4 \cdot (3 + 6) = 36$

27. $8 \cdot (5 - 3) \cdot 4 = 64$

28. $13 + (7 \cdot 3) = 34$

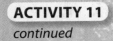
My Notes

Learning Targets:
- Use variables to represent numbers and write expressions to solve problems.
- Evaluate expressions containing variables.

SUGGESTED LEARNING STRATEGIES: Marking the Text, Look for a Pattern, Paraphrasing, Sharing and Responding

1. Ayana paid $3.00 for each ride she went on at the fair. Complete this table to show the cost of the given number of rides.

Number of Rides	Total Cost of Rides
1	
2	
3	
4	
5	
6	
7	

2. Describe any patterns you notice in the table.

3. How much would it cost Ayana to go on 6 rides?

4. Write a numeric expression for the cost of 8 rides.

5. Write a numeric expression for the cost of 12 rides.

Often **variables** are used to represent parts of an expression that may change or are unknown.

6. Let r represent the number of rides Ayana goes on. Write an expression using the variable r to represent the cost of r rides.

A **coefficient** is a number multiplied by a variable in an **algebraic expression** or equation.

In the expression $2a$, a is the variable, and 2 is the coefficient.

7. Identify the coefficient and the variable in the expression you wrote in Item 6.

MATH TERMS

A **variable** is a letter or symbol used in place of unknown numbers or quantities in expressions and equations. For example, in the expression $x + 5$, x is the variable.

A **coefficient** is a number that multiplies a variable. For example, 5 is the coefficient of $5x$.

An **algebraic expression** is a mathematical phrase that uses numbers, variables, or both with operations. For example: $x + 5$ or $5x$.

MATH TIP

You cannot *solve* an expression. You *evaluate* it for a specific value by substituting that value for the variable and simplifying.

8. Evaluate the expression you wrote in Item 6 when r is 12.

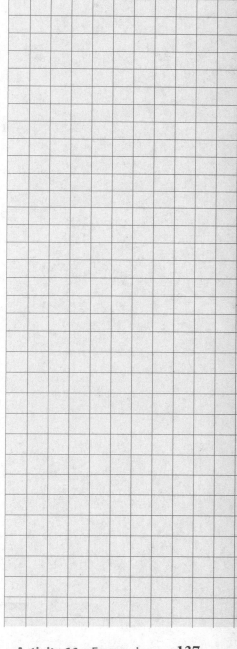

My Notes

MATH TIP

When evaluating an expression, use the order of operations. First, do the operations inside grouping symbols. Then evaluate expressions with exponents. Next, do multiplication and division from left to right. Finally, do addition and subtraction from left to right.

Example C

Evaluate each expression.

a. $2x + 3$ when $x = 4$
$2(4) + 3$ Substitute 4 in place of x and simplify
$8 + 3 = 11$

b. $x - 9$ when $x = 15$
$15 - 9 = 6$

c. $\frac{a}{12}$ when $a = 24$
$\frac{24}{12} = 2$

Try These C

Evaluate each expression.

a. $c + 11$ when $c = 5$

b. $15b$ when $b = 2$

c. $4a - 5$ when $a = 3$

d. $\frac{d}{6}$ when $d = 54$

9. General admission to the fair is $8.00, and rides cost $3.00 each.
  a. Write an expression to represent the cost for Zachary to attend the fair and go on r rides.

  b. Evaluate the expression to find his total cost if he goes on 6 rides.

10. Ayana attends the fair, buys r ride tickets, and buys g tickets to play games. Games cost $2.00 each.
  a. Reason abstractly. Write an expression to represent the cost for Ayana to attend the fair, go on r rides, and play g games.

  b. Evaluate the expression to find her total cost if she goes on 4 rides and plays 3 games.

A ***term*** is part of an expression containing a number, a variable, or both. Terms are separated in an expression by addition and subtraction symbols.
- In the expression $2a + 3$, there are two terms.
- The terms are $2a$ and 3.

11. Identify the terms in the expression you wrote in Item 10a.

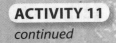

My Notes

Operations in an expression are identified by certain words.

Sum means "addition."
- The sum of 2 and 3 would be written $2 + 3$.

Product means "multiplication."
- The product of 5 and x would be written $5 \cdot x$, or just $5x$.

Difference means "subtraction."
- The difference of x and 3 would be written $x - 3$.

Quotient means "division."
- The quotient of x and 4 would be written $x \div 4$ or $\frac{x}{4}$.

Check Your Understanding

12. Identify the coefficient of the variable in each expression. Then evaluate the expression for the given value of the variable.
   a. $7x$ when $x = 3$
   b. $2b^2 + 4$ when $b = 5$
   c. $80 - 5y$ when $y = 9$

13. Write expressions for the following:
   a. Admission to a fair of $5.00 and going on r rides that cost 2 dollars each. Evaluate this expression when $r = 6$.
   b. The sum of 12 and b. Evaluate this expression when $b = 4$.
   c. The product of 9 and q. Evaluate this expression when $q = 3$.

14. Write the expression $6a$ in words.

15. Write the expression $3x + 7$ in words.

LESSON 11-2 PRACTICE

16. Evaluate each expression for the given value of the variable.
   a. $8a$ when $a = 2$ 16
   b. $\frac{x}{7}$ when $x = 21$ 3
   c. $c^3 - 1$ when $c = 4$ 63
   d. $2x + 9$ when $x = 5$ 19
   e. $4z - 2$ when $z = 3$ 10

17. Write an expression representing the product of 17 and c. Evaluate this expression for $c = 4$. 68

18. Write the expression $12a$ in words. twelve x a

19. **Reason abstractly.** Write an expression to represent the sum of $5x$ and 9, and evaluate this expression for $x = 5$.
   $5 \cdot 5 + 9 = 34$

Learning Targets:

- Use variables to represent quantities.
- Write expressions to represent quantities.

> **SUGGESTED LEARNING STRATEGIES:** Paraphrasing, Marking the Text, Note Taking, Create Representations

When writing mathematical expressions to find solutions to real-world problems, it is important to know words and phrases that represent the four mathematical operations.

Sum refers to addition, and *product* refers to multiplication. In the table below, add as many words as you can to define each operation.

Addition	Subtraction
sum	

Multiplication	Division
product	

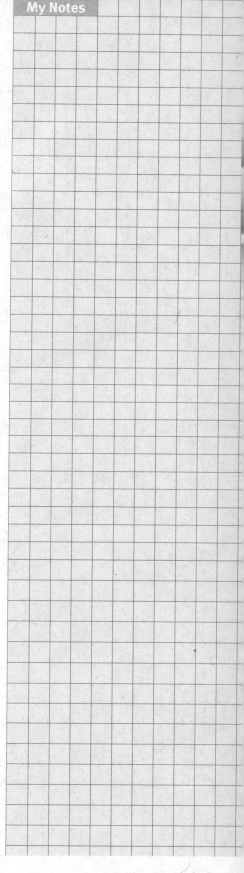

Example D

When writing algebraic expressions for verbal expressions, first determine the operation being done.

a. Fifteen more than a number
(*More than* means "addition," so 15 is being added to a number.)
$15 + n$

b. One half of a number
(*Of* means "multiplication," so $\frac{1}{2}$ is being multiplied by a number.)
$\frac{1}{2}n$

c. A number decreased by 7
(*Decreased by* means "subtraction," so 7 is being subtracted from a number.)
$n - 7$

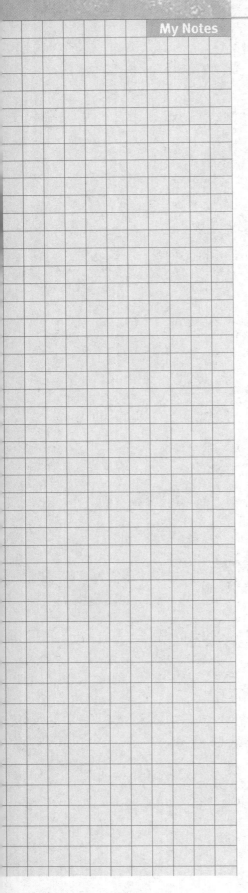

My Notes

d. The quotient of 12 and a number
(*Quotient* means "division," so 12 is being divided by a number.)
$12 \div n$ or $\dfrac{12}{n}$

Try These D

Tell which operation is being used, and write an algebraic expression for each verbal expression.

a. 4 increased by a number

$$x + 4$$

b. A number divided by 3

$$\dfrac{x}{3}$$

c. 9 more than a number squared

$$x^2 + 9$$

d. 12 less than twice a number

$$2x - 12$$

1. The area of a rectangle is found by multiplying the base and the height or the length times the width.
   a. Write an algebraic expression for the area of a rectangle.

   b. Use your expression to find the area of a rectangle with a length of 17 inches and a width of 13 inches.

2. The perimeter of a square is determined by finding the sum of the lengths of all four sides.
   a. Write two algebraic expressions to determine the perimeter of a square.

   b. Confirm that both expressions are equivalent by using both expressions to find the perimeter of a square with side lengths of 2.6 inches.

3. Use concrete or pictorial models to determine if the expressions $3x$ and $x + x + x$ are equivalent.

4. Use algebra tiles or other concrete or pictorial models to determine if the expressions $n \cdot n$ and n^2 are equivalent.

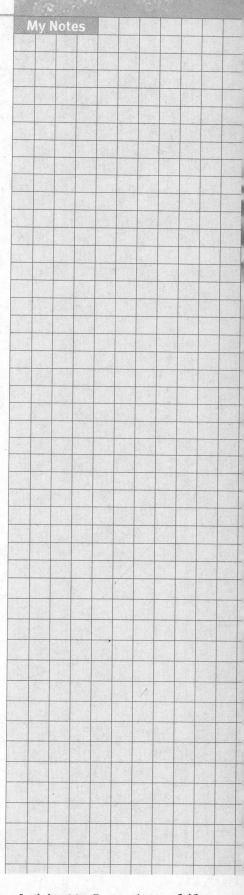

My Notes

5. The rental fee for a bicycle to ride on the beach is $10.00, plus $2.00 for each hour that you ride.
   a. **Model with mathematics.** Write an algebraic expression for the total cost of renting the bike.

   b. Use your expression to determine the cost to rent the bike for three and a half hours.

6. Ayana and Zachary drove to the fair at an average speed of 40 mph. It took them 0.5 hours to get there. Write and simplify a numerical expression to determine how far away their home is from the fair. Show your work.

The ***unit rate*** is the rate for one item. For example, if four apples cost $2.80, the unit cost, or cost per apple, is $2.80 divided by 4, or $0.70.

7. Zachary bought eight hot dogs at the fair. He paid a total of $12.00 for the food. Find the unit cost of one hot dog. Show your work.

8. Ayana is buying peanuts at the fair. She can buy a bag of 16 ounces of peanuts for $2.88 or a bag of 10 ounces for $1.75.
   a. Find the unit cost of each bag of peanuts.

   b. Which size bag is the better buy? Explain your reasoning.

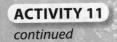

My Notes

Check Your Understanding

9. Write an algebraic expression for each verbal expression.
   a. Six more than a number
   b. Three times a number
   c. The quotient of a number and 7
   d. Four less than five times a number
   e. A number squared decreased by 2
   f. Twice a number increased by 16

10. An electrician charges a $50 house call fee and $65 per hour for the work.
    a. Write an algebraic expression to represent the situation.

    b. Is it less expensive to have the electrician work for 6 hours or have him come back for two 3-hour jobs? Explain.

11. A store sells peanut butter in 28-ounce jars for $4.29 and in 16 ounce jars for $2.49. Find the price per ounce for each size jar and determine which jar is the better buy. Explain.

LESSON 11-3 PRACTICE

12. Write an algebraic expression for each verbal expression.
    a. Five fewer than twice a number
    b. A number of coins split into 4 equal groups
    c. A number to the third power
    d. The product of 1.5 and a number
    e. Four times a number increased by 11

13. **Model with mathematics.** Three friends went to lunch. They all ordered the same meal. At the end of lunch, they gave the waiter a $12 tip.
    a. Write an algebraic expression to represent the situation.

    b. How much total money was spent if each meal cost $7.50?

14. Find the unit cost if a store sells a dozen eggs for $1.99.

Learning Targets:

● Apply the properties of operations to generate equivalent expressions.
● Identify when two expressions are equivalent.

> **SUGGESTED LEARNING STRATEGIES:** Summarizing, Marking the Text, Construct an Argument, Think-Pair-Share, Sharing and Responding

Wendy and Peter are going to a different fair. The admission for this fair is $15.00 and rides cost $2.00 each.

1. Wendy wrote the expression $2x + 15$ to represent the cost of attending the fair and going on x rides. Peter wrote the expression $15 + 2x$. Are these expressions equivalent? Explain.

In mathematics, the **_Commutative Property of Addition_** says that the order of the numbers being added can be changed and the outcome will still be the same. *Commutative* means to change order.

2. Is subtraction commutative? Explain your reasoning. Provide an example to support your response.

3. Is multiplication commutative? Explain your reasoning. Provide an example to support your response.

4. Is division commutative? Explain your reasoning. Provide an example to support your response.

5. Betsy and Patrik also are going to this fair. Betsy plans to go on eight rides and spend $6.00 for food in addition to her admission cost. She wrote the expression $(15 + 16) + 6$ to represent her total cost. Patrik thought she should use the expression $15 + (16 + 6)$ instead. Are these expressions equivalent? Explain.

The **_Associative Property of Addition_** says that when three or more numbers are being added, you can regroup and have the same outcome. For example, $(3 + 4) + 8 = 3 + (4 + 8)$.

6. Examine multiplication:
  a. What is the value of $3 \cdot (5 \cdot 2)$
  b. What is the value of $(3 \cdot 5) \cdot 2$
  c. Explain why multiplication is associative.

My Notes

> **MATH TERMS**
>
> A **mathematical property** is a rule or statement that is always true.

My Notes

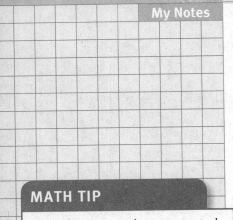

MATH TIP

Multiplication can be represented using several different symbols.

For example, the expressions 3 • 5 and 3 × 5 both mean "3 times 5."

Likewise, "4 times *a*" can be written 4 • *a*, 4 × *a*, or just 4*a*.

Usually in algebra the symbol × is not used for multiplication, because it could be easily confused with the variable *x*.

7. Are subtraction and division associative? Explain your reasoning. Provide examples to support your response.

8. Describe the similarities and differences between the Commutative and Associative Properties.

9. **a.** Apply the Commutative Property of Multiplication to create an expression equivalent to 5(6).

   b. Apply the Associative Property of Addition to create an expression equivalent to $(5 + 9) + x$.

10. Identify the property illustrated in each equation.
    a. $(2 \cdot 8) \cdot 9 = 2 \cdot (8 \cdot 9)$

    b. $3.6 + 5.7 = 5.7 + 3.6$

    c. $\left(\frac{1}{3} + \frac{1}{5}\right) + \left(\frac{1}{7} + 1\right) = \frac{1}{3} + \left(\frac{1}{5} + \frac{1}{7}\right) + 1$

The Additive Identity is the number that can be added to any number without changing its value.

11. **a.** What number will make $3 + \underline{\quad 0 \quad} = 3$ a true sentence?

    b. What number is the Additive Identity?

       0

The Multiplicative Identity is the number that can be multiplied by any number without changing its value.

12. **a.** What number will make $3 \cdot \underline{\quad 1 \quad} = 3$ a true sentence?

    b. What number is the Multiplicative Identity?

       1

13. **Make sense of problems.** Drew and Seth were in charge of collecting the money for their class field trip to the fair. They collected the estimated cost of $36.00 from each of the 16 girls and 14 boys in their class. Then they found out that the fair would give them the special price of $32.00 per person. To determine the total amount of money due back to the class, Drew wrote the expression $(16 + 14) \cdot 4$. Seth wrote the expression $16 \cdot 4 + 14 \cdot 4$. Explain why both boys are correct.

The expressions written by the boys illustrate the **Distributive Property**. In Seth's expression, the 4 has been distributed to both the 16 and the 14.

Distributive Property: $a(b + c) = ab + ac$ or $(b + c)a = ba + ca$

14. The Distributive Property can be used to simplify problems.

   a. Use the Distributive Property to rewrite the expression

   $19 \cdot 25 + 19 \cdot 75$ using parentheses.

   b. Evaluate the expression.

   $19(25 + 75) = 19 \cdot 100 = 1900$

   c. How does rewriting the expression make it easier to evaluate?

15. Drew and Seth sold greeting cards to raise money for the school band. They sold 21 boxes for $2.50 per box and need to find the total amount of money they collected. They don't have their calculators with them and need to find the total instead using the Distributive Property and mental math. Examine each method below.

$$\begin{aligned} \text{Seth:} \quad 21 \cdot 2.50 &= (20 + 1) \cdot 2.50 \\ &= 20 \cdot 2.50 + 1 \cdot 2.50 \\ &= \$50.00 + \$2.50 \\ &= \$52.50 \end{aligned}$$

$$\begin{aligned} \text{Drew:} \quad 21 \cdot 2.50 &= (10 + 10 + 1) \cdot 2.50 \\ &= 10 \cdot 2.50 + 10 \cdot 2.50 + 1 \cdot 2.50 \\ &= \$25.00 + \$25.00 + \$2.50 \\ &= \$52.50 \end{aligned}$$

Compare and *contrast* Seth's and Drew's methods.

16. Seth remembered that he sold several boxes of greeting cards to his math teacher, but he was not exactly sure how many boxes he sold her. Drew wrote the expression $\$2.50(x + 21)$, which he could use to determine the total amount of money they collected.

   a. Explain what each number and variable in Drew's expression represents.

   b. Use the Distributive Property to write an equivalent expression without parentheses.

My Notes

MATH TIP

If two numbers have a common factor, you can use the Distributive Property to write their sum as a product.
$28 + 12$
$4 \cdot 7 + 4 \cdot 3$
$4(7 + 3)$
The product $4(7 + 3)$ consists of the two factors 4 and $(7 + 3)$.

ACADEMIC VOCABULARY

To *compare* and *contrast* means to point out similarities and differences between two or more things.

CONNECT TO ALGEBRA

In algebra you will use the Distributive Property to simplify algebraic expressions.
For example:

$$n + n = 1 \cdot n + 1 \cdot n$$
$$= (1 + 1)n$$
$$= 2n$$

$$3(n + 5) = 3 \cdot n + 3 \cdot 5$$
$$= 3n + 15$$

Check Your Understanding

17. Use the Distributive Property to determine whether the following expressions are equivalent.
 a. $53 \cdot 4 + 53 \cdot 6 = 53(4 + 6)$
 b. $3 \cdot (4x - 5) = 12x - 5$
 c. $(y - 4) \cdot 2 = 2y - 8$

18. Use the Distributive Property to write equivalent expressions for each of the following.
 a. $3 \cdot (2 + x)$
 b. $6 \cdot 4 + 6 \cdot 3$
 c. $(4x + 3y + 2z) \cdot 7$
 d. $4(4x + 3y)$

19. Identify each property.
 a. $2 + 0 = 2$
 b. $15(1) = 15$
 c. $6(3 + 2) = 6(3) + 6(2)$

LESSON 11-4 PRACTICE

20. Use the Distributive Property to determine whether the following expressions are equivalent.
 a. $7(3x + 2) = 21x + 2$
 b. $(9y - 4) \cdot 3 = 27y - 12$
 c. $8 \cdot 9 + 8 \cdot 11 = 8(9 + 11)$

21. Use the Distributive Property to write equivalent expressions for each of the following.
 a. $4(5 + x)$
 b. $11 \cdot 3 + 11 \cdot 5$
 c. $(a + 5b + 6c) \cdot 8$
 d. $9(3x - 2y)$

22. Make use of structure. Identify each property.
 a. $12(10 + 2) = 12 \cdot 10 + 12 \cdot 2$
 b. $20(1) = 20$
 c. $0 + 20 = 20$

23. Use the Distributive Property to write each sum as a product. Identify the factors in the product.
 a. $26 + 10$
 b. $56 + 49$
 c. $42 + 18$

ACTIVITY 11 PRACTICE
Write your answers on notebook paper.
Show your work.

Lesson 11-1

For Items 1–10, evaluate each expression.

1. $2 \cdot 6 + 9$

2. $10 - 3 \cdot 2$

3. $8^2 + 19$

4. $3 \cdot 4 - 5 \cdot 1$

5. $36 - 20 \div 4 \cdot 3$

6. $8 \cdot 6 + 15 \div 5$

7. $(4 + 2)^2 \cdot 2$

8. $3 \cdot 36 \div (30 \div 5 \cdot 2)$

9. $8(2 + 9) \div 44$

10. $54 - 6 \cdot 3^2$

11. When Ayana arrived home from the fair she wanted to determine how much she and Zachary had left of the money they took to the fair.

    This expression represents the total amount of money Ayana and Zachary have left of the $60 each that they took to the fair.

    $60 \cdot 2 - [2 \cdot 8 + ((8 + 5) + 5) \cdot 3 + (1 + 2) \cdot 3 + 5]$

    Evaluate the expression to find how much money they returned home with. Show all work to justify your response.

Lesson 11-2

For Items 12–14, identify the terms in each expression. Then identify the coefficient of the variable and evaluate each expression when $x = 8$, $y = 4$, and $z = 6$.

12. $2y + 3$

13. $3x$

14. $4z - 7$

For Items 15–18, identify each expression as a sum, difference, product, or quotient. Then evaluate each expression for $x = 8$, $y = 4$, and $z = 6$.

15. $12 - x$

16. $y + z$

17. y^4

18. $\dfrac{2z}{3}$

19. Write an expression to represent the product of 15 and y. Evaluate your expression when $y = 3$.

20. Write an expression to represent the sum of x and $2y$. Evaluate your expression for $x = 4$ and $y = 7$.

21. Write expression $5a + 12$ in words.

22. Write the expression $2.6b$ in words.

23. Write an expression to represent admission to a zoo of $10.00 and the cost of special exhibits s at $4 each. Evaluate your expression when $s = 2$.

24. List all the factors of 15.

Lesson 11-3

For Items 25–33, write an algebraic expression for each verbal expression.

25. Eleven more than a number

26. A number decreased by 19

27. Two more than a number squared

28. A number divided by 6

29. A number less 22

30. Eight more than twice a number

31. The product of a number and 26

32. 19 less than three times a number

33. Ten more than the product of a and b

34. A number to the third power increased by 9
    A. $3n + 9$ **B.** $n^3 + 9$
    C. $(3n)9$ **D.** $9n^3$

35. A repairman charges $40 for a house call and $50 per hour. Write an algebraic expression to represent the situation.

36. A store sells grape jelly in 15-ounce jars for $3.59. Find the price per ounce.

Lesson 11-4

For Items 37–42, identify each property.

37. $5(a + 3b) = 5a + 15b$

38. $4x + 3 = 3 + 4x$

39. $7(8 \cdot 3) = (7 \cdot 8) \cdot 3$

40. $92 + 0 = 92$

41. $7(9) = 9(7)$

42. $66(1) = 66$

For Items 43–44, use the Distributive Property to determine whether the following expressions are equivalent.

43. $26(x + 3) = 26x + 3$

44. $a + a + a = 3a$

For Items 45–51, use the indicated property to write an expression equivalent to the given expression.

45. $6 + (9 + 7)$; Commutative Property of Addition

46. $6 + (9 + 7)$; Associative Property of Addition

47. $8(1)$; Multiplicative Identity Property

48. $12 \cdot 3 + 12 \cdot 7$; Distributive Property

49. $4(5)$; Commutative Property of Multiplication

50. $2(5 \cdot 10)$; Associative Property of Multiplication

51. $16 + 0$; Additive Identity Property

52. Write each sum as a product. Identify the factors in the product.
    a. $18 + 63$ **b.** $84 + 35$

MATHEMATICAL PRACTICES
Look For and Express Regularity in Reasoning

53. The length of a rectangle is three times the width. Which algebraic expression represents the perimeter of the rectangle?
    A. $3x + x$ **B.** $4x$
    C. $x + x + x + 3x$ **D.** $x + 3x + x + 3x$

Equations
Dog Gone
Lesson 12-1 Representing Situations with Equations

Learning Targets:

- Write one-variable, one-step equations to represent situations.
- Distinguish between expressions and equations.

> **SUGGESTED LEARNING STRATEGIES:** Marking the Text, Shared Reading, Create Representations, Discussion Groups, Sharing and Responding

Brynn has been volunteering at the animal shelter and has decided that she would like to adopt one of the puppies. Her parents have said that before she can have a puppy, they must fence in a portion of the backyard.

At the local home improvement store, her parents have determined that they can afford 360 feet of fencing materials. Brynn's parents have agreed to let her choose how she wants to build the fence as long as she takes into consideration the trees, storage building, and deck already in the back yard.

Brynn decides it will be easiest to fence in a rectangular area and remembers that the formula for finding the perimeter of a rectangle is $P = 2l + 2w$, where P represents the perimeter, l represents the length, and w represents the width. The formula $P = 2l + 2w$ is an example of an **equation**. In algebra, we use equations to determine solutions to problems. The value or values of a variable that make an equation true are the **solutions** to the equation.

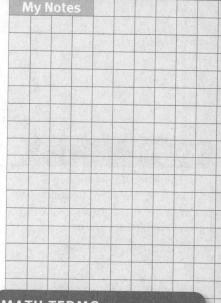

> **MATH TERMS**
>
> An **equation** is a statement showing that two numbers or expressions are equal, such as $4 + 3 = 7$. An equation has an equal sign while an expression does not.
>
> The **solution** of an equation is the numeric value of a variable that makes the equation a true statement.

1. Use substitution to rewrite the formula $P = 2l + 2w$ to represent the amount of fencing materials that Brynn's family can afford.

2. Brynn decides she can create an entrance from the existing deck to the fenced portion of the yard if she makes the enclosure 30 feet wide. Use substitution to rewrite the formula $P = 2l + 2w$ to represent this new information.

It is important to represent real-world situations with algebraic expressions and equations. Solving the resulting equations helps determine answers to real-life problems.

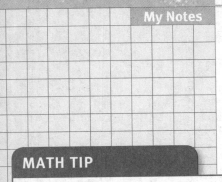

My Notes

Example A

Write an equation to represent this situation.

What number do you add to 15 to get 23?

Step 1: Write a verbal model.
A number + 15 = 23

Step 2: Define variables for unknown quantities.
Let n = the number

Step 3: Write an equation using a variable for any unknown quantity.
$n + 15 = 23$

Try These A

Write an equation to represent each situation.

a. What number do you add to 86 to get 95?

b. What number do you multiply 7 by to get 56?

3. **Reason abstractly.** Madison and Tanisha went out to lunch. The bill for their lunches came to $18.94. Madison knows that her lunch cost $9.72. How much did Tanisha's lunch cost?
   a. Write a verbal model for the situation.

   b. Define a variable for the unknown quantity.

   c. Write an equation using a variable for any unknown quantity to represent the situation.

Expressions consist of variables, numbers, and operation symbols, while **equations** also contain an equal sign.

4. Determine below whether each is an equation or an expression.
   a. $5x - 9$
   b. $2x + 6 = 50$
   c. $8x^2 - 64 = 0$
   d. $90(3a + 2b - c)$

Check Your Understanding

Write an equation for each situation. Show your verbal model and define the variable you use.

5. What number do you subtract from 59 to get 31?

6. What number do you multiply by 10 to get 210?

7. What number do you divide by 12 to get 9?

8. Brynn needs to save \$125 to build a doghouse for her new puppy. She has saved \$68. How much more does she need to save?

Identify each as an expression or an equation.

9. $8x - 3 = 5$

10. $8x - 3$

11. $2 = 4x$

LESSON 12-1 PRACTICE

Write an equation for each situation. Show your verbal model and define the variable you use.

12. What number must be multiplied by 5 to get 35?

13. What number is subtracted from 12 to get 9?

14. The recycling club has a goal to recycle 2,000 pounds of newspaper this year. They have already recycled 1,585 pounds. How many more pounds do they need to recycle to meet their goal?

15. **Reason abstractly.** Mrs. Smith is having a graduation party for all of the eighth-grade students in her school. She is making 120 cupcakes to serve at the party. She needs to buy trays to hold the cupcakes. Each tray will hold 24 cupcakes. How many trays will she need to buy?

16. Brynn can feed her puppy for \$1.99 per week. How many weeks will a bag of puppy chow last if it costs \$11.94?

Identify each as an expression or an equation.

17. $4x$

18. $14x + 2y + 3$

19. $6x^2 = 24$

20. $y - 5 = 2$

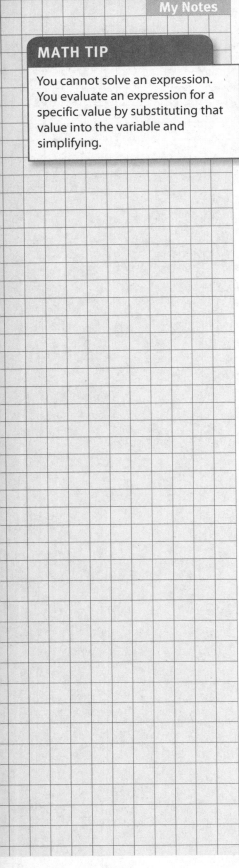

MATH TIP

You cannot solve an expression. You evaluate an expression for a specific value by substituting that value into the variable and simplifying.

Learning Targets:

- Understand what it means to solve an equation.
- Use substitution to determine which values from a specified set make an equation true.

SUGGESTED LEARNING STRATEGIES: Paraphrasing, Think-Pair-Share, Guess and Check, Simplify the Problem, Share and Respond

Equations can be solved using many methods. These include using mental math, using guess and check, solving algebraically, or substituting in values for the variable to see which value makes the equation true.

Brynn wrote the equation $2l + 2(30) = 360$ to represent the length of the enclosure she could build for her new puppy with 360 feet of fencing materials, if the width of the enclosure was 30 feet.

1. **Attend to precision.** Brynn decided to find the length of the fence by substituting to test possible lengths. Substitute the following values into the equation for l and see if they result in a true statement. Show your work.
    a. 100 feet

    b. 200 feet

    c. 150 feet

    d. What length should Brynn use for her fenced area? Justify your answer.

2. Mental math can also be used to solve some equations.
    a. Explain how you could use mental math to solve $2l + 60 = 360$.

    b. Use mental math to determine a value for l that makes the equation a true statement. This is the solution of the equation.

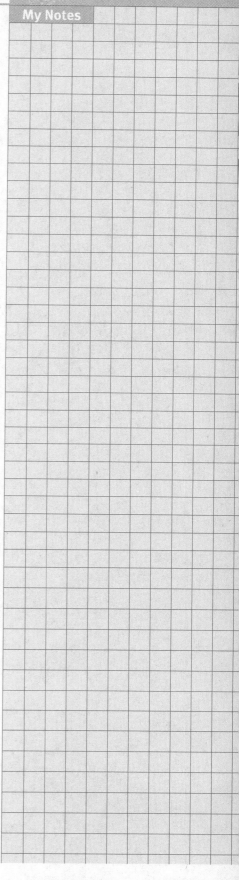

Example B

Use this set of possible solutions to determine the solution to each equation.

$\{0, 6, 15, 18\}$

a. $2x - 4 = 32$

Step 1: Substitute in for x each value from the set of possible solutions.

Step 2: Determine which value produces a true equation.
$2(0) - 4 = 0 - 4 = -4 \neq 32$
$2(6) - 4 = 12 - 4 = 8 \neq 32$
$2(15) - 4 = 30 - 4 = 26 \neq 32$
$2(18) - 4 = 36 - 4 = 32$

Solution: 18 is the solution of the equation $2x - 4 = 32$

b. $\dfrac{y}{3} + 2 = 7$

$\dfrac{0}{3} + 2 = 0 + 2 = 2 \neq 7$

$\dfrac{6}{3} + 2 = 2 + 2 = 4 \neq 7$

$\dfrac{15}{3} + 2 = 5 + 2 = 7$

$\dfrac{18}{3} + 2 \neq 7$

15 is the solution of the equation $\dfrac{y}{3} + 2 = 7$

Try These B

Use this set of possible solutions to determine the solution to each equation.

$\{0, 11, 13, 15\}$

a. $61 - m = 50$
b. $3k = 39$

My Notes

Check Your Understanding

Use this set of possible solutions to determine a solution to each equation using substitution.

{3, 8, 10, 14, 15, 16}

3. $4 = 0.5z - 4$

4. $11 = x - 3$

5. $\dfrac{63}{x} = 21$

6. $21 + a = 29$

7. $\dfrac{y}{3} + 1 = 6$

8. $8x - 2 = 78$

LESSON 12-2 PRACTICE

Use this set of possible solutions to determine a solution to each equation using substitution.

{1, 2, 5, 6, 12, 20}

9. $13x = 26$

10. $6x + 9 = 45$

11. $3a - 12 = 48$

12. $\dfrac{y}{4} - 2 = 1$

13. $4 = z - 1$

14. $x^2 + 3 = 4$

15. Attend to precision. In Lesson 12-1, Item 8, you wrote an equation for this situation: Brynn needs to save $125 to build a doghouse for her new puppy. She has saved $68. How much more does she need to save? Now use this set of possible solutions and substitution to solve the equation.
{$193, $67, $57, $125}

ACTIVITY 12 PRACTICE

Write your answers on notebook paper. Show your work.

Lesson 12-1

For Items 1–8, write an equation to represent each situation. Include a verbal model and define any variables you use.

1. What number do you add to 17 to get 51?

2. What number do you multiply 6 by to get 66?

3. Morris and Luther went shopping. Their total bill was $52.96. Morris knew he spent $31.24. How much did Luther spend?

4. Gigi has 64 baseball cards. How many should she give to Carla so she will have only 49 left?

5. What number do you divide by 9 to get 8?

6. The local hockey team needs to win 11 games to reach the playoffs. They have already won 8 games. How many more games must they win to reach the playoffs?

7. Sam is making 100 cookies. He can fit 20 cookies on each cookie sheet. How many cookie sheets will be need?

8. The perimeter of a rectangle is 400 feet and the width is 80 feet. What is the length of the rectangle?

For Items 9–12, tell if each is an equation or an expression.

9. $6x - 17$

10. $3x + 9 = 12$

11. $58 - a = 17$

12. $x^2 + 4$

13. Sigfried is calculating the percent of tax he paid if the tax on his $10.00 dinner was $0.60. Which equation could he use to represent this situation, where x represents the percent of tax?
    a. $10 + x = 60$
    b. $10.00x = 0.60$
    c. $0.60 + x = 10$
    d. $0.60x = 10.00$

14. Eight less than a number is 15. Which equation represents this situation, where n represents the number?
    a. $n - 8 = 15$
    b. $8 - n = 15$
    c. $8 < n = 15$
    d. $\frac{8}{n} = 15$

15. Explain the difference between an equation and an expression.

16. Ross and Kristen disagreed about how to write an equation to represent the following situation.

    Ross had twice as many DVDs as Kristen. Together they had 93 DVDs. How many did Kristen have?

    They agreed that x should represent the number of DVDs that Kristen had. Ross wrote the equation $x + 2x = 93$, while Kristen wrote the equation $2x = 93$. Whose equation is correct? Explain your choice.

Lesson 12-2

17. Explain what it means to solve an equation.

For Items 18–27, use substitution to determine which number in the given set is a solution of each equation.

$$\{0, 1, 3, 4, 5, 6, 7, 8, 9, 12, 20\}$$

18. $4x - 10 = 14$

19. $\frac{y}{2} + 3 = 5$

20. $19 - a = 14$

21. $6b = 48$

22. $3y + 11 = 47$

23. $9 - x^2 = 9$

24. $c + 15 = 27$

25. $\frac{7}{r} + 1 = 2$

26. $p - 14 = 6$

27. $42 - 5y = 7$

For Items 28–32, use substitution to determine which number in the given set is a solution of the each equation.

$$\{1, 2, 3, 4, 5, 6, 10\}$$

28. $2x + 3 = x + 7$

29. $x^2 - 8x + 15 = 0$

30. $a^2 = 25$

31. $3y + 6 = 7y - 34$

32. $x^2 - 2x = 8$

For Items 33–35, Harley is fencing off a rectangular garden in his backyard. To have room for all the vegetables that he wants to grow, the area of the garden must be 100 square feet. He remembers that the formula $A = lw$ gives the area of a rectangle, where A represents the area, l represents the length, and w represents the width.

33. Write an equation to represent this situation.

34. Harley finds that the area in his backyard that gets enough sun for the garden is only 5 feet wide. Substitute this value to write a new equation representing this situation.

35. Use mental math to find the length of Harley's garden. Explain your reasoning.

MATHEMATICAL PRACTICES
Model with Mathematics

36. Lupe is measuring the dimensions of her triangular lot. She knows that the lot is in the shape of an isosceles triangle (two sides are equal), and the perimeter can be calculated by adding the lengths of the three sides. She knows that the perimeter is 450 feet and that the side that is different in length from the other two is 100 feet. She wants to calculate the length of the other two sides.

   a. Draw a diagram of this situation.

   b. Write an equation that Lupe can use to find the length of the other two sides of her lot, where x represents the length of one side.

   c. Lupe is not sure if the length of the other two sides is 100 feet, 125 feet, 150 feet, 175 feet, or 200 feet. Use substitution to find the solution to your equation and the length of the sides of Lupe's lot.

Write your answers on notebook paper. Show your work.

1. Twins Terry and Tony attend Riverdale Middle School. They are on a student council committee that is deciding what the ticket price will be for a school dance. Terry and Tony know the following:
   - The decorations for the gym will cost $189.26.
   - The cost of a security guard is $52.50 per hour
   - The dance will be 3 hours long.
   - The deejay charges $50.98 plus $23.50 per hour.
   - The refreshments will cost $2.25 per student.
   - The student council has raised $349.49 to help pay for the dance.
   - Ninety-five students will attend and share the cost of the dance.

   a. Use the Distributive Property to write an expression to find the cost of the security guard and the deejay.

   b. Simplify the expression you wrote for part a to find the cost of the security guard and the deejay.

   c. How much will the refreshments cost?

   d. Write an expression for the total cost of the dance.

   e. How much money will the student council need to collect from ticket sales to break even?

2. Write a letter to the twins telling them what you think the ticket price for the dance should be. Use the information provided and your work in Item 1 to justify your recommendation.

3. Terry and Tony had 50 balloons to use for decorations. They put 30 on the tables and 4 at each end of the refreshment table. Their advisor thought they needed balloons at the entrance and brought 10 more. The expression $50 - 30 - 4 \times 2 + 10$ shows the number of balloons they have for the entrance. Tony thinks they will have 42 balloons for the entrance but Terry says there will only be 22. Who is correct? Explain your reasoning.

4. To help pay for the next school event, Terry and Tony want to make a profit from ticket sales for this dance. They determine that they would like to bring in a total of $475 from ticket sales.

   a. If x represents the price per ticket, write an equation to represent this situation.

   b. Some student council dance committee members believe they should charge $4.00 per ticket, while others think they should charge $4.50 per ticket. Terry and Tony believe the price per ticket should be $5.00. Use substitution to find the solution to your equation from part a and to determine how much each ticket should cost.

Scoring Guide	Exemplary	Proficient	Emerging	Incomplete
	The solution demonstrates these characteristics:			
Mathematics Knowledge and Thinking (Items 1a–e, 2, 3, 4a–b)	• A clear understanding of the order of operations and the Distributive Property. • Effective understanding of and accuracy in writing, evaluating, and solving expressions and equations.	• A functional understanding of the order of operations and the Distributive Property. • Writing, evaluating, and solving expressions and equations that usually result in correct answers.	• Partial understanding of the order of operations and the Distributive Property. • Difficulty with writing, evaluating, and solving expressions and equations.	• Little or no understanding of the order of operations and the Distributive Property. • Little or no understanding of writing, evaluating, and solving expressions and equations.
Problem Solving (Items 1e, 2)	• An appropriate and efficient strategy that results in a correct answer.	• A strategy that may include unnecessary steps but results in a correct answer.	• A strategy that results in some incorrect answers.	• No clear strategy when solving problems.
Mathematical Modeling / Representations (Items 1a, 1d, 4a)	• Clear and accurate representation of problems as expressions and equations.	• Some difficulty in representing problems as expressions and equations.	• Difficulty in writing expressions and equations leading to errors.	• No understanding of representing problems as expressions and equations.
Reasoning and Communication (Items 2, 3)	• Precise use of appropriate math terms and language to explain solutions to expressions and equations and the role of the order of operations.	• An adequate explanation of solutions to expressions and equations and the role of the order of operations.	• A misleading or confusing explanation of solutions to expressions and equations and the role of the order of operations.	• An incomplete or inaccurate explanation of solutions to expressions and equations and the role of the order of operations.

Solving Addition and Subtraction Equations

Music to My Ears

Lesson 13-1 Modeling and Solving Addition Equations

ACTIVITY 13

Learning Targets:

- Write a one-step addition equation to model a situation.
- Solve an addition equation of the form $x + a = b$, where a, b, and x are all nonnegative integers.

SUGGESTED LEARNING STRATEGIES: Shared Reading, Summarizing, Think-Pair-Share, RAFT, Self Revision/Peer Revision, Work Backward

Example A

Samantha wants to buy a new electronic tablet. She has $70 from her recent birthday, but the tablet she wants costs $340. How much more does she need to save to be able to buy the tablet?

This situation can be modeled with an equation.

Step 1: Define a variable.
Let x represent the amount she needs to save.

Step 2: Write a verbal model for this situation.
$70 + \text{amount needed} = \$340$

Step 3: Write an equation.
$70 + x = 340$

Step 4: Use mental math to determine the solution.
What number added to 70 gives 340?
$x = 270$

Step 5: Use substitution to check your solution.
$70 + x = 340, x = 270$
$70 + 270 = 340$
$340 = 340$

Solution: Samantha needs to save $270 to buy the tablet.

Try These A

Onil's cheerleading squad wants to buy matching sweaters. They have 16 sweaters, but there are 22 cheerleaders. How many more sweaters do they need to buy?

a. Define a variable.

b. Write a word phrase to model this situation.

c. Write an equation.

d. Solve the equation.

e. Check the solution using substitution.

My Notes

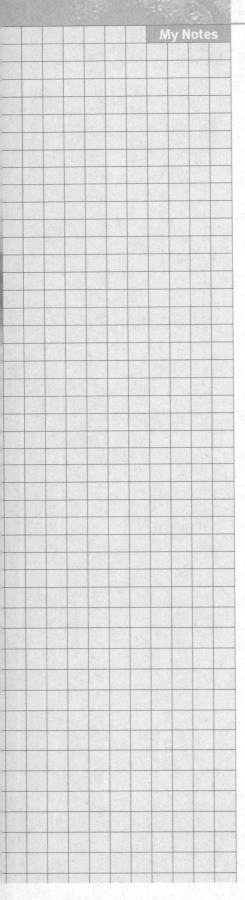

My Notes

The equations you wrote in the previous problems are addition equations. An addition equation can be solved using several methods that include mental math, guess and check, a balance scale, or an algebraic method. The solution can be graphed on a number line.

1. **Make sense of problems.** Samantha has 29 songs downloaded to her new tablet. She wants to have a total of 100 songs on the tablet. How many more songs does she need to download?

   a. Define a variable and write a word phrase to model the situation.

   b. Write an equation and use mental math to solve the equation.

   c. Check the solution using substitution.

   d. Graph the solution on a number line.

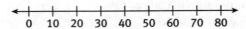

2. Quin has 28 state quarters collected. He wants to have a complete set of the 50 state quarters. How many more quarters does he need to collect?

   a. Define a variable and write a verbal model.

   b. Write an equation and use mental math to solve the equation.

   c. Check the solution using substitution.

   d. Graph the solution on a number line.

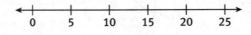

Lesson 13-1
Modeling and Solving Addition Equations

Check Your Understanding

3. Shaunika is filling her swimming pool. The pool has 21 inches of water in it. She wants it to have 42 inches of water. How many more inches of water does she need to put in the pool?

   a. Define a variable and write a verbal model.

   b. Write an equation and use mental math to solve the equation.

   c. Check the solution using substitution.

   d. Graph the solution on a number line.

   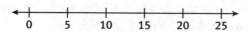

4. There are 5 inches of snow on the ground. How many more inches of snow must fall to make the snow 12 inches deep? Write, solve and check an equation for this situation. Define the variable.

LESSON 13-1 PRACTICE

Evaluate each expression.

5. **Make sense of problems.** Trevor wants to buy a car that costs $23,600. He has $5,000 for a down payment. How much more will Trevor owe on the car? Write, solve and check an equation for this situation. Define the variable.

6. Moira is planting 100 tulip bulbs in her front yard. She has planted 42 bulbs. How many more bulbs does Moira have to plant? Write, solve and check an equation for this situation. Define the variable.

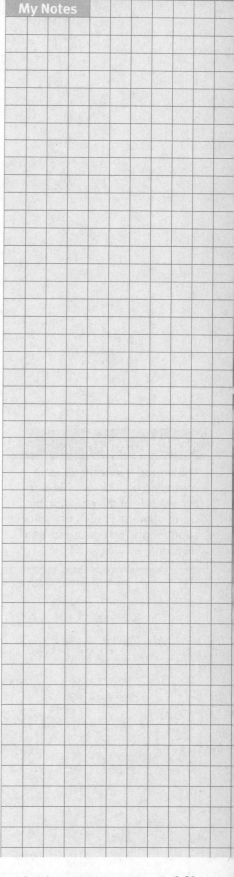

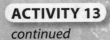

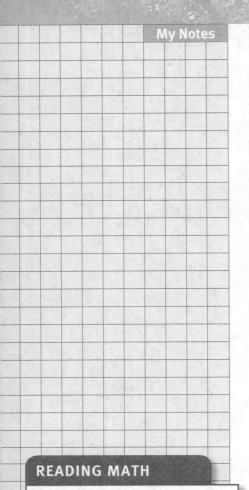

Learning Targets:
- Write addition equations to represent situations.
- Solve one-step addition equations of the form $x + a = b$, where a, b, and x are all nonnegative rational numbers.
- Given an equation of the form $x + a = b$, where a, b, and x are all nonnegative rational numbers, write a corresponding real-world problem.

SUGGESTED LEARNING STRATEGIES: Sharing and Responding, Create a Plan, Create Representations

Example B

Mario wants 5 books to take on vacation. He has 2 books that he has not read yet. How many more books does he need to buy?

Step 1: Define a variable and write a verbal model.
 Let x represent the number of books he needs to buy.
 2 + number of books he needs = 5

Step 2: Write an equation.
 $x + 2 = 5$

Step 3: Solve the equation.

In addition to mental math, another method to solve an equation is using a balance scale. When using a balance scale, the goal is to get the quantity being determined, or x, on one side of the scale alone. This is called "isolating the variable."

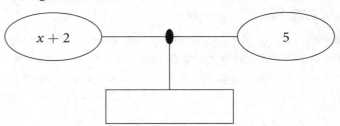

Subtract 2 from the left side to isolate the x, because $+2$ and -2 are a zero pair. To keep the scale balanced, you must also subtract 2 from the right side.

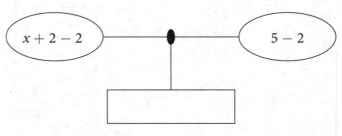

READING MATH

The phrase *isolate the variable* means "to get the variable alone on one side of the equation by using operations such as addition, subtraction, multiplication, and division."

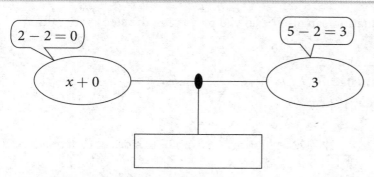

Use the Additive Identity Property to simplify $x + 0$.
The solution is $x = 3$.

Check by substitution.

$x + 2 = 5$
$3 + 2 = 5$
$5 = 5$

Try These B

Solve $x + 4 = 11$ using a balance scale. Check your solution.

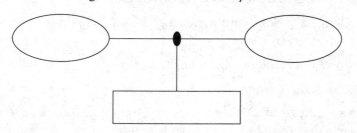

Addition equations can also be solved algebraically.

Example C

Solve the equation $x + 15 = 25$.

Step 1: Since this is an addition equation, use the inverse operation of subtraction. Subtract 15 from both sides.
$x + 15 - 15 = 25 - 15$

Step 2: Simplify both sides of the equation.
$x + 0 = 10$

Step 3: Use the Additive Identity Property to isolate the variable.
$x = 10$

Step 4: Check the solution by substitution.
$10 + 15 = 25$
$25 = 25$

Solution: $x = 10$

Try These C

Solve the equation $x + 9 = 34$ algebraically.

MATH TERMS

Inverse operations are operations that "undo" each other. Addition and subtraction are inverse operations. Multiplication and division are inverse operations.

CONNECT **TO** **AP**

In AP mathematics, understanding inverse operations is important in understanding the relationship between the processes called differentiation and integration.

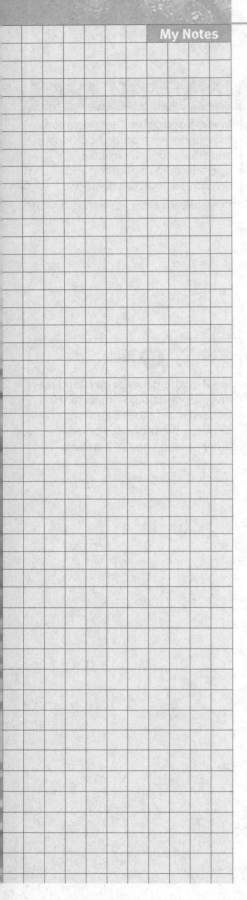

An equation can also be solved by writing the steps vertically.

Example D

Solve $x + 22 = 36$

$$x + 22 = 36$$
$$\underline{-22 \quad -22}$$ Subtract 22 from both sides of the equation to
$$x + 0 = 14$$ isolate x.
$$x = 14$$

Try These D

Solve $x + 34 = 52$.

1. Samantha has scored 2,160 points in a video game on her tablet. To win the current level she needs to have 8,500 points. How many more points must she score to win the level?

   a. Define a variable and write an equation.

   b. Solve the equation algebraically.

   c. Check the solution.

2. **Make sense of problems.** Alfred has made 8 cookies to give to his friends. Since he has 15 friends that he wants to give cookies to, how many more cookies does he need to make? Define a variable, write an equation, and solve your equation algebraically. Check your solution.

3. Olivia has 6 of the CDs by her favorite group. The group has recorded 22 CDs. How many more of this group's CDs must she buy to have the complete collection? Define a variable, write an equation, and solve your equation algebraically. Check your solution.

4. Write a real-world problem that could be represented by the equation $y + 11 = 19$.

5. Write a real-world problem that could be represented by the equation $a + 68 = 79$.

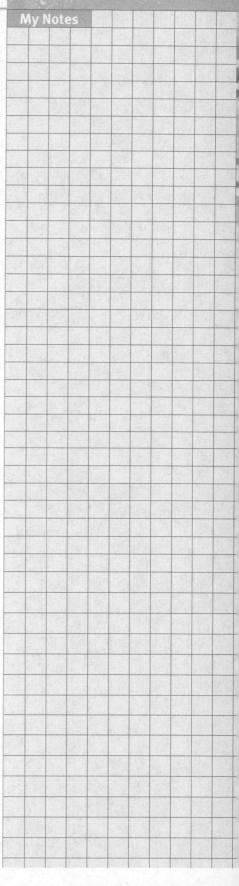

Check Your Understanding

6. Samantha has 27 pictures on her new tablet. How many more must she take so she will have 81 pictures? Define a variable, write an equation, and solve it algebraically. Check your solution.

7. Zander has $\frac{2}{3}$ of a cup of milk. How much more milk does he need to have $1\frac{1}{2}$ cups of milk? Define a variable, write an equation, and solve it algebraically. Check your solution.

8. Write a real-world problem that could be represented by the equation $b + 36 = 52$.

LESSON 13-2 PRACTICE

9. Lamont has read 152 pages of a 450-page book. How many more pages does he have to read to finish the book? Define a variable, write an equation, and solve it algebraically. Check your solution.

10. **Make sense of problems.** Tim can run a mile in 5.8 minutes. Shannon can run a mile in 8.2 minutes. How much longer does it take Shannon than Tim to run a mile? Define a variable, write an equation, and solve it algebraically. Check your solution.

11. Write a real-world problem that could be represented by the equation $x + 15 = 94$.

12. Write a letter to a friend explaining how to solve an addition equation using the balance scale method.

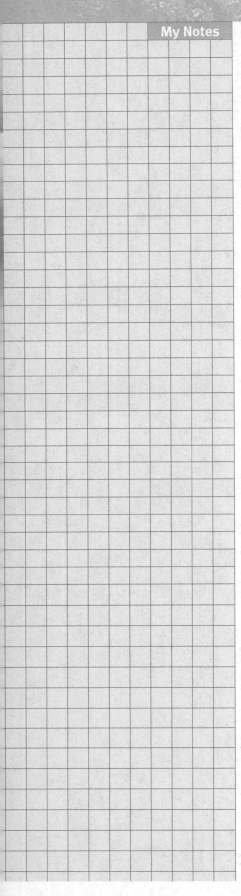
My Notes

Learning Targets:

- Write a subtraction equation to represent a situation.
- Solve a subtraction equation of the form $x - a = b$, where a, b, and x are all nonnegative rational numbers.

SUGGESTED LEARNING STRATEGIES: Summarizing, Think-Pair-Share, RAFT, Self Revision/Peer Revision, Work Backward

Many real-world problems can be represented and solved using a subtraction equation very much like those represented and solved using an addition equation.

Example E

Samantha has apps on her tablet. If she deletes 7 of them she will have 17 left. How many apps did she have to begin with?

Step 1: Define a variable.
Let x represent the number of applications she had to begin with.

Step 2: Write a verbal model.
number of apps she had to begin with $- 7 = 17$

Step 3: Write an equation.
$x - 7 = 17$

Step 4: Use mental math to solve the equation.
From what number can you subtract 7 and get 17?
$x = 24$

Step 5: Use substitution to check the solution.
$24 - 7 = 17$
$17 = 17$

Solution: Samantha had 24 apps to begin with.

Try These E

Shiro is driving from Houston, Texas, to San Antonio, Texas. After driving 50 miles, he still has 150 miles to go. How many miles is the trip from Houston to San Antonio?

a. Define a variable, write a verbal model and an equation.

b. Solve the equation and check using substitution.

My Notes

1. After Yadra lent $9.12 to Raquel, she had $24.36 left. How much money did Yadra have before the loan? Define a variable and write a verbal model and equation for this situation. Then solve the equation and check the solution.

2. Samantha was entering her contacts on her new tablet. She has entered 25 contacts and still has 22 left to enter. How many total contacts will she have on her tablet? Define a variable and write a verbal model and equation for this situation. Then solve the equation and check the solution.

3. Confirm your solution to the equation in Item 2 by using the balance scale method.

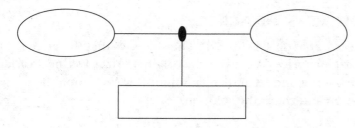

4. **Critique the reasoning of others.** Joshua believes a subtraction equation can be solved using a balance scale by subtracting a number from each side. Is he correct? Explain.

My Notes

Check Your Understanding

5. Enzo still owes $750 on his new furniture. He has already paid $600 on it. What was the original cost of the furniture? Define a variable and write a verbal model and equation for this situation. Then solve the equation and check the solution.

6. Yusra's dog is overweight. The vet says the dog needs to lose 7 pounds to get down to the desirable weight of 45 pounds. How much does Yusra's dog weigh? Define a variable and write a verbal model and equation for this situation. Then solve the equation and check the solution.

LESSON 13-3 PRACTICE

7. You see a coat on sale for $78. The sign says that the price is $15 off the original price. What was the original price? Define a variable and write a verbal model and equation for this situation. Then solve the equation and check the solution.

8. **Model with mathematics.** Payat put $420 from his savings account into a certificate of deposit to earn more interest. He then had $80 left in his savings account. How much did Payat have in his savings account before he opened the certificate? Define a variable and write a verbal model and equation for this situation. Then solve the equation and check the solution.

9. **Critique the reasoning of others.** Marsha said she could solve $x - 3 = 7$ using the balance scale method by adding 3 to each side of the scale. Do you think her reasoning is correct? Explain.

Learning Targets:

- Write subtraction equations to represent situations.
- Solve subtraction equations by adding the same number to both sides of the equation.
- Given an equation of the form $x - a = b$, where a, b, and x are all nonnegative rational numbers, write a corresponding real-world problem.

SUGGESTED LEARNING STRATEGIES: Marking the Text, Think Aloud, Sharing and Responding, Create a Plan, Create Representations, Discussion Groups

A subtraction equation can be solved algebraically much like an addition problem.

Example F

Solve $x - 3 = 17$.

Step 1: Add 3 to each side of the equation.
$x - 3 + 3 = 17 + 3$

Step 2: Simplify both sides.
$x + 0 = 20$

Step 3: Use Additive Identity Property to isolate the variable.
$x = 20$

Step 4: Substitute to check the solution.
$x - 3 = 17, x = 20$
$20 - 3 = 17$
$17 = 17$

Solution: $x = 20$

MATH TIP

The inverse operation of subtraction is addition.

Try These F

Solve $x - 11 = 5$ algebraically.

1. Wayne is playing a card game. He has dealt 17 cards out and has 35 left to deal. How many cards did he have to start?

   a. Define a variable and write a subtraction equation.

   b. Solve the equation algebraically.

   c. Use substitution to check the solution.

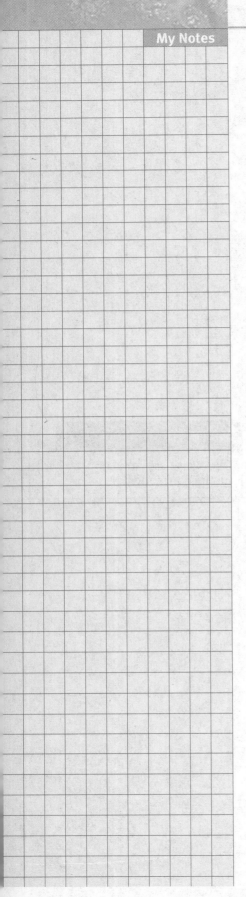

My Notes

2. The Tigers lost 7 yards on their first play. After that play they were on their own 33 yard line. What yard line were they on before that play?

   Define a variable and write an equation. Solve the equation algebraically and check the solution.

3. Write a real-world problem that could be represented by the equation $x - 9 = 40$.

4. Write a real-world problem that could be represented by the equation $x - 2 = 15$.

5. **Construct viable arguments.** Would $13 - x = 9$ be solved the same way as $x - 13 = 9$? Explain.

6. Glenn is writing a term paper. He has written 2,000 words and still has 1,700 words left to write. How long will the term paper be? Define a variable and write an equation. Solve the equation algebraically and check the solution.

7. Lindsey decreased her time on a downhill ski course by 15 seconds. Her new time is 86 seconds. What was her old time? Define a variable and write an equation. Solve the equation algebraically and check the solution.

8. Bob is printing party invitations. He has printed 17 and has 31 more invitations to print. How many invitations is he sending out to his party? Define a variable and write an equation. Solve the equation algebraically and check the solution.

9. On Tuesday, there were 23 students absent from school. The total number of students at school that day was 372 students. How many students attend the school? Define a variable and write an equation. Solve the equation algebraically and check the solution.

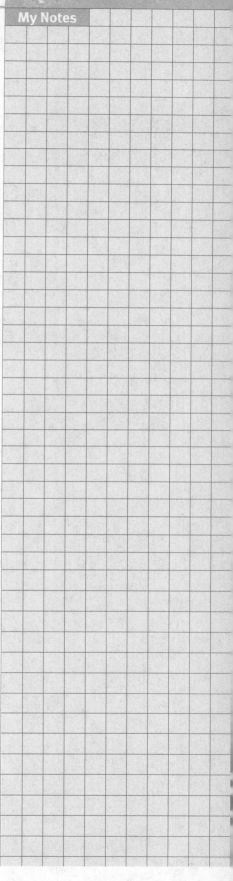

My Notes

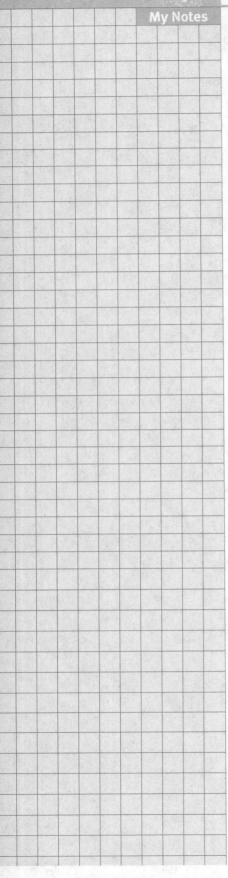

My Notes

Check Your Understanding

10. Solve each equation algebraically.
   a. $a - 7.29 = 55.64$
   b. $w - \frac{2}{3} = \frac{1}{2}$
   c. $a - 9 = 11$
   d. $b - 28 = 2$
   e. $c - 49 = 96$

11. Manny is putting his DVDs away. He put 11 of them away and still has 43 left to put away. How many DVDs does Manny have? Define a variable and write an equation. Solve the equation algebraically and check the solution.

12. Write a real-world problem that could be represented by the equation $c - 4 = 26$.

LESSON 13-4 PRACTICE

13. Solve each equation algebraically.

   a. $a - 1.23 = 4.72$

   b. $x - 4 = 7$

   c. $z - 17 = 28$

   d. $c - 71 = 59$

   e. $w - \frac{3}{4} = \frac{7}{12}$

14. Samantha was scanning photos. She has scanned 123 but still has 296 left to scan. How many pictures did she start with? Define a variable and write an equation. Solve the equation algebraically and check the solution.

15. Write a real-world problem that could be represented by the equation $a - 50 = 9$.

16. **Construct viable arguments.** Explain why $x + 8 = 12$ and $12 - x = 8$ have the same solution.

ACTIVITY 13 PRACTICE

Lesson 13-1

For Items 1–4, define a variable and write a verbal model and an equation. Then solve the equation and check the solution using substitution.

1. Lee is 32 years younger than his mother and his mother is 67 years old. How old is Lee?

2. Sumatra bought a loaf of bread 24 inches long. She cut it into two pieces. If one piece was 9 inches long, how long was the other piece?

3. Mt. McKinley in Alaska is 20,320 feet high. It is 9,081 feet higher than Mt. Hood in Oregon. How tall is Mt. Hood?

4. Emma has 11 pairs of shoes. She has three more pairs of shoes than Louisa has. How many pairs of shoes does Louisa have?

For Items 5–9, solve each equation using mental math or guess and check. Then check the solution.

5. $x + 11 = 26$

6. $12 + a = 19$

7. $51 = 47 + b$

8. $y + 81 = 152$

9. $890 + x = 1,359$

Lesson 13-2

For Items 10–12, define a variable and write a verbal model and an equation. Then solve the equation and check the solution using substitution.

10. Joella makes $12.75 per hour. This is $2.50 more than her younger sister makes per hour. How much does Joella's sister make per hour?

11. The enrollment at the University of Texas, Austin, in 2011 was 51,112. This was 11,245 more than the enrollment at Texas A&M University. What was the enrollment at Texas A&M University?

12. During the first hour on opening day 2,120 people entered the amusement park. By the end of that day 8,596 people had entered the park. How many people entered the park after the first hour?

For Items 13–14, write a real-world problem that could be represented by the equation.

13. $z + 2 = 9$

14. $15 + x = 40$

For Items 15–17, solve each equation, and then check your solution.

15. $a + 97 = 125$

16. $12.95 = y + 3.19$

17. $\frac{2}{3} + x = \frac{3}{4}$

Lesson 13-3

For Items 18–21, define a variable, write a verbal model and an equation. Then solve the equation and check the solution using substitution.

18. Devery is going on a rafting trip. She has rafted 12 miles and has 16 miles left to go. How many miles long is the trip?

19. Terry is hiking on the trail to Mt. LeConte in the Great Smoky Mountains. He has hiked 2.1 miles and has 4.5 left before he reaches the summit. How many miles long is the hike?

20. McKenzie is putting away holiday decorations. She has put 36 decorations away and still has 97 left to put away. How many holiday decorations did she have out?

21. There are seven tuba players in the high school band and 51 band members who play other instruments. How many band members are there?

For Items 22–25, use mental math or guess and check to solve each equation, then check your solution.

22. $x - 4 = 10$

23. $a - 15 = 3$

24. $b - 17 = 18$

25. $4 = c - 26$

Lesson 13-4

For Items 26–28, define a variable, write a verbal model and an equation. Then solve the equation and check the solution using substitution.

26. Grandma is knitting a scarf. She has knit 10 inches of the scarf and still has 38 inches left to finish. How long will the scarf be when it is completed?

27. Elroy is taking a train to downtown. The train has made 11 stops already and will make another 23 stops before it reaches its destination. How many total stops are there on the train route?

28. The football team is losing the game in the fourth quarter. There are still 6,700 fans in attendance but 2,500 fans have already left. What was the total attendance at the game before the fans began to leave?

For Items 29–30, write a real-world problem that could be represented by the equation.

29. $x - 12 = 20$

30. $a - 15 = 3$

For Items 31–32, choose the correct solution of the equation.

31. $x - 57.6 = 24.3$
    a. 81.9   b. 57.6   c. 33.3   d. 24.3

32. $x - \frac{1}{5} = \frac{1}{2}$
    a. $\frac{1}{5}$ b. $\frac{3}{10}$ c. $\frac{1}{2}$ d. $\frac{7}{10}$

MATHEMATICAL PRACTICES
Reason Abstractly and Quantitatively

33. Describe the strategies for solving equations. Explain when and why you would use each strategy.

Solving Multiplication and Division Equations

Trash Talk

Lesson 14-1 Modeling and Solving Multiplication Equations

Learning Targets:

- Write a one-step multiplication equation to model a situation.
- Solve a multiplication equation of the form $ax = b$, where a, b, and x are all positive integers.

SUGGESTED LEARNING STRATEGIES: Marking the Text, Visualization, Guess and Check, Note Taking, Think-Pair-Share, Discussion Groups, Look for a Pattern

In 2010, Americans generated about 250 million tons of trash and recycled and composted nearly 85 million tons of the trash they produced. According to the Environmental Protection Agency (EPA), Americans recycled and composted about 1.5 pounds of the average 4.5 pounds of waste produced per person per day.

1. Using this information, complete the table below to determine how much trash one person generates in a week.

Day	Total Amount of Trash Generated
1	
2	
3	
4	
5	
6	
7	

2. Describe patterns in the table.

3. **Reason quantitatively.** How much trash will one person generate in 4 weeks? Explain your answer.

4. Write a numeric expression for the amount of trash the average American has generated after 40 days.

5. Let d represent the number of days. Write an algebraic expression for the amount of trash the average American has generated after d days.

6. How many days does it take for the average American to generate 279 pounds of trash? Write and solve an algebraic equation representing this situation.

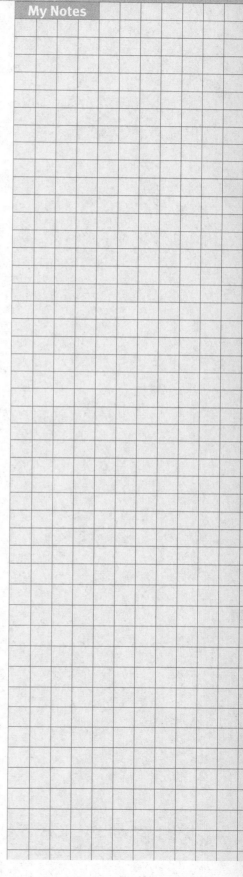

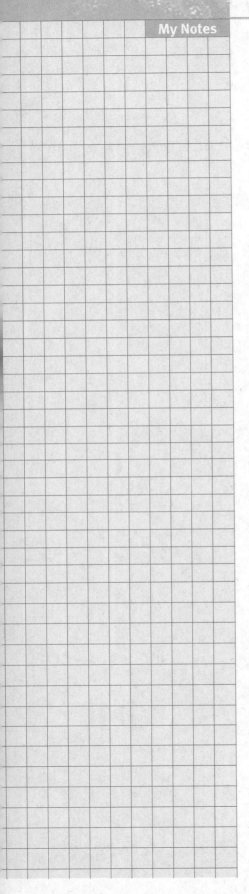

My Notes

7. The amount of trash the average American sends to the landfill each month is the difference between the total amount of trash they collect and the amount of trash they recycle.
   a. Write an algebraic expression to represent the amount of trash the average American sends to the landfill in d days.
   b. If an average American sends 93 pounds of trash to the landfill, write an algebraic equation that could be used to find the number of days, d.
   c. Use guess and check or mental math to solve the equation you wrote in part b.
   d. Check your solution from part c, using substitution.

The equations you wrote and solved above are multiplication equations. A multiplication equation is one in the form $ax = b$, where a and b are numbers. Multiplication equations can be solved by guess and check, by mental math, or by using algebra.

Example A
Gabrielle has 8 apples that weigh a total of 56 ounces. How much does each apple weigh?

Step 1: Define a variable.
Let x = weight of one apple.

Step 2: Write an algebraic equation to represent this situation.
$8x = 56$

Step 3: Use mental math to solve the equation.
What number times 8 gives 56? $x = 7$

Step 4: Use substitution to check your solution.
$8(7) = 56; 56 = 56$

Solution: Each apple weight 7 ounces.

Try These A
A box of 150 paper clips costs $3.00. How much does one paper clip cost?
a. Define a variable and write an equation for this situation.

b. Use mental math to solve the equation. Then check the solution.

Check Your Understanding

8. Cherado ordered concert tickets for himself and 5 friends. The total price of the tickets was $270. How much was each ticket? Define a variable and write an equation. Solve the equation and check your solution.

9. Roselinda bought 40 stamps. She paid $18.00 for the stamps. How much did each stamp cost? Define a variable and write an equation. Solve the equation and check your solution.

10. Use guess and check or mental math to solve each equation.
   a. $14x = 56$
   b. $240 = 12a$
   c. $8q = 72$

LESSON 14-1 PRACTICE

11. The Circle X Ranch has 1,200 steers. They separate the steers equally into 5 different areas. How many steers are in each area? Define a variable and write an equation. Solve the equation and check your solution.

$$5x = 1200$$
$$x = 240$$

12. Julio made $9.00 per hour working at a stable. How many hours did he work in a week if his weekly pay before deductions was $243? Define a variable and write an equation. Solve the equation and check your solution.

13. Use guess and check or mental math to solve each equation.
   a. $5x = 75$ x=15
   b. $17a = 34$ a=2
   c. $320 = 64k$ k=5

14. Reason quantitatively. If an average American recycles 1.5 pounds of trash a day, how many pounds do they recycle in a year (365 days)? $1.5 \cdot 365 = 547.5$

Learning Targets:

- Write multiplication equations to represent situations.
- Solve multiplication equations of the form $ax = b$, where a, b, and x are all positive rational numbers.
- Given an equation of the form $ax = b$, where a, b, and x are all positive rational numbers, write a corresponding real-world problem.

SUGGESTED LEARNING STRATEGIES: Marking the Text, Create a Plan, Note Taking, Think-Pair-Share, Discussion Groups, Activating Prior Knowledge

In the previous activities, you learned about isolating the variable. To solve a multiplication equation, you must also isolate the variable.

The inverse operation of multiplication is division, so to isolate the variable in a multiplication equation, you divide both sides of the equation by the **coefficient** of x.

MATH TERMS

A **coefficient** is a number that multiplies a variable.

Example B

Solve $5x = 30$

Step 1: $\dfrac{5x}{5} = \dfrac{30}{5}$ Divide both sides by 5 (coefficient of x)

Step 2: $1x = 6$ Simplify both sides

Step 3: $x = 6$ Apply the Multiplicative Identity Property:

Step 4: Check your solution: $5(6) = 30$
$$30 = 30$$

Solution: $x = 6$

Try These B

Solve $9x = 108$. Show work. Check your solution.

$$x = \frac{108}{9} = 12$$

a. Pencils cost $0.88 each. How many pencils can you buy for $13.20? Define a variable and write an equation. Solve the equation and check your solution.

$$15$$

b. **Reason abstractly.** Barkley averaged 75 yards per game. How many games will it take him to run 600 yards? Define a variable and write an equation. Solve the equation and check your solution.

1. a. Write a real-world problem that could be represented by the equation $40x = 200$.

   b. Solve the equation in part *a*.

2. Myrna is buying a car that costs $19,500. If she wants to pay for it in 48 months, how much will each payment be? Define a variable and write an equation. Solve the equation and check your solution.

3. If an average American composted 1.5 pounds of trash every day, how many people would it take to compost 114 pounds of trash in a day? Define a variable and write an equation. Solve the equation and check your solution.

4. Solve each equation algebraically.
   a. $5b = 160$

      $b = 32$

   b. $2.6z = 10.4$

      $z = 4$

My Notes

MATH TIP

Instead of dividing both sides of an equation, you could also multiply each side by the reciprocal of the coefficient of the variable. For example, to solve $3x = 6$ you could multiply each side by $\frac{1}{3}$ instead of dividing by 3.

Check Your Understanding

5. The sixth grade class, which consists of 130 students, is going on a field trip by bus. Each bus can hold 26 students. How many busses will they need? Define a variable and write an equation. Solve the equation and check your solution.

6. One-third of the girls in the sixth-grade class have long hair. Eleven girls have long hair. How many girls are in the sixth-grade class? Define a variable and write an equation. Solve the equation and check your solution.

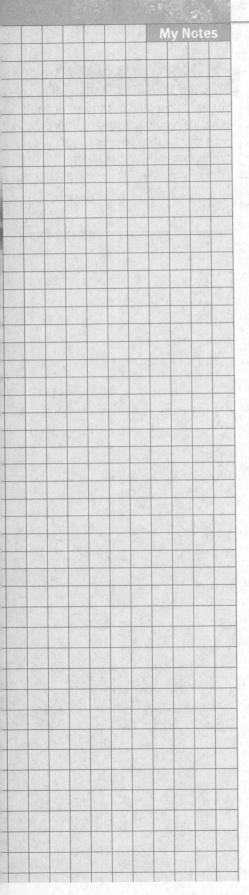

My Notes

A multiplication equation that has a fraction as a coefficient can still be solved by using the inverse operation of division.

Example C

Solve $\frac{2}{3}x = 6$.

Method 1

Step 1: Divide each side by $\frac{2}{3}$:

$$\frac{\frac{2}{3}x}{\frac{2}{3}} = \frac{6}{\frac{2}{3}}$$

Step 2: Simplify each side:

$$x = 6 \cdot \frac{3}{2}$$

Solution:

$$x = 9$$

Method 2

Step 1: Multiply each side by 3:

$$3 \cdot \frac{2}{3}x = 3 \cdot 6$$

Step 2: Simplify each side:

$$2x = 18$$

Step 3: Divide each side by 2:

$$\frac{2x}{2} = \frac{18}{2}$$

Solution:

$$x = 9$$

Try These C

Solve each equation.

a. $\frac{3}{4}x = 9$

b. $\frac{1}{2}a = 12$

7. Solve each equation and check your solutions.
   a. $3x = 210$ $x = 70$
   b. $11a = 22$ $a = 2$
   c. $\frac{4}{7}k = 20$ $k = 35$

8. Write a real-world problem that can be represented by the equation $8x = 48$.

LESSON 14-2 PRACTICE

9. Sales tax is 7.5%. How much did Tammy's lunch cost before tax if the tax on it was $0.72? Define a variable and write an equation. Solve the equation and check your solution.

10. How many egg cartons are needed to pack 216 eggs if each carton holds 12 eggs? Define a variable and write an equation. Solve the equation and check your solution.

11. **Reason abstractly.** A book of stamps contains 20 stamps. How many books must you buy to get 300 stamps? Define a variable and write an equation. Solve the equation and check your solution.

12. **Make use of structure.** Three-fourths of the students in the class did their homework last night. If 18 students in the class did their homework, how many students are there in the class? Write an equation for this situation. Solve your equation algebraically two different ways.

13. Write a real-world problem that could be represented by the equation $60h = 270$.

14. Solve each equation algebraically.
    a. $7a = 63$ $a = 9$
    b. $2.3b = 36.8$ $b = 16$
    c. $12 = 1.5x$ $x = 8$
    d. $\frac{3}{5}x = 21$ $x = 35$
    e. $\frac{3}{5}x = \frac{12}{25}$ $x = \frac{4}{5}$
    f. $\frac{5}{7}n = \frac{15}{28}$ $n = \frac{3}{4}$

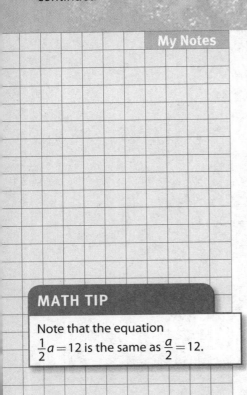

My Notes

Learning Targets:
- Write a division equation to represent a situation.
- Solve a division equation by multiplying both sides of the equation by the same number.

A division equation is an equation of the form $\frac{x}{a} = b$, where a and b are numbers and $a \neq 0$. To solve a division equation you multiply both sides of the equation by the denominator in order to isolate the variable.

Example D

Solve $\frac{x}{4} = 9$

Step 1:   Multiply both sides by 4: $4 \cdot \frac{x}{4} = 4 \cdot 9$

Notice that $4 \cdot \frac{1}{4} = 1$ and $1 \cdot x = x$.

Step 2:   Simplify both sides: $1x = 36$

Solution: $x = 36$

Try These D

Solve $\frac{a}{6} = 8$.

MATH TIP

Note that the equation $\frac{1}{2}a = 12$ is the same as $\frac{a}{2} = 12$.

---

1. Emil was dividing his candy among 15 friends and himself. If each person received 4 pieces, how many pieces of candy did Emil have to start with? Define a variable and write an equation. Solve the equation and check your solution.

2. A candy bar costs $0.89. How much would it cost to buy 24 candy bars? Define a variable and write an equation. Solve the equation and check your solution.

Lesson 14-3
Solving Division Equations

3. The cost of a ski trip is to be divided equally among 16 members of the ski club. Each club member will pay $250. What is the total cost of the trip? Define a variable and write an equation. Solve the equation and check your solution.

4. A punch recipe makes 24 servings of 6 ounces each. How many total ounces of punch does the recipe make? Define a variable and write an equation. Solve the equation and check your solution.

5. Make use of structure. Compare and contrast the method of solving a multiplication equation to that of solving a division equation.

6. Write a real-world problem that could be represented by the equation $\frac{b}{7} = 19$.

My Notes

Check Your Understanding

7. Write a division equation for each situation.
   a. Twenty-two books fit on a shelf in the library. How many books can be displayed on 6 shelves?
   b. Marguerite can save 130 pictures on a DVD. How many pictures can be stored on 7 DVDs?
   c. A pet store has 19 goldfish tanks. The store can place 12 fish in each tank. How many goldfish can it keep?

8. Solve each equation.
   a. $\dfrac{x}{12} = 5$
   b. $16 = \dfrac{a}{0.3}$

LESSON 14-3 PRACTICE

9. Write a division equation for each situation.
   a. The choir is lining up on stage in three rows. There are 24 choir members in each row. How many choir members are there?
   b. Little league baseball has 12 teams with 15 children on each team. How many children play little league baseball?

10. Solve each equation.
    a. $\dfrac{x}{3} = 26$
    b. $14 = \dfrac{a}{9.6}$

11. **Make sense of problems.** Write a real-world problem that can be represented by the equation $\dfrac{x}{6} = 16$.

ACTIVITY 14 PRACTICE
Write your answers on notebook paper.
Show your work.

Lesson 14-1
For Items 1–7,

a. Define a variable.
b. Write an equation.
c. Solve the equation.
d. Check the solution.

1. The Houston Rockets scored 66 points in the second half. There are 24 minutes in a half. What was their average number of points per minute?

2. The temperature rose 20°F from 10 A.M. to 3 P.M. On average, how many degrees did the temperature rise per hour?

3. Sandy was playing a word game. Her total score for the last 7 turns was 154 points. What was her average score per turn?

4. A 1,000-pound horse eats about 25 pounds of hay a day. How many days would it take the horse to eat 400 pounds of hay?

5. Gold costs $1,654 per ounce. How many ounces are needed to be worth $16,540?

6. Three-fourths of the students in honors algebra are eighth graders. There are 21 eighth graders in honors algebra. How many total students are in honors algebra?

7. It takes two-thirds of a yard of fabric to make a pillowcase. How many pillowcases can be made from 16 yards of fabric?

For Items 8–11, use guess and check or mental math to solve the equation.

8. $7x = 42$

9. $12 = 3a$

10. $200p = 1,400$

11. $25z = 225$

Lesson 14-2
For Items 12–15,

a. Define a variable.
b. Write an equation.
c. Solve the equation.
d. Check the solution.

12. Kiesha has $250 in two-dollar bills in her teller drawer at the bank. How many bills does she have?

13. There are 16 windmills along a six-mile stretch of road. If they are equally spaced, how many feet apart are the windmills? (1 mile = 5,280 feet)

14. Clayton left a 15% tip for the waitress. If the amount of the tip was $3.30, how much was the bill before the tip?

15. A donut shop sells glazed donuts for $5.88 a dozen. How much would one donut cost?

For Items 16–20, solve each equation and check your solutions.

16. $6x = 36$

17. $0.75a = 14.25$

18. $350 = 140r$

19. $7.8s = 499.2$

20. $\frac{1}{5}k = 15$

21. $\frac{5}{6}x = \frac{25}{36}$

22. $\frac{4}{9}x = \frac{8}{27}$

For Items 23–25, write a real-world problem that could be represented by the equation.

23. $8x = 96$

24. $10n = 420$

25. $\frac{4}{5}y = 16$

Lesson 14-3

For Items 26–30, define a variable and write a division equation. Solve the equation algebraically and check the solution.

26. If $1 is equivalent to 0.77 Euros, find the number of Euros equivalent to $20.

27. Zita wants to buy an MP3 player that is on sale for 25% off. The original price of the MP3 player was $200. What is the amount of the discount?

28. The population of Australia in January, 2013, was about 23 million. If the population of the United States then, divided by 13.7, was approximately equal to the population of Australia, what was the population of the United States?

29. The average American composted about 1.5 pounds of trash per day. How many pounds would the average American compost in 90 days?

30. The area of Texas in square miles is approximately 5 times the area of Arkansas. If the area of Arkansas is 53,178 square miles, what is the area of Texas?

For Items 31–35, solve each equation and check your solutions.

31. $\frac{x}{17} = 3$

32. $\frac{r}{6} = 9$

33. $\frac{y}{3} = 7$

34. $\frac{x}{3.8} = 4$

35. $12.9 = \frac{n}{10}$

For Items 36–39, write a real-world problem that can be represented by each equation.

36. $\frac{x}{10} = 15$

37. $\frac{n}{21} = 6$

38. $32 = \frac{k}{4}$

39. Would the equations $\frac{x}{8} = 2$ and $\frac{8}{x} = 2$ have the same solution? Explain.

MATHEMATICAL PRACTICES
Critique the Reasoning of Others

40. Pam said the equations $\frac{x}{16} = 4$ and $\frac{x}{4} = 16$ have the same solution. Is she correct? Explain.

Expressions and Equations

Up In the Air
Lesson 15-1 Representing Situations with Inequalities

Learning Targets:

- Write inequalities to represent constraints or conditions within problems.
- Use substitution to determine whether a given number makes an inequality true.
- Graph solution sets of inequalities.
- Given an inequality, write a corresponding real-world problem.

> **SUGGESTED LEARNING STRATEGIES:** Interactive Word Wall, Marking the Text, Summarizing, Note Taking, Discussion Groups, Activating Prior Knowledge

Geri wants to become a commercial airline pilot someday. She found the following information while doing research on this career.

- The airplane's captain must be at least 23 years old.
- The captain must have a minimum of 1500 hours of flying experience.
- By law, pilots can fly a maximum of 100 hours in a month.
- By law, pilots may not fly more than 32 hours during any consecutive 7 days.

Each piece of information that Geri found can be modeled by using an *inequality*. Phrases like *at least, more than*, and *a maximum* express a quantity that is greater than another.

1. List some phrases that could be used to express a quantity that is less than another.

The phrases above, and others like them, are clues to help solve the problem. They help to explain the rules of the situation.

Let's look at one of the rules about being an airline pilot.

A captain must be at least 23 years old. The words *at least* tell you that someone who is 23 years old can be a pilot. If the person is not 23, then he or she must be older than 23 to be a pilot.

The inequality modeling this situation is written as follows:

$$x \geq 23, \text{ where } x \text{ represents the age of the person.}$$

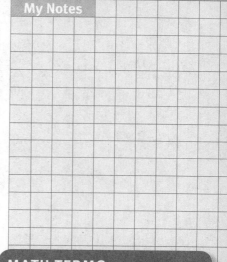

MATH TERMS

An **inequality** is a mathematical statement showing that one quantity is greater than or less than another. Inequalities use these symbols:

$>$ *is greater than*

$<$ *is less than*

$\geq$ *is greater than or equal to*

$\leq$ *is less than or equal to*

My Notes

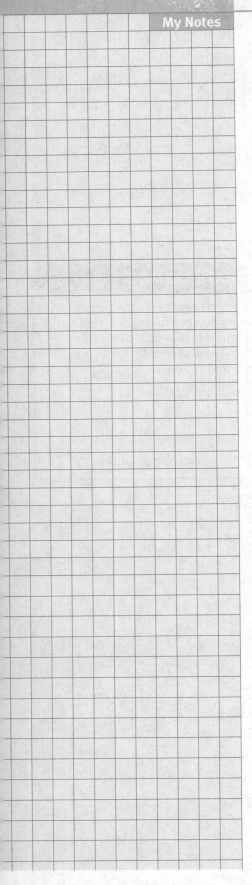

Example A

Linda was told she had to spend less than $15 on flight snacks. Write the inequality that represents this statement.

Step 1:   Define the variable:
Let $x =$ the amount of money Linda can spend.

Step 2:   Determine which symbol should be used in the inequality. Linda needs to spend *less than* $15, so use the symbol $<$.

Solution: Write the inequality. $x < 15$

Try These A

Write inequalities for the following statements.
a. The temperature was less than 20° F on the morning of the test.

b. More than 40 students were in her flight school class.

c. Training uniforms cost at least $50.

d. No more than 25 students in the class will get a job with the airline.

Much like the solution to an equation, a ***solution of an inequality*** is a number that makes a statement true when it is substituted for the variable in the inequality.

18 is one possible solution to the inequality $p < 25$ because $18 < 25$ is a true statement.

Commercial airplanes are required to fly at least 150 feet above the highest fixed object in a residential area. The highest building in Geri's town is 240 feet tall.

2. Define a variable and write an inequality to describe the situation.

3. State three possible solutions to the inequality.

4. Give three values for the variable *a* that are not solutions to the inequality.

Check Your Understanding

Determine two possible solutions for each of the following inequalities.

5. $x \leq 3.5$

6. $m > \frac{5}{4}$

7. Daria did not want to spend more than $200 for a flight from San Francisco to San Diego. Write the inequality that models this situation and determine two possible solutions.

The graph of an inequality shows all its possible solutions. Inequalities with one variable are graphed on a number line.

Example B

Graph all possible solutions of the inequality, $a > 3$.
a. Draw a number line.

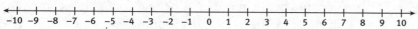

b. Draw an open dot at 3.

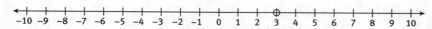

c. The solution is all values greater than 3, so draw a line with an arrow to the right where the values are larger than 3.

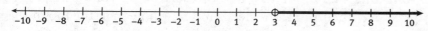

MATH TIP

When graphing inequalities use an open point to show an endpoint that is not be included in the graph, $<$ or $>$.

Use a filled point to show an endpoint that is included as part of the solution to the inequality, $\leq$ or $\geq$.

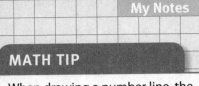

MATH TIP

When drawing a number line, the scale may be altered to best describe the situation. It is not always necessary to scale by ones.

Try These B

a. Model with mathematics.
Graph all possible solutions of the inequality $y \leq 1$.

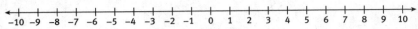

b. Graph all possible solutions of the inequality $6 \geq x$.

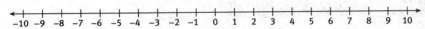

c. Graph all possible solutions of the inequality $x > 5$.

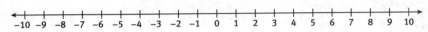

8. Look at the inequalities in Try These B above.
 a. Name two solutions for each inequality.
 b. How many more solutions do you think you can find to each inequality?

An inequality such as $y \leq 1$ or $y > 5$ has infinitely many solutions. That means that the number of solutions has no limit.

In the previous items, inequalities were written from the real-world scenario about becoming a pilot. Real-world problems can also be written from an inequality.

Example C

Write a real-world problem this inequality could represent.

$$x \leq 10$$

Step 1: Think about what the number 10 could represent.
It could be the number of people going on the same flight.
It could be the height of a room in feet.
It could be the number of seats remaining on a flight.

Step 2: Pick one of your choices.
The height of a room in feet.

Step 3: Make up a problem that could occur in the real world.

Solution: Lenora wants a new dresser and mirror for her bedroom. She needs to know how high the top of the dresser could be, so she measures the height of her room. The height of her room is 10 feet. The inequality above shows that Lenora's dresser and mirror can be no taller than 10 feet.

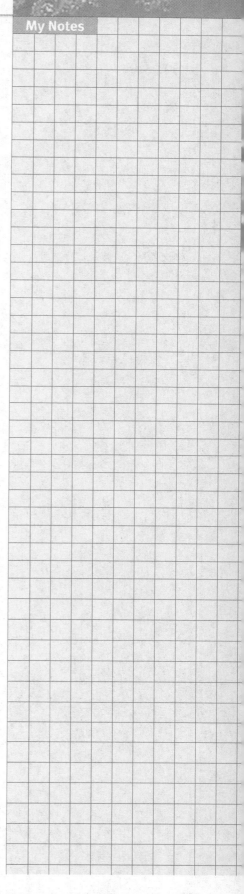

My Notes

Example D

Write a real-world problem this inequality could represent.

$$125 < x$$

Step 1: Think about what the number 125 could represent.
It could be the number of airplanes sitting at the airport.
It could be the number of bags that need to go through security.
It could be the number of songs in a music collection for flight entertainment.

Step 2: Pick one of your choices.
The number of songs in a music collection for flight entertainment

Step 3: Make up a problem that could occur in the real world.

Solution: Travel Right Airlines has 30 jazz songs, 45 rock songs, 30 easy listening songs, and 20 rap songs ready to play on a flight. The rest are movie sound tracks. The inequality above represents that the number of songs in the music collection is greater than 125.

Try These C and D

Reason abstractly. Write a real-world problem each inequality could represent.

a. Use the inequality $x < 5.5$ to write a problem about the height a paper airplane can reach.

b. Use the inequality $21 \leq x$ to write a problem about the number of people who want to sign up for a trip.

c. Use the inequality $x \leq 105$ to write a problem about the number of snacks served during a flight.

d. Use the inequality $x \geq \frac{7}{4}$ to write a problem about the diameter of an airplane engine.

e. Use the inequality $x \geq 40$ to write a problem about the number of seats on a Ferris wheel.

f. Use the inequality $x \leq 16$ to write a problem about the number of students who sign up for the class trip to Paris.

g. Use the inequality $x \leq 12.7$ to write a problem about the cubic feet of space in an overhead compartment on an airplane.

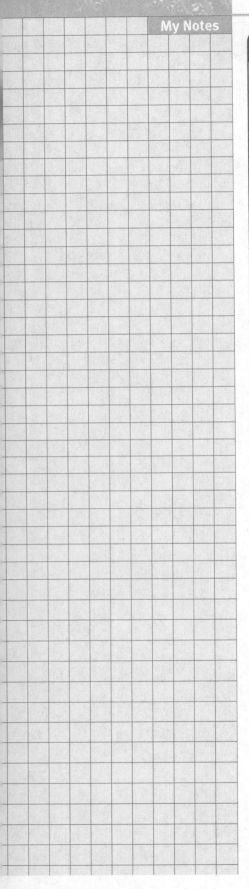

Check Your Understanding

Define a variable and write an inequality to represent this situation.

9. No one under 23 is allowed to captain an airplane.

10. Write two possible solutions to the inequality $x < \frac{9}{5}$.

11. Graph all possible solutions to the inequality $x \leq 2$.

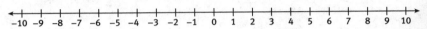

12. Write a problem about the number of pieces of luggage for the inequality $7 < x$.

LESSON 15-1 PRACTICE

Define a variable and write an inequality to represent these situations.

13. She finished the license test in no more than 30 minutes.

14. The captain must have a minimum of 1500 hours of flying experience.

15. **Reason quantitatively.** What are two values that are not solutions for $11.4 > y$?

16. What are three possible solutions for $x > \frac{10}{8}$?

17. Graph all possible solutions for $x > \frac{3}{2}$.

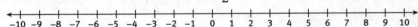

18. Graph all possible solutions for $x > 9$.

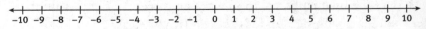

19. Use the inequality $x \leq 20$ to write a problem about people waiting for a flight.

Learning Targets:

- Write one-step inequalities to represent constraints or conditions within problems.
- Use substitution to determine whether a given number makes an inequality true.
- Solve one-step inequalities.
- Graph the solution sets of one-step inequalities.

> **SUGGESTED LEARNING STRATEGIES:** Paraphrasing, Marking the Text, Think Aloud, Create a Plan, Sharing and Responding, Create Representations, Simplify the Problem

A pilot training class has space for at most 25 students. There are already 12 students who have signed up for the class. How can the number of spaces remaining in the class be represented?

An inequality can be written similar to an equation, except that instead of using an equal sign, you use an inequality symbol.

Example E

Find the number of students that can still sign up for pilot training if there is space for at most 25 students and 12 have already signed up.

Step 1: Define the variable.
The variable x can represent the number of spaces remaining in the class.

Step 2: The words *at most* in the statement above mean that the numbers represented are 25 or less than 25. The symbol used to write this inequality is $\leq$.

Step 3: Write the inequality.
Put the maximum number of students who can sign up for the class on the side indicating that 25 is the greatest amount, and the number who have signed up and can still sign up, on the side indicating that these values are less than 25.

$$x + 12 \leq 25$$

Solution: This inequality says that there do not have to be 25 students in the class. Any number of students below 25 is also acceptable.

Try These E

Write inequalities to represent the following situations.

a. A pilot training class needs a minimum of 10 students to run. At this time, 7 students have signed up for the class.

My Notes

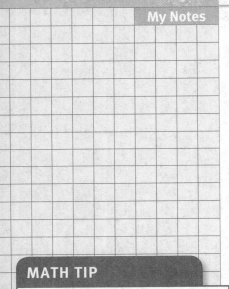

My Notes

b. A hot-air balloon needs to be at least 100 feet in the air to fly safely. It is already 37 feet in the air.

c. A block is 6 inches high. The tower must be over 100 inches high.

The person registering students for the pilot training class does not know that there is a maximum number of students that can sign up, or that some students have already signed up. She signs up 15 more students. Is there a way to know if she signed up too many people?

> **MATH TIP**
>
> Show a question mark over the inequality symbol to show that you are not sure if it is true or not.

Example F

Use substitution to determine if 15 additional people are too many for the class.

Step 1: Write the inequality using the information that is given. Let x represent the additional students that can sign up for the class.

$$x + 12 \le 25$$

Step 2: Substitute the value 15 for x and solve.

$$15 + 12 \overset{?}{\le} 25$$

$$27 \overset{?}{\le} 25$$

Solution: You know that 27 is not less than 25, so 15 additional students cannot sign up for the class.

Try These F

Determine if the given value of x makes the inequality true.

a. $x - 5 > 17,$ $x = 12$

b. $x + 9 > 21,$ $x = 15$

c. $4x \le 50,$ $x = 13$

To determine the values that make an inequality true, an inequality can be solved like an equation is solved.

Example G

You know that 15 students are too many to add to the class, but how many more can sign up without going over the limit?

Step 1: Write the inequality.
$$x + 12 \leq 25$$

Step 2: Subtract 12 from both sides of the inequality to isolate the variable.
$$x + 12 - 12 \leq 25 - 12$$
$$x \leq 13$$

Solution: $x \leq 13$.

This solution tells you that any number of students, less than or equal to 13, can sign up for the class without exceeding the limit of 25.

Try These G

Solve each inequality.

a. $x + 21 \leq 46$

b. $2x > 11$

c. $x - 1.2 < 4.8$

d. $x + \frac{3}{2} \geq 6$

Graph the solution of an inequality on a number line.

Example H

Graph the solution to the inequality $x + 12 \leq 25$.

a. From Example G you know the solution is $x \leq 13$.

b. The inequality includes an equal sign, showing that 13 is included in the solution, so the point at 13 will be solid.

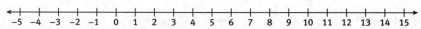

c. The solution is all numbers less than 13, so the arrow goes to the left.

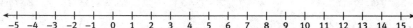

Try These H

Solve and graph each inequality.

a. $x + 5 < 13$

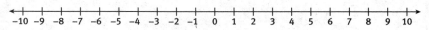

b. $x - 3 \geq 9$

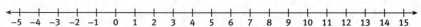

c. $3x \leq 24$

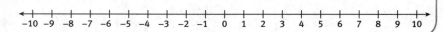

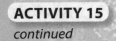

My Notes

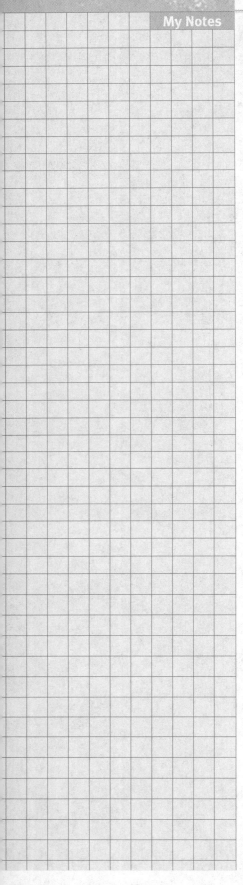

Check Your Understanding

Write an inequality to represent this situation.

1. The parachute needs at least six people to hold it. There are two people holding it now.

2. Determine if $\frac{3}{4}$ is a solution for $x + \frac{1}{3} > 2$.

3. Determine if 4.7 is a solution for $x - 2.4 < 5$.

4. Solve $2.3 + x < 7.7$.

5. Solve $3x < 8$.

6. Solve this inequality and graph the solution $x + 23 < 31$.

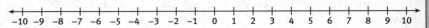

LESSON 15-2 PRACTICE

7. A captain can fly a maximum of 100 hours a month. He has flown 52 hours. Write the inequality that represents this situation.

8. **Model with mathematics.** A paper airplane contest needs at least 65 people to enter. So far, 43 people have entered. Write the inequality that represents this situation.

9. Determine if 4.4 is a solution for $x + 1.9 > 7$.

10. Determine if $\frac{5}{2}$ is a solution for $\frac{5}{4} + x \leq 3$.

11. Solve $x - 15 < 2$.

12. Solve $2.5x \geq 12.5$.

13. Solve $1.5 + x < 6.5$ and graph the solution.

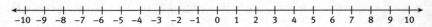

14. Solve $\frac{4}{3} + x > 3$ and graph the solution.

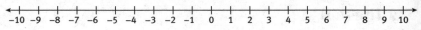

ACTIVITY 15 PRACTICE
Write your answers on notebook paper.
Show your work.

Lesson 15-1
Write an inequality to represent each situation in Items 1–4.

1. A number is at least 6.

2. 7 is less than a number.

3. No more than 150 people will fit on the plane.

4. The maximum score on the pilot's test is 95 points.

5. Is $\frac{4}{5}$ a solution of $x \leq 2$?

6. Which of the following is a solution of
   $x > 10.4$?
   a. 5.2   b. 7.4
   c. 9.6   d. 11.2

7. Consider the inequality $x \geq 10.2$.
   a. Is 7 a solution? Explain.
   b. How many solutions does the inequality have? How can you show this?

8. Explain why 5 is a solution to both $x < 10$ and $10 > x$.

9. Graph $x < 8.5$.

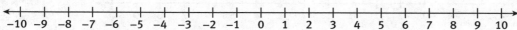

10. Graph $\frac{3}{2} \leq x$.

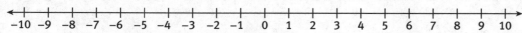

11. Graph $x \geq 3$.

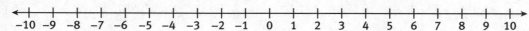

12. Use the inequality $x < 5.5$ to write a problem about the distance a paper airplane flew.

13. Use the inequality $x \geq 50$ to write a problem about the number of hours of flight training required.

14. Use the inequality $x > 15$ to write a problem about the number of balloons it takes to lift a small box off the ground.

15. Use the inequality $x > 5$ to write a problem about the wind speed it takes to keep a kite in the air.

Lesson 15-2

For Items 16–18, write an inequality to represent each situation.

16. A helium balloon can stay in the air for up to 6 hours. It has been in the air 2.5 hours.

17. An airplane can go 3,500 miles on a single filling of fuel. It has gone 1,250 miles.

18. An airplane captain must have a minimum of 1500 hours of flying experience. Tom has 715.

19. Is $\frac{4}{5}$ a solution of $\frac{5}{4} + x \le 2$?

20. Is 10.3 a solution of $x - 2.5 > 8$?

21. Which of the following is a solution for $x + 3.2 \ge 10.2$?
    A. 5.7   **B.** 4.0
    C. 7   **D.** 6.5

22. Solve $\frac{6}{4} + x \le \frac{9}{2}$.

23. Solve $x + 11.3 > 15.2$.

24. Solve $x - 9.25 < 3.5$.

25. Solve $8x > 112$.

26. Solve $7x \le 139$.

27. Solve and graph $x + 3.5 < 9.5$.

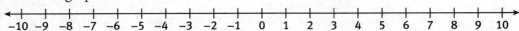

28. Solve and graph $4x \ge 14$.

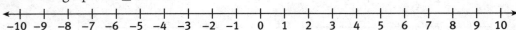

29. Solve and graph $x - \frac{3}{5} \le \frac{12}{5}$.

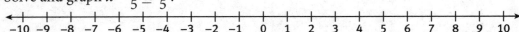

MATHEMATICAL PRACTICES
Reason Abstractly

30. How is an inequality similar to an equation? How are they different? Provide examples to support your answers.

Expressions and Equations

Moving Right Along
Lesson 16-1 Representing Relationships

Learning Targets:

- Create a table representing a relationship given a verbal description.
- Write an equation to represent a relationship given a verbal description or a table.
- Investigate rate of change.
- Graph equations of the form $y = ax$.

> **SUGGESTED LEARNING STRATEGIES:** Shared Reading, Role Play, Visualization, Quickwrite, Critique Reasoning, Think-Pair-Share, Create Representations, Look for a Pattern

One sunny day Sen T. Pede and his friend Lady Bug start out from the elm tree and move toward a rose bush that is 45 feet away. Sen crawls at 5 feet per minute and Lady crawls at 3 feet per minute.

1. **Model with mathematics.** Use the diagram below to show where each critter is exactly three minutes after they start their journey. Place the letter S at Sen's location and the letter L at Lady's location.

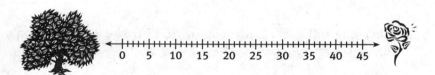

2. Complete this table to show how far Sen and Lady are from the elm tree for each time value.

Time Since Leaving Elm Tree (min.)	0	1	2	3	4	5
Sen's Distance from Elm Tree (ft)						
Lady's Distance from Elm Tree (ft)						

3. Describe a pattern you see in Sen's row of the table. Use words and mathematical symbols.

4. Sen crawls d feet in m minutes. Write an equation using d and m to represent the relationship between how long Sen has been traveling and how far he has travelled from the elm tree.

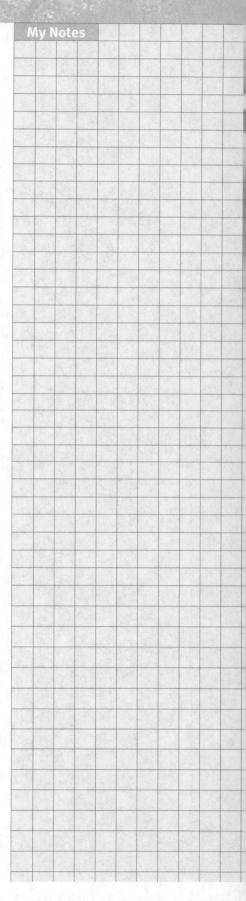
My Notes

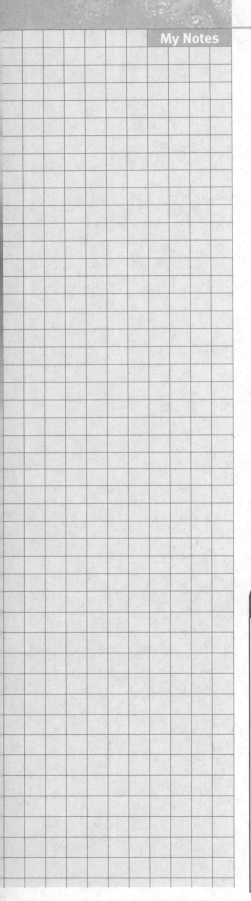

My Notes

5. How far will Sen be from the elm tree after seven minutes? Use your equation to justify your response.

6. How long will it take Sen to crawl 40 feet? Use your equation to justify your response.

7. **Make use of structure.** Describe a pattern you see in Lady's row in the table. You may use words and mathematical symbols.

8. Lady crawls *d* feet in *m* minutes. Write an equation to represent the relationship between how long Lady has been traveling and how far she has travelled from the elm tree.

9. How far will Lady be from the elm tree after eight minutes? Use your equation to help justify your response.

10. **a.** How long will it take Lady to crawl 36 feet? Use your equation to justify your response.

   b. After Sen reaches the rose bush, how long will he wait for Lady to arrive? Explain how you determined your answer.

Check Your Understanding

11. **a.** Lee walks his dog every morning before school. He travels 4 feet per second. Make a table to show how far Lee travels during the first 5 minutes of his walk.
    b. Using the table created for Lee walking his dog, write an equation for this relationship if Lee travels *d* feet in *m* minutes.
    c. How far will Lee travel in the first 15 minutes of his walk?

12. **a.** Joey can ride his skateboard 50 feet every minute. Write an equation that determines his distance *d* in *m* minutes.
    b. How far will Joey ride his skateboard in 1 hour?

13. **a.** Sam can read 3 books each month. Write an equation that determines how many books *b* he reads every month *m*.
    b. **Make sense of problems.** How many books can Sam read in 2 years?

Work with your group to answer Items 14–18.

14. Plot the data points from Item 2. Label the axes. Let the vertical axis show distance and the horizontal axis show time.

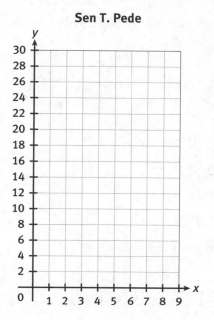

Sen T. Pede

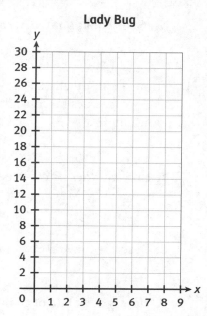

Lady Bug

WRITING MATH

Ordered pairs are written as (x, y). For example: $(5,7)$ is an ordered pair where $x = 5$ and $y = 7$.

15. Write your equations from Items 4 and 8 under the corresponding graphs. What connections, if any, can you make between the graphs of the data points and the equations you wrote from the data?

16. Use Sen's graph to determine how far he would travel in 8 minutes. Explain how you used the graph to determine your response. Verify your response using Sen's equation.

17. Use Lady's graph to determine how long it would take Lady to travel 30 feet. Explain how you used the graph to determine your response. Verify your response using Lady's equation.

18. If Sen's graph were to be extended, it would contain the point (12,60).
   a. Explain what the coordinates in this ordered pair tell you about Sen.

   b. Explain how Sen's equation can be used to justify the fact that the point (12,60) is on Sen's graph.

My Notes

On another day, Sen and Lady want to go to the lake for a picnic. However, the lake is much farther away than the rose bush. They decide they will use their equations to determine how long it will take them to reach the lake.

19. Use Sen's equation to determine how far he can crawl in one hour.

20. Think about the distances Sen crawls.
   a. How far does he crawl between time $m = 20$ minutes and $m = 21$ minutes?

   b. How far does he crawl between time $m = 25$ minutes and $m = 26$ minutes?

   c. Describe how far Sen crawls as a ***rate of change***.

   d. How is Sen's rate of change represented in his equation?

21. Use Lady's equation to determine how far she can crawl in one hour.

22. Describe how far Lady crawls as a rate of change between time:
   a. $m = 32$ minutes and $m = 33$ minutes

   b. $m = 32$ minutes and $m = 34$ minutes

   c. How is Lady's rate of change represented in her equation?

23. If the lake is 540 feet from the elm tree, how long will it take each critter to reach the lake? Show your work or explain how you determined your answer.

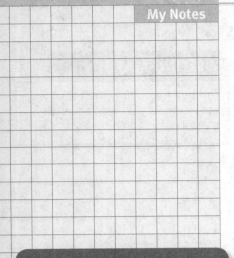

MATH TERMS

Rate of Change is a relationship that compares the change in one variable to the corresponding change in a related variable.

For example, for each hour you study for a test your grade increases by 5 points. The rate of change is 5 points per 1 hour.

If the rate of change remains the same in a problem situation, it is called a **constant rate of change**.

Check Your Understanding

24. Archie crawls 7.5 feet per minute. Create a table that shows how many feet he crawls over 5 minutes.
25. **Model with mathematics.** Write an equation that determines the distance traveled d per minute m.
26. How many feet has Archie traveled after 2 hours?
27. If Archie traveled 112.5 feet, how long has he been crawling?
28. After 20 minutes Archie has traveled 150 feet. Using the rate of change, how far has he traveled after 21 minutes?

LESSON 16-1 PRACTICE

29. Leo spends $5 per week on music.
    a. Make a table that shows how much he spends over 4 weeks.
    b. Write an equation that determines the dollars spent d per week w.
    c. Determine how much he has spent over 6 weeks.
    d. If the equation was $d = 7w$, how much is he spending each week?

30. Shelby walks at a constant rate. The equation that represents this relationship is $d = 4t$, where d is the distance in miles and t is the time in hours.
    a. What does the coefficient 4 tell you about Shelby?
    b. **Make use of structure.** What question is answered by the equation $d = 4(32)$?

31. Andy bikes 20 miles in 1 hour. After 5 hours, he has biked 100 miles.
    a. Make a table starting at hour 5 and going to hour 10, showing the number of miles he has traveled.
    b. Write an equation that relates the number of hours to the miles he travels.
    c. Write an equation to determine how many miles he has traveled at 21 hours, when he has gone 400 miles after 20 hours.
    d. How far does he bike between hours 31 and 32?

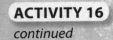

My Notes

Learning Targets:

- Graph equations of the form $y = kx$ or $y = x + b$.
- Create a table and graph a relationship given a verbal description.
- Explain how one variable depends on another variable.
- Describe a relationship given a graph.

> **SUGGESTED LEARNING STRATEGIES:** Marking the text, Summarizing, Visualization, Create Representations, Look for a Pattern

Sen and Lady have a turtle friend, Archimedes, who sometimes goes along on their adventures.

1. Archimedes crawls d feet in minutes. The equation that shows the relationship between d and m for his pace is $d = 7.5m$.
   a. Use appropriate units to describe what information the coefficient 7.5 gives about how Archimedes moves.

   b. Create a table of values and plot the data.

MATH TERMS

An **independent variable** is the variable for which input values are substituted in an equation.

A **dependent variable** is the variable whose value is determined by the input or value of the independent variable.

For Sen, Lady, and Archimedes, the **independent variable** is m, the time in minutes each crawls. The **dependent variable** is distance, because it depends on how long each critter crawls.

2. The data points appear to be *linear*. What do you think this means?

MATH TERMS

In an **ordered pair**, the first number describes the horizontal position and the second number describes the vertical position. The numbers are the coordinates of the point.

3. If all the points on Archimedes' graph are connected with a line, the line contains the **ordered pair** (2.5, 18.75). An ordered pair locates points in the coordinate plane.
   a. What does this ordered pair mean in this context?

   b. Should the data points on the graphs in Item 14 in Lesson 16-1 be connected with a line?

4. Solve the equation $540 = 7.5m$. What question is answered by the solution to the equation?

5. Solve the equation $d = 7.5(540)$. What question is answered by the solution to the equation?

My Notes

Check Your Understanding

Bailey sells bouquets of flowers at the farmers' market in the city. Each day that she goes to the market, she sells 7 bouquets.

6. **Model with mathematics.** Create a table of values showing how many bouquets she sells over 7 days.

7. Graph the data showing days on the *x*-axis and bouquets on the *y*-axis.

8. Identify the dependent and independent variables.

9. **Make use of structure.** Explain how you could use the graph to determine the number of bouquets sold after 10 days.

Fox and Raccoon are waiting for Archimedes to meet up with them. Fox crawls at a rate of 9 feet per minute. Raccoon crawls at a rate of 1 foot per minute and always starts 9 feet in front of Fox.

10. After 3 minutes, compare how far each critter crawled. How do their paces compare?

11. Make two tables of values using the same inputs for both Fox and Raccoon. Describe any similarities and differences between the tables.

12. Fox's pace is described by the equation $d = 9m$, and Raccoon's pace is described by the equation $d = m + 9$. Compare and contrast their equations.

13. How does Fox's graph compare to Raccoon's graph?

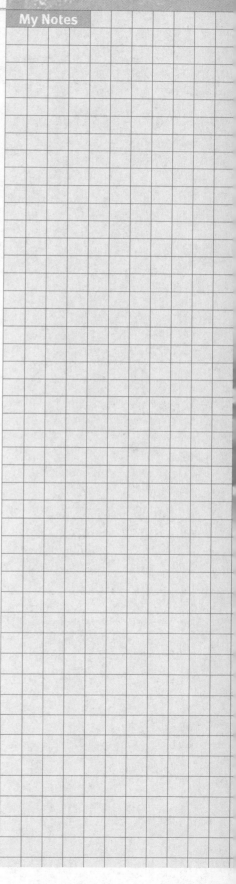

Archimedes takes a box of crackers to share at a picnic with Sen, Lady, and other friends. Archimedes did not have breakfast so he knows he will eat 3 crackers and the other critters will each eat one cracker.

The equation $y = x + 3$ relates the amount crackers, y, Archimedes brings with the number of critters, x, who will eat the crackers.

14. Complete the following table.

Input, x	$x + 3$	Output, y
1	1+3	4
2	2+3	5
4	4+3	7
7	7+3	10

15. Plot the points on the graph below.

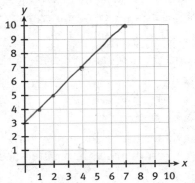

16. How is the rate of change represented in the equation, table, and graph? X axis point increases by 3.

17. Interpret the meaning of the rate of change in this context.

$$x = y - 3$$

18. State the dependent and independent variables. Justify your answers.

19. Compare and contrast the equations $y = x + 3$ and $y = 3x$.

x+3 ≤ x·3

20. Suppose the equation $y = 3x$ relates the number of crackers, y, with the number of critters, x, eating them.

a. Explain how the table of values would differ from the table in Item 14.  y would equal 3·x.

b. Describe the similarities and differences between the graph of $y = 3x$ and the graph in Item 15.

Itsy Spider has spun a web and is sitting 2 centimeters from its center. The graph of Itsy's equation $d = 5m + 2$ shows the relationship between the time she walks and distance she walks as she moves outward on her web.

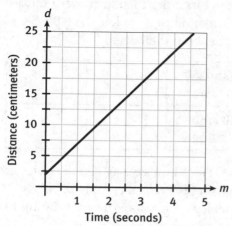

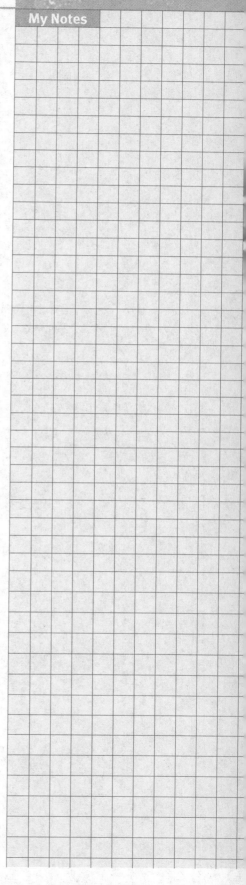

21. Write the ordered pairs for 4 ordered pairs on the graph.

22. Describe the relationship modeled by the graph between the independent variable, the time Itsy walks (m), and the dependent variable, the distance Itsy walks (d).

23. What do the 5 and 2 in Itsy's equation mean in this context?

5 is the slope

2 is the y-intercept

24. a. What is the rate of change shown on the graph?

b. What does the rate of change mean in this context?

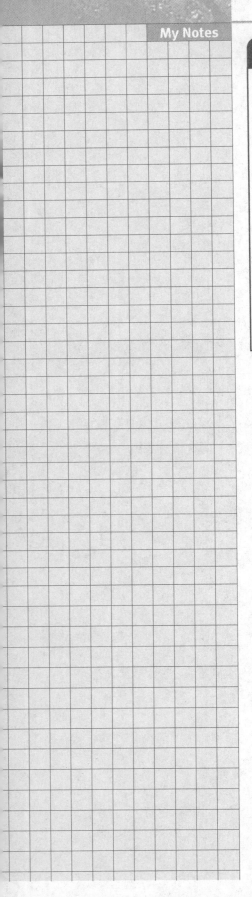

My Notes

Check Your Understanding

25. Brianna is three years older than her sister Lindsay.
   a. Use this information to complete the table below to show the relationship between their ages.

Lindsay's Age	1	2	3	4
Brianna's Age	4	5	6	7

   b. Plot the data. Place Lindsay's age on the horizontal (x) axis and Brianna's age on the vertical (y) axis.
   c. Use the variables x and y to write an equation to represent Brianna's age if Lindsay's age is x.
   d. Describe each of the variables as either independent or dependent.

LESSON 16-2 PRACTICE

26. Use the equation $y = 2x + 2$ for this problem.
   a. Create an input/output table.
   b. Graph the ordered pairs from the table.
   c. Describe each of the variables as the independent or the dependent variable.

27. Use the graph below to describe the relationship between the variables.

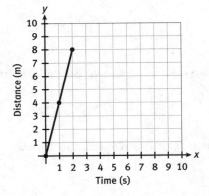

ACTIVITY 16 PRACTICE

Write your answers on notebook paper. Show your work.

Lesson 16-1

1. A car can travel 60 miles per hour.
   a. Create a table showing how far the car travels in 5 hours.
   b. Write an equation to determine the distance d that the car can travel in t hours.
   c. How long will it take the car to travel 540 miles? Explain your reasoning.
   d. How far will the car travel in 12 hours? Explain your reasoning.

2. Use the equation $d = 5m$ for Sen and $d = 3m$ for Lady.

   One day, Sen and Lady wanted to go to the lake for a picnic. However, the lake is much farther away than the rose bush is. They decide to use their equations to determine how long it will take them to reach the lake.
   a. Use Sen's equation to determine how far he can crawl in one hour.
   b. Use Lady's equation to determine how far she can crawl in one hour.
   c. If the lake is 540 feet from the elm tree, how long will it take Sen and Lady to reach the lake?

3. Sen and Lady have a friend Archie who moves according to the equation $d = 7.5m$.
   a. Solve the equation $540 = 7.5m$. Explain what the solution to the equation means in this context.
   b. Solve the equation $d = 7.5(540)$. Explain what the solution to the equation means in this context.

4. Emma decided to start a snow globe collection. She started with 3, and every year she added one more.
   a. Create a table showing the growth in Emma's snow globe collection over 5 years.
   b. Write an equation to determine the number of snow globes she has after y years.
   c. Use the equation to determine how many snow globes she will have after 15 years.
   d. How many years will it take her to get 25 snow globes?

Lesson 16-2

5. Niall paints three paintings a week.
   a. Create a table showing the number of paintings Niall completes over 4 weeks.
   b. Graph the data. Place weeks on the horizontal axis, and paintings completed on the vertical axis.
   c. Write an equation representing the relationship between the number of weeks and the number of paintings completed.
   d. Describe each of the variables as independent or dependent.
   e. How many weeks will it take Niall to paint 24 paintings?

6. a. Copy and complete the table for the equation $y = 3x - 2$.

Input, x	$3x - 2$	Output, y
2		
3		
1.5		
2.5		

   b. Graph the data.

7. After buying three paintings from Niall (from Item 5), Naeem was inspired to paint. He paints one painting a week. Who will have more paintings over 4 weeks? Explain your reasoning.

8. Harry got a job assembling birdhouses. There were 2 birdhouses already completed as examples for him. Each week, he assembled 2 more.
   a. Create a table showing the total number of birdhouses Harry completed over 5 weeks. Show the input and the output.
   b. Plot the data.
   c. Write an equation that shows the relationship between the number of weeks and the total number of birdhouses Harry completed.
   d. How many birdhouses will he build after 10 weeks? Explain your reasoning.
   e. When will he complete 28 birdhouses? Explain your reasoning.

9. Compare and contrast the graphs of parts 5b and 8b.

MATHEMATICAL PRACTICES
Make Sense of Problems

10. Describe the relationship represented in the graph below.

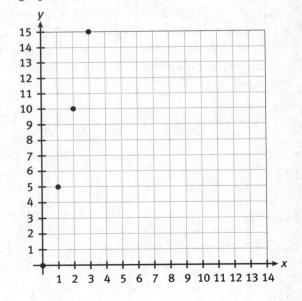

Write your answers on notebook paper. Show your work.

1. The Middle School is holding a book fair. The costs of different types of books are in the table.

Book Type	Cost ($)
paperback	7.50
hardcover	12.50
books on tape	8.75
reference book	10.25

   a. Paige brought $5.00 to the book fair. She wants to buy three paperback books. Write and solve an equation to determine how much more money she will need to make this purchase.
   b. Lesley has $17 to spend, which she uses to buy a reference book. Write and solve an equation to show how much Lesley will receive in change.
   c. Write and graph an inequality to represent the *maximum* amount of money Lesley has to spend on another book.
   d. Use the inequality and its graph to explain whether Lesley has enough money to buy a paperback book.

2. Darius's parents sent money to the book fair to be split among the four children in his family. After they gave the money to the cashier, she told each child they had $11.50 to spend. Write and solve an equation to show the total amount of money Darius's parents sent to the book fair.

3. Marcus wants to buy several paperback books.
   a. Create a table of values to show the cost of buying up to five paperback books.
   b. Plot the data on a graph.
   c. Write an equation that represents the cost to Marcus of buying the books and identify the independent and dependent variables. Explain your reasoning in making your choices.
   d. If Marcus wanted to buy eight paperback books, what would be the cost?
   e. Marcus's friend has $97.50 to spend on paperback books. How many paperbacks can he buy? Explain which representation you used in determining your answer.

Scoring Guide	Exemplary	Proficient	Emerging	Incomplete
	The solution demonstrates these characteristics:			
Mathematics Knowledge and Thinking (Items 1a-d, 2, 3a-e)	• A clear understanding of tables, graphs, independent and dependent variables. • Effective understanding of and accuracy in writing and solving equations; writing and graphing inequalities.	• A functional understanding of tables, graphs, independent and dependent variables. • Writing and solving equations, and writing and graphing inequalities that usually result in correct answers.	• Partial understanding of tables, graphs, independent and dependent variables. • Difficulty with writing and solving equations, and writing and graphing inequalities.	• An inaccurate understanding of tables, graphs, independent and dependent variables. • Little or no understanding of writing and solving equations, and writing and graphing inequalities.
Problem Solving (Items 1a-b, 2, 3e)	• An appropriate and efficient strategy that results in a correct answer.	• A strategy that may include unnecessary steps but results in a correct answer.	• A strategy that results in some incorrect answers.	• No clear strategy when solving problems.
Mathematical Modeling / Representations (Items 1a-d, 2, 3a-c)	• Clear and accurate modeling using tables and graphs. • Clear and accurate representation of problems as equations and inequalities.	• Graphing data and creating tables of data with little difficulty. • Some difficulty in representing problems as equations and inequalities.	• Partially accurate graphing of data and use of tables. • Difficulty in writing equations and inequalities leading to errors.	• Inaccurate or incomplete graphs and tables. • No understanding of representing problems as equations and inequalities.
Reasoning and Communication (Items 1d, 3c, 3e)	• Precise use of appropriate math terms and language to explain independent and dependent variables. • Accurately explain a situation using an inequality.	• An adequate explanation of independent and dependent variables. • Relating an inequality to a situation with little difficulty.	• A misleading or confusing explanation of independent and dependent variables. • Poor understanding of relating an inequality to a situation.	• An incomplete or inaccurate description of independent and dependent variables. • No understanding of how to relate an inequality to a situation.

Ratios

Unit Overview
In this unit you will study ratios, rates, proportions, and percents as you explore applications and use them to solve problems.

Key Terms
As you study this unit, add these and other terms to your math notebook. Include in your notes your prior knowledge of each word, as well as your experiences in using the word in different mathematical examples. If needed, ask for help in pronouncing new words and add information on pronunciation to your math notebook. It is important that you learn new terms and use them correctly in your class discussions and in your problem solutions.

Academic Vocabulary
- benchmark

Math Terms
- ratio
- equivalent ratios
- rate
- dimensional analysis
- conversion factor
- unit rate
- unit price
- proportion
- percent
- average

ESSENTIAL QUESTIONS

? Why is it important to understand calculations with ratios, rates, and percents?

? Why are proportional relationships important in mathematics?

EMBEDDED ASSESSMENTS

These assessments, following activities 19 and 21, will give you an opportunity to demonstrate your ability to work with ratios, rates, and percents to solve mathematical and real-world problems involving proportional relationships.

Embedded Assessment 1:

Ratios and Rates   p. 245

Embedded Assessment 2:

Understanding and Applying Percents   p. 273

1. Label the scale on each number line as indicated.

   a.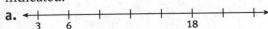
   3   6   18

   b. 1 to 2
   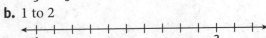
   1   2

2. Identify each pair of fractions that are equal.

   a. $\frac{2}{3}$ and $\frac{4}{5}$

   b. $\frac{5}{8}$ and $\frac{10}{16}$

   c. $\frac{3}{7}$ and $\frac{7}{15}$

   d. $\frac{2}{5}$ and $\frac{5}{10}$

   e. $\frac{3}{5}$ and $\frac{9}{15}$

3. Use division to find an equivalent decimal. Round quotients to the nearest hundredth.

   a. $\frac{3}{8}$

   b. $\frac{6}{11}$

   c. $\frac{6}{9}$

   d. $\frac{5}{7}$

4. Complete each of the following:

   a. 1 foot = _____ inches
   b. 1 yard = _____ inches
   c. 1 hour = _____ minutes
   d. 1 hour = _____ seconds
   e. 1 cup = _____ ounces
   f. 1 pound = _____ ounces
   g. 1 dime = _____ pennies

5. Place the following numbers in a Venn diagram to create a visual representation.
   A: Whole numbers less than 12
   B: Prime numbers less than 15

   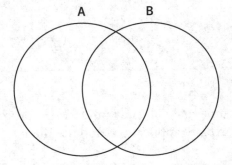

6. Find the value of each of the following.

   a. $\$3.68 \div 4$
   b. $\$8.94 \div 6$
   c. $\$10.32 \div 8$

7. **a.** Shade $\frac{1}{3}$ of the figure.

   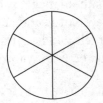

   b. Shade $\frac{2}{5}$ of the figure.

8. Solve each of the following for x.

   a. $7x = 21$
   b. $4x = 10$
   c. $1.2x = 24$
   d. $2.5x = 6$

Understanding Ratios
All About Pets
Lesson 17-1 Understanding Ratios

Learning Targets:

- Understand the concept of a ratio and use ratio language.
- Represent ratios with concrete models, fractions, and decimals.
- Give examples of ratios as multiplicative comparisons of two quantities describing the same attribute.

> **SUGGESTED LEARNING STRATEGIES:** Interactive Word Wall, Visualization, Create Representations, Look for a Pattern

A **ratio** is a comparison of two quantities. Ratios can represent a comparison of part-to-part, part-to-whole, or whole-to-part. Ratios can be written as fractions, or using the word "to" or a colon.

MATH TERMS

Each part of a **ratio** is called a term. Terms can be:

- Numbers, such as 4 and 8: $\frac{4}{8}$, 4 to 8, 4:8
- Variables, such as x and y: $\frac{x}{y}$, x to y, x:y
- The product of a number and a variable, such as $3x$ and $9y$: $\frac{3x}{9y}$, $3x$ to $9y$, $3x$:$9y$

Example A

Use the tags below. Find each of these ratios:

a. stars to bones
b. stars to total number of tags
c. total number of tags to bones

Write each ratio three different ways. State whether the ratio is a part-to-part, part-to-whole, or whole-to-part.

Solution:

a. stars to bones

part-to-part: $\dfrac{\text{number of stars}}{\text{number of bones}} = \dfrac{4}{8}$; 4 to 8, 4:8

b. stars to total number of tags

part-to-whole: $\dfrac{\text{number of stars}}{\text{number of tags}} = \dfrac{4}{12}$; 4 to 12; 4:12

c. total number of tags to bones

whole-to-part: $\dfrac{\text{number of tags}}{\text{number of bones}} = \dfrac{12}{8}$; 12 to 8; 12:8

MATH TIP

Like fractions, ratios can sometimes be rewritten in lowest terms.

$\dfrac{4}{8} = \dfrac{1}{2}$, 1 to 2, or 1:2

$\dfrac{4}{12} = \dfrac{1}{3}$, 1 to 3, or 1:3

$\dfrac{12}{8} = \dfrac{3}{2}$, 3 to 2, or 3:2

Try These A

Use ratios to compare the pet toys shown. Write each ratio three different ways. State whether the ratio is a part-to-part, part-to-whole, or whole-to-part.

a. balls of yarn to mice

b. white balls of yarn to total number of toys

c. gray mice to white mice

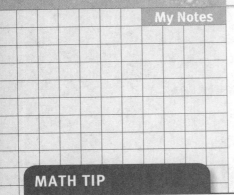

A ratio is also a multiplicative comparison of two quantities. The ratio of circles to the total number of shapes below is $\frac{2}{5}$.

This means $\frac{2}{5}$ of all the shapes are circles and that for every 2 circles added, a total of 5 shapes will be added.

Suppose a set of shapes with the pattern above includes 8 circles. You know that $2 \times 4 = 8$, so multiply the number of shapes in the repeating part of the set (2 circles + 3 squares = 5 shapes) by 4 to find the total number of shapes when there are 8 circles: $5 \times 4 = 20$ total shapes.

MATH TIP

Like fractions, ratios can be written as decimals. The ratio $\frac{3}{4}$ is the quotient of $3 \div 4$ or 0.75.

Example B

Make sense of problems. In January, for every 3 cats adopted, 4 dogs were adopted. A total of 16 dogs were adopted. How many cats were adopted?

Step 1: Write a ratio comparing the number of cats to the number of dogs adopted.

$$\frac{\text{number of cats}}{\text{number of dogs}} = \frac{3}{4}$$

The number of cats adopted is $\frac{3}{4}$ times the number of dogs adopted.

Step 2: Multiply the ratio times the number needed to create an equivalent ratio showing 16 dogs.

$$\frac{3}{4} \times \frac{4}{4} = \frac{12 \text{ cats}}{16 \text{ dogs}}$$

Solution: 12 cats were adopted.

Check: Does the ratio of 12 cats to 16 dogs equal $\frac{3}{4}$?

$$\frac{12}{16} = \frac{12 \div 4}{16 \div 4} = \frac{3}{4}$$

Try These B

At the dog park on Monday, 2 dogs out of every 5 were terriers. A total of 20 dogs were at the park.

a. How many terriers were there? Explain how you got your answer.

b. The ratio of Irish terriers to the total number of terriers was 1:4. How many of the terriers were Irish terriers? Explain how you got your answer.

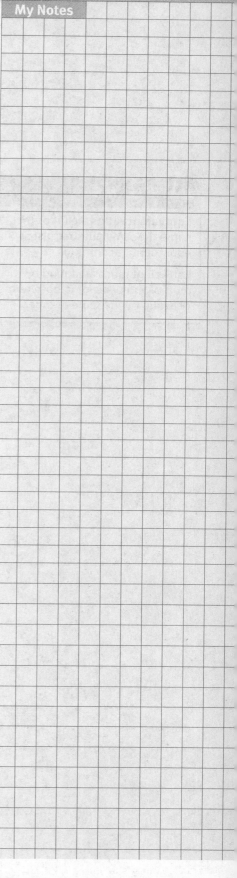

Check Your Understanding

1. For a given ratio, how many equivalent ratios can be written? Explain your reasoning.

2. How can you check to see if the ratio 1:2 is equivalent to another ratio?

3. Find as many whole-number ratios equal to 50:100 as you can, using division.

LESSON 17-1 PRACTICE

4. Use ratios to compare the dog bowls shown. Write each ratio three different ways. State whether the ratio is a part-to-part, part-to-whole, or whole-to-part.

   a. white bowls to total number of bowls
   b. black bowls to gray bowls
   c. all bowls to bowls that are not gray

5. At the veterinarian's office, 4 animals out of every 5 seen were cats. A total of 35 animals were seen.
   a. How many cats were seen?
   b. The ratio of male cats to all cats seen was 6:7. How many of the cats seen were males?

6. There are twelve rabbits in a cage. The ratio of white rabbits to all rabbits is 3:4. How many white rabbits are in the cage?

7. **Make sense of problems.** Each veterinarian has seen 40 animals today. Two out of every 5 animals Vet A has seen have been dogs. Three out of every 8 animals Vet B has seen have been dogs. Which vet saw more dogs today? Explain your reasoning.

8. **Reason abstractly.** The ratio of red collars to black collars sold at one store is 9 to 10. In one month 30 black collars are sold. Is 57 a reasonable number for the total number of red and black collars sold that month? Explain your reasoning.

9. There are 15 black mice in a cage. The ratio of all mice to black mice is 5:1. How many mice are in the cage?

My Notes

MATH TERMS

Equivalent ratios are ratios that name the same number, just as equivalent fractions do.

Equivalent ratios are found by multiplying or dividing both terms of a ratio by the same number.

Learning Targets:

● Make tables of equivalent ratios relating quantities.
● Use tables to compare ratios.
● Plot the pairs of values on the coordinate plane and describe the relationship.

SUGGESTED LEARNING STRATEGIES: Interactive Word Wall, Visualization, Create Representations, Identify a Subtask

Relationships that have *equivalent ratios* are called **proportional relationships**. All the columns in a **ratio table** show equivalent ratios.

Example A

Reason quantitatively. A recipe for a homemade dog treat calls for a mixture of 8 ounces of oats to 12 ounces of finely chopped liver. Complete the ratio table.

	8 ÷ 4	8 ÷ 2		8 × 2	8 × 10
Oats (oz)			8	16	
Liver (oz)	3	6	12		120
	12 ÷ 4	12 ÷ 2		12 × 2	12 × 10

a. How many ounces of liver are needed with 16 oz of oats?

Solution: 24 oz of liver are needed with 16 oz of oats.

b. How many ounces of oats are needed with 120 oz of liver?

Solution: 80 oz of oats are needed with 120 oz of liver.

c. Use the table to name four ratios equivalent to $\frac{8}{12}$.

Solution: The ratios $\frac{2}{3}$, $\frac{4}{6}$, $\frac{16}{24}$, and $\frac{80}{120}$ are equivalent to $\frac{8}{12}$.

Try These A

a. In one recipe for dog biscuits, the ratio of cups of water to cups of flour used is 3:9. Complete the ratio table.

	3 ÷ 3		3 × 2	3 × 4	3 × 6	3 × 9
Water (c)		3	6	12		
Flour (c)	3	9			54	81
	9 ÷ 3		9 × 2	9 × 4	9 × 6	9 × 9

b. How many cups of water are needed with 81 cups of flour?
c. How many cups of flour are needed with 12 cups of water?
d. Use the table to name five ratios equivalent to 3:9.

A relationship is proportional if the graph of the relationship is a set of points through which a straight line can be drawn and the straight line passes through the point (0, 0).

Example B

At the animal food store, 20 dog biscuits cost $6. Is the relationship between the number of biscuits and the cost proportional?

Step 1: Make a ratio table.

Number of Biscuits, x	10	**20**	40	60
Total Cost ($), y	3	**6**	12	18

Step 2: Graph the relationship between the number of biscuits x and the cost y.
Plot the ordered pairs (x, y) from the table: (10, 3), (20, 6), (40, 12), and (60, 18).

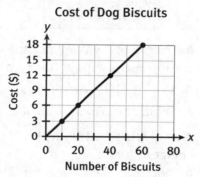

Solution: A line passes through all the points and through (0, 0). This means that the relationship is proportional.

Try These B

Graph each relationship in the My Notes section to the right. Determine if the relationship is proportional or not proportional. Explain your reasoning

a.

Number of Hours, x	2	4	6	8	9
Total Cost ($), y	15	25	35	45	50

b.

Number of Hours, x	2	4	6	8	9
Total Cost ($), y	6	12	18	24	27

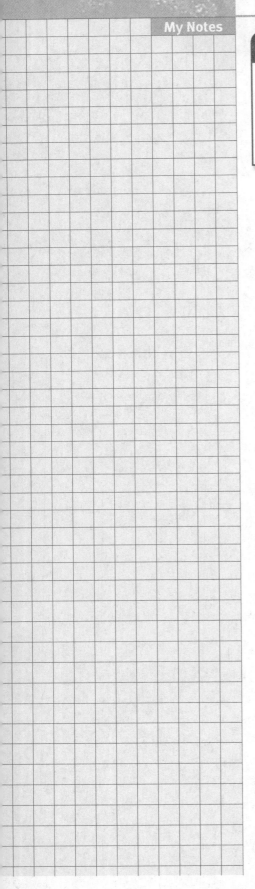

My Notes

1. How can you use a ratio table to find the value of *x* in the ratio *x*:20 if the ratio is equivalent to 5:2? Explain your reasoning.

2. Name two ways to determine if the *x*- and *y*-values in a table have a proportional relationship.

LESSON 17-2 PRACTICE

3. **Reason quantitatively.** The recipe for a homemade dog treat calls for a mixture of 2 eggs for every 8 cups of flour.
   a. Complete the ratio table.

Number of Eggs	1	2	6		
Cups of Flour		8		40	64

   b. How many eggs are needed with 40 cups of flour?
   c. How many cups of flour are needed with 6 eggs?
   d. Use the table to name four ratios equivalent to $\frac{2}{8}$.
   e. Which ratio is equivalent to 2:8 in lowest terms?

4. **Model with mathematics.** For every 4 days of dog sitting Julie charges $20.
   a. Complete the table to find the amount Julie should charge for 1, 2, and 8 days of dog sitting.

Number of Days, *x*	1	2	4	8
Total Cost ($), *y*			20	

   b. Graph the relationship between the number of days *x* and the cost *y*.
   c. Is the relationship between the number of days and the cost proportional? Justify your answer.
   d. Use your graph to determine how much Julie should charge for 6 days of dog sitting.
   e. Is 4:20 equivalent to 10:50? Explain using the graph.

5. Are $\frac{2}{3}$ and $\frac{5}{6}$ equivalent ratios? Justify your answer.

6. Are $\frac{2}{7}$ and $\frac{6}{21}$ equivalent ratios? Justify your answer.

7. Are $\frac{2}{4}$ and $\frac{3}{6}$ equivalent ratios? Justify your answer.

ACTIVITY 17 PRACTICE
Write your answers on notebook paper.
Show your work.

Lesson 17-1

1. Write a ratio in three different ways to represent the number of boys to the number of girls in the class.

Girls	Boys
12	15

2. Write a ratio for each situation.
   a. 310 heartbeats per 5 minutes
   b. $68 for 8 hours of work
   c. Work 40 hours in 5 days

3. A recent study shows that out of 100 pieces of a popular multicolored snack, there will usually be the following number of pieces of each color.

Brown	Yellow	Red	Blue	Orange	Green
13	14	13	24	20	16

   a. The numbers for two colors form a ratio that is equal to $\frac{7}{12}$. What are the colors? What is their ratio?
   b. If there were 500 pieces, about how many would be red?

4. Katie is making lemonade from a powder mix. The ratio of scoops of powder mix to water is 4 scoops to 1 gallon.
   a. How much water should Katie mix if she uses 12 scoops of mix?
   b. How much powder mix should Katie use if she plans to use 5 gallons of water?

5. There are a total of 60 plastic blocks. Three out of every 5 blocks are red. Is it reasonable for Briana to think there are enough red blocks to make a design that uses 32 red blocks? Explain your reasoning.

6. Which of the following expressions is not a ratio?
   A. $\frac{2}{3}$
   B. 2:3
   C. 2 to 3
   D. $2 + 3$

7. Which of the following compares the number of stars to the number of circles?

   ☆☆☆◯◯☆◯◯☆◯◯☆☆☆

   A. $\frac{6}{8}$
   B. 4:3
   C. 3:4
   D. 8 to 14

8. How does a ratio comparing the number of squares to the total number of shapes compare to a ratio comparing the number of arrows to the total number of shapes?

9. There are three types of animals in the pictures in Mica's album: horses, cows, and sheep. The ratio of horses to total number of animals in the pictures is 2:8. The ratio of cows to total number of animals in the pictures is 1:4.
   a. What can you conclude about the number of horses and the number of cows in the pictures?
   b. There are 40 animals pictured in Mica's album. How many are either horses or cows?

10. Write a ratio in lowest terms for each type of relationship for the following shapes.

   ◯▢◯◯◯▢◯◯◯▢◯◯◯▢◯◯

   a. part-to-whole
   b. part-to-part
   c. whole-to-part

Lesson 17-2

11. Complete the ratio table to show ratios equivalent to 9:33.

45	3			63
		330	132	

12. Which of the following ratios is not equivalent to 9:33?

A. $\dfrac{54}{198}$ B. $\dfrac{18}{66}$

C. $\dfrac{1}{25}$ D. $\dfrac{6}{22}$

13. The ratios 4:5 and x:80 have a proportional relationship. What is the value of x?

A. 79   B. 100
C. 81   D. 64

14. The following is a graph of the number of hours driven versus the number of miles traveled. Use the graph to answer parts a–c.

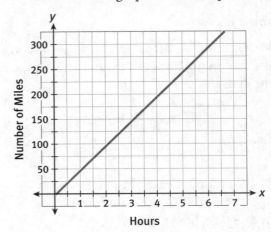

a. Is the relationship between the number of hours driven and the number of miles traveled proportional? Explain your reasoning.

b. After 3 hours of driving, how many miles would be traveled?

c. Find the value of x.

$$\frac{2}{100} = \frac{x}{250}$$

MATHEMATICAL PRACTICES
Construct Viable Arguments

15. Graph the following relationship. Determine if the relationship is proportional or not proportional. Explain your reasoning

Number of Pens, y	2	4	8	12
Total Cost ($), x	10	12	16	20

Solve Problems Using Ratios
A Picture Is Worth . . .
Lesson 18-1 Solve Problems Using Ratios

Learning Targets:

- Use ratio and rate reasoning to solve problems.
- Use ratio reasoning to convert measurement units.
- Apply quantitative reasoning, including predicting and comparing, to solve real-world problems involving ratios and rates.

> **SUGGESTED LEARNING STRATEGIES:** Close Reading, Construct Arguments, Create Representations, Identify a Subtask

Everyone tells Chris that his stories and drawings are great. Career Week is coming at his school and Chris is very excited to meet someone who has worked with movies and video game design. Chris decided to do some research before Career Week and was surprised to find out how much math is involved in filming and animation.

Animation is a series of pictures that flip by quickly in order, making something look like it is moving. A *rate* is a ratio that compares two quantities having different units. So, for animation, the number of pictures that go by in a second is called the frame rate, or "fps." Two different frame rates are shown below.

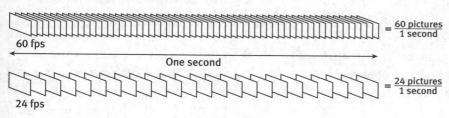

60 fps $= \dfrac{60 \text{ pictures}}{1 \text{ second}}$

One second

24 fps $= \dfrac{24 \text{ pictures}}{1 \text{ second}}$

MATH TERMS

A **rate** is a ratio that compares two quantities with different units.

rate: $\dfrac{\text{miles}}{\text{hour}} \longrightarrow \dfrac{110 \text{ miles}}{2 \text{ hours}}$

rate: $\dfrac{\text{cost}}{\text{ounces}} \longrightarrow \dfrac{\$3.18}{12 \text{ ounces}}$

MATH TIP

Rates written with a 1 as the second term are called unit rates.

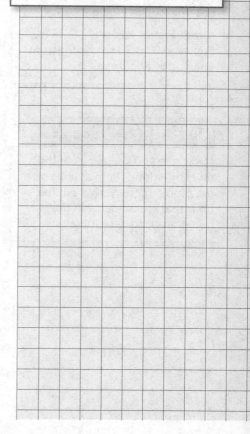

Example A

a. **Reason quantitatively.** If a swimming fish is filmed at 120 frames in one second, there are 120 photos of the fish. If you played the film at 10 frames per second, how long would the film play?

Write and solve an equation using the play rate and s, the length of the film in seconds.

$$\frac{\text{number of photos}}{1 \text{ second}} = \text{play rate} \times \text{number of seconds}$$

$$\frac{120}{1 \text{ sec}} = \frac{10}{1 \text{ sec}} \times s$$

$$120 = 10s$$

$$\frac{120}{10} = \frac{10s}{10}$$

$$12 = s$$

Solution: The film would play for 12 seconds.

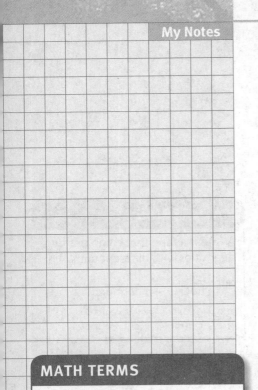

b. If Chris films the swimming fish at four times the initial speed of 120 frames in 1 second, he will have more photos of the fish. How many photos will he have with the faster filming?

Multiply the frame rate times the speed.

Number of photos = frame rate × new speed

$$= \frac{120 \text{ photos}}{1 \text{ second}} \times 4$$
$$= 480$$

Solution: Chris will have 480 photos at the new speed.

Try These A

If a swimming fish is filmed at 100 frames in one second, there are 100 photos of the fish.

a. If you played the film at 20 frames every second, how long would the film play?

b. If Chris films the swimming fish at three times the initial speed, he will have more photos of the fish. How many photos will he have with the faster filming?

You can use **dimensional analysis** to solve problems that require one unit to be converted to another. In Example B, the **conversion factor** is found first.

MATH TERMS

Dimensional analysis is a problem-solving method that uses the multiplicative identity property of one. It states that any number or expression can be multiplied by one without changing its value.

A **conversion factor** is a form of the value "1" used to change from one unit to another.

MATH TIP

Make sure you keep track of the units by writing them as you solve the problem. Then cross out the units that are the same in the numerator and denominator.

Example B

Make sense of problems. How many frames would be needed for a 1-minute film if it is filmed at 1,000 frames every second?

Step 1: Determine the number of seconds in 1 minute. This is the conversion factor.

1 minute = 60 seconds

Step 2: Multiply 1,000 frames per second by 60 seconds per minute.

$$\frac{1,000 \text{ frames}}{\text{second}} \times \frac{60 \text{ seconds}}{1 \text{ minute}} = \frac{60,000 \text{ frames } \cancel{\text{seconds}}}{1 \cancel{\text{second}} \text{ minute}}$$
$$= \frac{60,000 \text{ frames}}{1 \text{ minute}}$$

Solution: There are 60,000 frames in a 1-minute movie.

Try These B

How many frames would be needed for a 1-minute film if it is filmed at 2,500 frames every second?

Example C

A bean seed is filmed as it grows. It is being filmed at a rate of 1 frame per minute. Predict how many hours of the bean's growth will be shown in 2,910 frames.

Step 1: Determine the number of frames in 1 hour to be used as the conversion factor.

1 hour = 60 minutes, or 60 frames in 1 hour

The conversion factor is $\dfrac{1 \text{ hour}}{60 \text{ frames}}$.

Step 2: Multiply and cross out the units that are the same in the numerator and denominator.

$$\frac{2{,}910 \text{ frames}}{\text{film}} \times \frac{1 \text{ hour}}{60 \text{ frames}} = \frac{2{,}910 \ \cancel{\text{frames}} \ \text{hours}}{60 \ \cancel{\text{frames}} \ \text{film}}$$
$$= \frac{2{,}910 \ \text{hours}}{60 \ \text{films}}$$

Step 3: Divide 2,910 by 60 and label the solution.

$$\frac{2{,}910 \text{ hours}}{60 \text{ films}} = 48.5 \text{ hours per film}$$

Solution: 2,910 frames will produce a 48.5-hour movie of the bean's growth.

Try These C

A rock candy crystal is filmed as it grows from a sugar solution. It is being filmed at a rate of 1 frame per hour. Predict how many days of the candy's growth will be shown in 840 frames.

MATH TIP

When finding the conversion factor, think about multiplying by one.

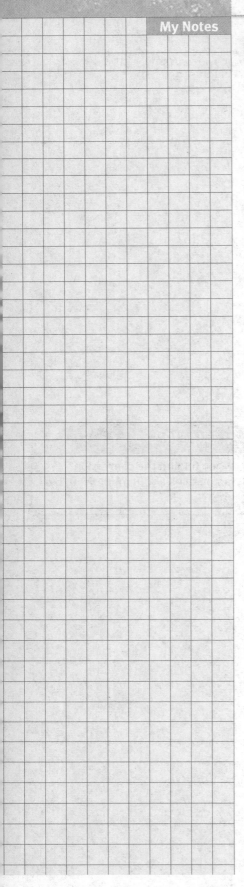

My Notes

Check Your Understanding

1. **Construct viable arguments.** Explain how determining the solution for Try These C was different from determining the solution for Try These B.

2. Explain the process you use to determine how many centimeters of film are in 7 meters of film.

3. A package of film weighs $28\frac{4}{5}$ ounces. What is the weight of the package in pounds?

LESSON 18-1 PRACTICE

4. Chris found out that animators earn an average salary of $46,885 per year. He wondered how much an animator earns per month.
   a. What is the conversion factor to convert dollars per year to dollars per month? (*Hint: Think about your final answer. Should it be smaller or larger than the yearly amount?*)
   b. What is the average monthly salary for an animator? Show your work.

5. Chris is wondering how many hours are left until Career Week starts. It is in $2\frac{1}{2}$ days.
   a. What is the conversion factor that will be used to convert days to hours?
   b. How many hours are in $2\frac{1}{2}$ days? Show your work.

6. **Make sense of problems.** Do conversion factors always, sometimes, or never have a numerator and denominator that are equivalent? Explain your choice.

7. A flower is filmed as it goes from slowly opening in the morning to closing up at night. It is being filmed at a rate of 1 frame per 30 seconds. Predict how many frames of the flower's blooming will be shown during 14 hours of daylight.

Learning Targets:

● Use ratio and rate reasoning to solve problems by reasoning about double number line diagrams and equations.

● Use ratio reasoning to convert measurement units.

● Represent mathematical and real-world problems involving ratios and rates using scale factors and proportions.

SUGGESTED LEARNING STRATEGIES: Visualization, Self Revision/Peer Revision, Discussion Groups, Sharing and Responding, Create Representations

You can use double number line diagrams to help you solve some rate problems.

Example A

Reason quantitatively. Chris may take some new photos at the beach before Career Week. Film should be stored at temperatures below 55°F. When Chris leaves for the beach, the outside temperature is 37°F. The temperature is predicted to rise 4° every hour.

a. Predict how many hours Chris will be able to shoot photos at the beach before the temperature is too warm to store his film in the car.

Use a double number line showing temperature and hours.

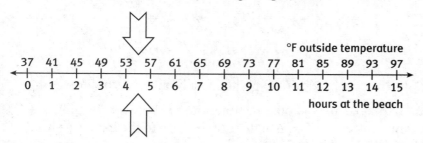

Since 55°F is halfway between 53°F and 57°F, the number of hours should be halfway between 4 and 5 hours, or 4.5 hours.

Solution: Prediction: 4.5 hours

b. Confirm your prediction using dimensional analysis.

$$55° - 37° = 18° \text{ and } \frac{18 \text{ degrees}}{1} \times \frac{1 \text{ hour}}{4 \text{ degrees}} = \frac{18}{4} = 4.5 \text{ hours}$$

Solution: Chris will be able to shoot photos for
18° ÷ 4° per hour = 4.5 hours.

Try These A

a. Chris often sells his photos to the local newspaper for $3 each, up to a limit of $40. Use a double number line to predict how many photos Chris can sell before the limit is reached.

b. Confirm your prediction using dimensional analysis.

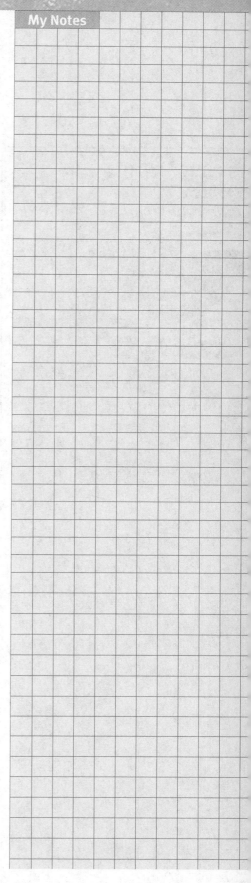

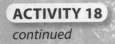

My Notes

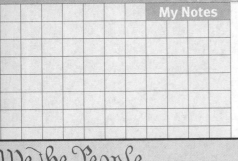

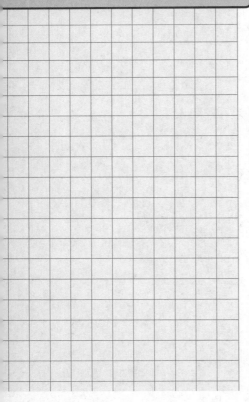

Chris has to think about the sizes of photos as he converts between sizes. Sizes are measured in inches in the United States and in the metric system internationally. For instance, an 8″ by 10″ photo in the United States is considered to be a 203 mm by 254 mm photo in other countries.

Example B

The U.S. Department of State requires that a passport photo be sized so that it is a square 2 inches by 2 inches.

a. What is the size of the photo in millimeters?

Step 1: Find the conversion factor.

There are approximately 2.54 centimeters per inch and 10 millimeters per centimeter.

$$\frac{2.54 \text{ cm}}{1 \text{ in.}} \times \frac{10 \text{ mm}}{1 \text{ cm}} = \frac{2.54 \text{ cm}}{1 \text{ in.}} \times \frac{10 \text{ mm}}{1 \text{ cm}}$$
$$= \frac{25.4 \text{ mm}}{1 \text{ in.}}$$

There are 25.4 millimeters per inch. This is the conversion factor.

Step 2: Convert the dimension in inches to millimeters.

$$\frac{25.4 \text{ mm}}{1 \text{ in.}} \times \frac{2 \text{ in.}}{\text{side}} = \frac{25.4 \text{ mm}}{1 \text{ in.}} \times \frac{2 \text{ in.}}{\text{side}}$$
$$= \frac{50.8 \text{ mm}}{\text{side}}$$

Solution: Each side of the photo must be about 51 millimeters.

b. In the passport photo, the head must be between 25 and 35 millimeters from the bottom of the chin to the top of the head. If the head is also a square, what is the minimum and maximum amount of area the person's head must take up?

Step 1: Find the area of the photo in square millimeters.

Since each side of the photo is about 51 millimeters, the area is $51 \text{ mm} \times 51 \text{ mm} = 2{,}601 \text{ mm}^2$.

Step 2: Find the area of the head in square millimeters.

mimimum area: $25 \text{ mm} \times 25 \text{ mm} = 625 \text{ mm}^2$

maximum area: $35 \text{ mm} \times 35 \text{ mm} = 1{,}225 \text{ mm}^2$

Solution: The person's head must take up from 625 mm^2 to $1{,}225 \text{ mm}^2$ of the photo.

Try These B

Chris resized a 5 in. by 7 in. photo into a passport photo. What is the original size of the photo in millimeters?

Lesson 18-2
Convert Between Measurements Using Ratios

You can resize a figure by any scale factor so that the new figure is the exact same shape as the original figure.

Example C

Chris wants to resize an 8-inch by 10-inch photo by the scale factor $\frac{3}{4}$. What will be the dimensions of the new photo?

Step 1: Convert the 8-inch side using x, the width of the new photo.

$$\frac{3}{4} = \frac{x \text{ in.}}{8 \text{ in.}} \qquad \text{Write a proportion using } x.$$
$$4x = 24 \qquad \text{Cross-multiply.}$$
$$\frac{4x}{4} = \frac{24}{4} \qquad \text{Divide each side by 4.}$$
$$x = 6 \qquad \text{Simplify.}$$

Step 2: Convert the 10-inch side using y, the length of the new photo.

$$\frac{3}{4} = \frac{y \text{ in.}}{10 \text{ in.}} \qquad \text{Write a proportion using } y.$$
$$4y = 30 \qquad \text{Cross-multiply.}$$
$$\frac{4y}{4} = \frac{30}{4} \qquad \text{Divide each side by 4.}$$
$$y = 7.5 \qquad \text{Simplify.}$$

Solution: The new photo will be 6 inches by 7.5 inches.

Try These C

Chris wants to resize a 12-inch by 14-inch photo by the scale factor $\frac{2}{3}$. What will be the dimensions of the new photo?

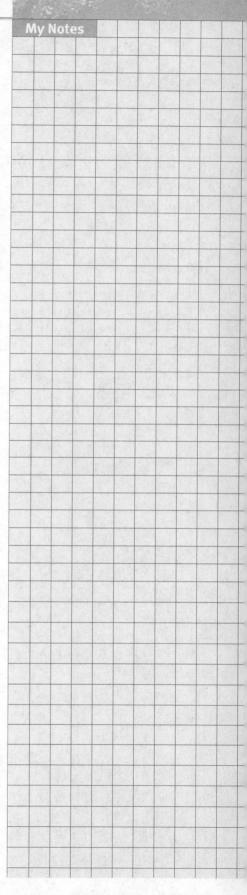

My Notes

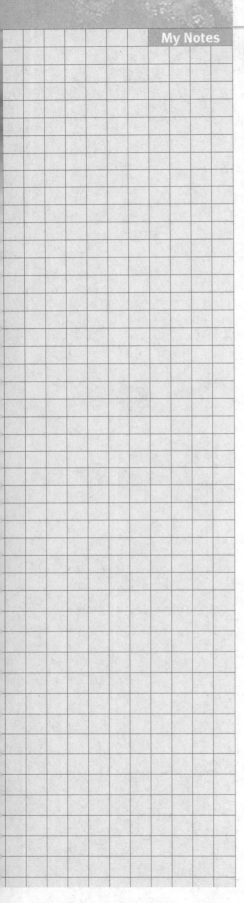

My Notes

1. Chris may sell some photos of the beach online for $2 each. Use a double number line to predict how many photos he needs to sell to earn at least $21.

2. Chris wants to resize a 4-inch by 6-inch photo by a factor of $\frac{4}{3}$. What are the dimensions of the new photo?

LESSON 18-2 PRACTICE

3. **Reason quantitatively.** Chris's work was a hit during Career Week. The filmmaker told Chris that she would pay him to illustrate some of her story lines on her next project at the rate of $120 per 8-hour day.
   a. How much did Chris earn by working on the project for 20 hours?
   b. Make a graph of the relationship between the number of hours Chris worked and the amount he earned.
   c. Look at your graph. How much does Chris earn for 6 hours of work?

4. For the project, Chris included resized pictures of Career Week. He resized his 5-inch by 7-inch pictures by a factor of $\frac{1}{2}$. What are the dimensions of the new photos?

5. Chris noticed that $\frac{3}{4}$ of his flash drive contained photos he took during the week. His flash drive holds 16 GB. If 1 GB = 1,024 MB (megabytes), and 1 MB = 1,048,576 bytes, how many bytes were photos taken during Career Week?

6. Chris found out that $\frac{7}{8}$ of the students in his school attended Career Day. If his school has 928 students, how many students attended that day?

7. The temperature outside school at noon on Career Day was 48°F, and it dropped 2°F each hour. If Career Day lasted 6 hours, what was the temperature outside at the end of Career Day?

ACTIVITY 18 PRACTICE
Write your answers on notebook paper.
Show your work.

Lesson 18-1

1. If a horse is filmed during a race at 100 frames in one second, there are 100 photos of the horse.
   a. If you played the film at 10 frames every second, how long would the film play?
   b. If you tripled the speed of filming, how many photos would you have with the faster filming?

2. How many frames would be needed for a 1-minute film if it is filmed at 500 frames every second?

3. A rubber ball is filmed as it bounces on a sidewalk at 25 frames every second. Predict how many seconds of film will be shown in 1,750 frames. Justify your answer.

4. How many seconds of film is in 120 minutes of video?
   A. 2
   B. 720
   C. 120
   D. 7,200

5. How many ounces are in 2.5 pounds of seeds bought to film one scene of a movie?
   A. $\frac{5}{32}$
   B. 30
   C. 40
   D. 400

6. The average salary for a photographer in Chris's town is $54,800 per year.
   a. What is the conversion factor to convert dollars per year to dollars per week?
   b. What is the average weekly salary for a photographer?

7. One yard of film is how many inches?
   A. 12
   B. 24
   C. 36
   D. 48

8. The filmmaker took 66 inches of film during Career Week.
   a. How many feet of film did she take?
   b. If she filmed at a rate of 400 frames per second and it took 1 minute to film 1 inch of film, how many photos did she take? Justify your answer.

9. There are two grades of students at Career Day: sixth and seventh. The sixth graders spent an average of 1.5 minutes at each booth, while the seventh graders spent an average of 2.5 minutes at each booth. Each student visited every booth and checked it off a list.
   a. How many sixth graders visited the first booth in 3 hours?
   b. What is the total number of hours spent by 400 seventh graders visiting 10 booths?

10. A typical scanning format for high-definition television is 25 frames per second, with each frame being 1,920 pixels wide and 1,080 pixels high. How many pixels are displayed in a minute?
    A. 48,000
    B. 2,880,000
    C. 2,073,600
    D. 3,110,400,000

Lesson 18-2

11. An online seller is offering photo images for $0.99 each. Use a double number line to predict how many images can be bought with $17.50.
A. 8 **B.** 17
C. 18 **D.** 175

12. Suppose you earn $7.80 per hour. How much will you earn if you work a 20-hour week?

13. The filmmaker drove her car a distance of 250 miles to get to Chris's school. She traveled the first 200 miles in 4 hours. At this rate, how long will it take her to make the complete trip?
A. 1 hr **B.** 4 hr
C. 5 hr **D.** 5.5 hr

14. Howard made a poster for the school advertising Career Week. He first sketched his design on an 8.5 in. by 11 in. sheet of notebook paper. Then he expanded his design using a scale factor of 4.
a. What are the dimensions of the poster?
b. What is the area of the poster?
c. What is the ratio of the area of the poster to the area of the sketch?

15. Suppose you resized an 8-inch by 10-inch photo to be an 11-inch by 14-inch photo. Did you use the same scale factor for each of the dimensions? Explain.

16. Your teacher taught you how to enlarge a diagram by drawing squares on the diagrams and then copying the image within each square to a larger square that has each dimension equal to 4 times the corresponding dimension of the smaller square. If the area of the original image is 32 square inches, what is the area of the enlarged image?
A. 32 in.^{2} **B.** 64 in.^{2}
C. 128 in.^{2} **D.** 512 in.^{2}

17. Chris saved some of his photos on his computer tablet. The height of his tablet is 9.5 inches, and the width is 7.31 inches. What are the dimensions of the tablet in millimeters?

MATHEMATICAL PRACTICES
Attend to Precision

18. A store is advertising a new, smaller computer tablet with a height of 7.87 inches and a width of 5.3 inches. What is the area of the face of the smaller tablet in square centimeters?

Understanding Rates and Unit Rate

Zooming!

Lesson 19-1 Understanding Rates and Unit Rates

Learning Targets:

- Understand the concept of a unit rate $\frac{a}{b}$ associated with the ratio $a : b$ with $b \neq 0$.

- Use rate language in the context of a ratio relationship.

- Give examples of rates as the comparison by division of two quantities having different attributes.

SUGGESTED LEARNING STRATEGIES: Marking the Text, Interactive Word Wall, Graphic Organizer, Self Revision/Peer Revision

For the last 28 years, students have participated in the Science Olympiad. The 2012 Science Olympiad drew 6,200 teams from 50 states. In this activity, you will use ratios and rates to describe some Science Olympiad events.

One Science Olympiad event requires teams to build a mousetrap car that both is fast and can go certain distances.

Several teams of students have decided to compete in the Mousetrap Car event. They will use mousetraps to act as the motor of their car. Seven of the students want to use wooden mousetraps, and 9 of the students want to use plastic mousetraps.

1. Write a ratio in fraction form that shows the relationship of the number of team members who want wooden traps to the number of team members who want plastic traps.

When wooden traps are compared to plastic traps, you compare different types of traps (*wooden* and *plastic*), but they have the same unit (*traps*). This is a ratio because the units are the same.

2. The coaches know that the students will need extra traps. These are needed so that the students can practice. Write a ratio equivalent to the one you wrote in Item 1 that shows the relationship of wooden traps to plastic traps, assuming each member will need 8 traps.

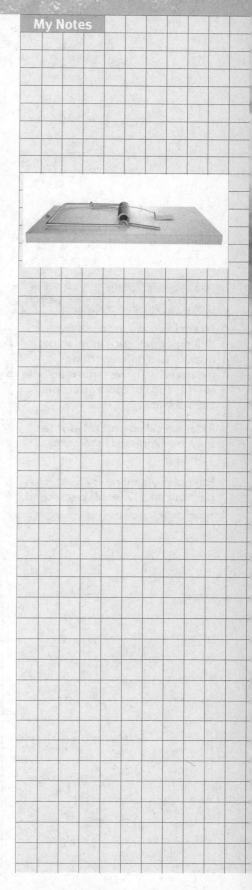

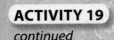
ACTIVITY 19
continued

My Notes

3. Use this ratio to determine:
   a. How many of each type of trap to buy.

   b. The total number of traps needed. Show your work.

Another way to figure out the total number of traps needed is to write a ratio comparing traps to people.

4. Write the average number of traps per 1 person as a ratio in fraction form.

You have just written is a special type of ratio known as a **rate**. This rate shows a relationship between quantities measured with *different units* (*traps* and *people*).

When the rate is *per 1 unit*, such as traps per 1 person, it is called a **unit rate**. Unit rates are easy to spot because they are often written with the word *per* or with a slash (/) (for example, traps **per** team member or traps/team member).

5. Name at least 2 other rates expressed with the word *per*.

6. Describe a situation that uses a unit rate.

Check Your Understanding

7. A factory can produce small wheels for the mousetrap cars at a rate of 18,000 wheels in 3 hours. What is the unit rate per hour?

8. Use the unit rate you found in Item 4 to find the total number of traps needed for the Mousetrap Car event. Fill in the values you know.

Unit Rate	Rate for Total
Traps/1 Person	Total Traps/Total People

$$\frac{traps}{person} = \frac{traps}{16 \text{ people}}$$

9. How does this compare to your answer in Item 3b? Explain.

10. Use the Venn diagram below to compare and contrast ratios, rates, and unit rates. Give an example of each in the diagram.

My Notes

MATH TIP

Remember that the regions of the Venn diagram that are outside the common regions should be information that is unique to that topic.

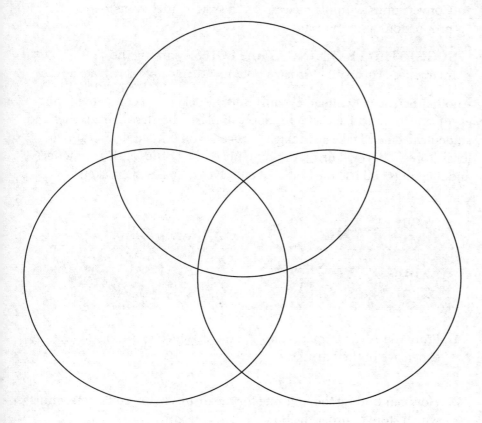

LESSON 19-1 PRACTICE

11. Find the missing value. $\dfrac{\$40}{8 \text{ mousetraps}} = \dfrac{\$5}{1 \text{ mousetrap}}$

12. The science teacher bought 20 mousetraps for $59.99. What was the unit cost for each mousetrap?

13. Solve: $\dfrac{48 \text{ mousetraps}}{6 \text{ people}} = \dfrac{x \text{ mousetraps}}{1 \text{ person}}$. $x = 8$

14. Students spent an average of $5.50 to buy materials for the Science Olympiad. If they each built 3 mousetrap cars, what was their unit cost per car?

15. Give an example of a rate that is not a unit rate. Explain your choice.

16. Make sense of problems. Do rates always have to be expressed as a quotient? Explain how you know.

17. A recipe has a ratio of 2 cups of flour to 3 cups of sugar. How much flour is there for each cup of sugar? $\dfrac{2}{3} : 1$

18. A punch recipe has a ratio of 3 pints of sparkling water to 5 pints of fruit juice. How much sparkling water is there for each pint of fruit juice?

My Notes

MATH TERMS

When a problem involves working with money, the unit rate is called the **unit price**. The unit price tells you the cost of one item, in this case the price of 1 bottle.

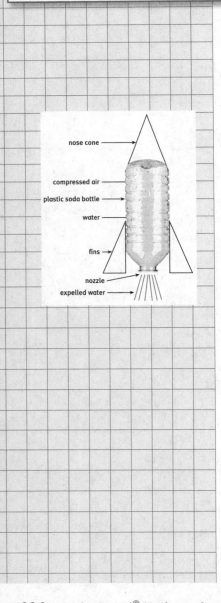

nose cone
compressed air
plastic soda bottle
water
fins
nozzle
expelled water

Learning Targets:

● Solve unit rate problems.
● Convert units within a measurement system, including the use of proportions and unit rates.

SUGGESTED LEARNING STRATEGIES: Marking the Text, Interactive Word Wall, Visualization, Identify a Subtask, Create a Plan

Another Science Olympiad event is Bottle Rockets. To compete in this event, a team must have a large supply of plastic bottles. The coaches and students decide to take advantage of specials on bottled drinks at two local stores. They will drink the contents of the bottles at their practices and meetings and use the bottles themselves to make the rockets.

Kroker's Market:

2 bottles for $2.98
or $1.59 each

Slann's Superstore:

3 bottles for $4.35
or $1.59 each

1. From the advertisements above, predict which store has the less expensive bottled drinks.

2. How can finding the unit rate for the drinks help you to determine which store to order the bottled drinks from?

3. Use the price chart for Kroker's Market.
   a. Determine the unit price per bottle if you buy the drinks using Kroker's 2-bottle deal.

   b. How much do the students save by using the 2-bottle deal instead of buying 2 bottled drinks at the regular price?

4. Use the price chart for Slann's Superstore.
   a. Determine the unit price per bottle if you buy the drinks using Slann's 3-bottle deal.

   b. How much do the students save by using the 3-bottle deal instead of buying 3 bottled drinks at the regular price?

5. **Reason quantitatively.** To decide where they will get the better deal, the students cannot simply compare unit rates. Since they need a specific number of bottled drinks, the better deal may depend on how many bottled drinks they are buying.

   a. Determine how much it would cost to buy 7 bottles from Kroker's Market. (*Hint: The students can use the deal for every 2 bottled drinks they buy, but the seventh bottle will be at regular price.*) Show your work.

   b. Determine how much it would cost to buy 7 bottled drinks from Slann's Superstore. Show your work.

   c. Where should the students buy their drinks if they want to buy 7 bottles? Explain.

The students now have all of the bottles that they need. They have just a few more supplies to purchase.

One needed supply is $\frac{1}{2}$-inch PVC pipe to build bottle launchers for practice and competition. They do not need a specific amount of pipe, because they will use the extra pipe in the future. They want to find the best deals on this pipe by the foot.

6. The table shows rates for the cost of $\frac{1}{2}$-inch PVC pipe at three different wholesalers.

Big S Supplies	Build It Again, Sam	Building Stuff
$1.45/2 feet	$3.98/5 feet	$1.77/2 feet
$28.77/50 feet		

   a. Find the unit rate for each of the prices at each of the suppliers above. Show all of your work.

Big S Supplies	Build It Again, Sam	Building Stuff

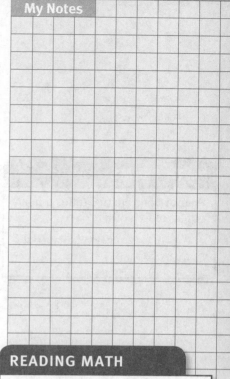

READING MATH

Symbols are sometimes used to represent units in a measurement. For example, ″ is used for inches, i.e., 9″ = 9 inches. Similarly, ′ is used for feet, i.e., 8′ = 8 feet.

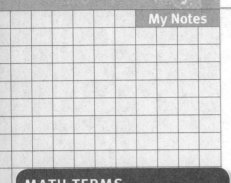

My Notes

MATH TERMS

Proportions are two ratios that are equal to each other.

$\frac{3}{5} = \frac{9}{15}$ is a proportion because the two ratios are equal.

b. Where should the PVC pipe be purchased? Explain why.

c. Explain why the numbers in the table make it easier to use unit rates to compare prices than using equivalent ratios.

Now, look at just the two pipe prices at Big S Supplies. When trying to decide which PVC pipe to buy at Big S Supplies, a ***proportion*** can also be used.

In this case, let c represent the unknown cost of the pipe for 50 feet.

$$\frac{\$1.45}{2 \text{ feet}} = \frac{c}{50 \text{ feet}}$$

To determine a rule that can be used to solve for c, think about what you already know about solving equations.

7. Write the steps you would use in solving this proportion.

$$\frac{\$1.45}{2 \text{ feet}} = \frac{c}{50 \text{ feet}}$$

8. Construct viable arguments. How can you use this proportion to determine which is the less expensive PVC pipe at Big S Supplies? Explain your reasoning.

9. The length of a car measures 20 feet. What is the length of a model of the car if the scale factor is 1 inch:2.5 feet?

Check Your Understanding

10. The table shows rates for the cost of buying toy rocket packages. The packages cannot be broken up. What is the unit rate for each of the prices shown?

ABC Toys	Z Science Supply	K Museum Store
$49.95/5 rockets	$29.99/2 rockets	$34.95/3 rockets

11. Where should the teacher buy the toy rockets? Explain why.

12. Suppose the teacher wanted to buy exactly 6 toy rockets. Where should she buy them? Explain.

13. Explain why unit rates may be used to compare prices.

LESSON 19-2 PRACTICE

14. Gordon read 18 pages of a book about rockets in 40 minutes. What was the unit rate per minute? Per hour?

15. Renaldo earned $45 organizing the science section of the library. If he worked for 6 hours, what was his hourly rate of pay?

16. **Make sense of problems.** The price of jet fuel in North America during the last week of 2012 was recorded as $3,062 for 1,000 gallons. What was the unit price of the jet fuel?

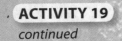
My Notes

Learning Targets:

● Use ratio and rate reasoning to solve problems.

● Represent mathematical and real-world problems involving ratios and rates using scale factors and proportions.

> **SUGGESTED LEARNING STRATEGIES:** Marking the Text, Predict and Confirm, Look for a Pattern

Some contestants in the Mousetrap Car event try to build the fastest car. Below are some Mousetrap Car record holders:

• One car raced 5 meters in 1.25 seconds.
• Another car raced 10 meters in 4.30 seconds.
• Another car raced 7 meters in 2.81 seconds.

1. Work with your group. Predict which of these mousetrap cars is the fastest.

2. What is the average speed of the mousetrap car that covered 5 meters in 1.25 seconds?

   To determine this, you must find the number of meters for one second. Find the meters per second by finding an equivalent ratio. Divide by 1 in the form of $\frac{1.25}{1.25}$.

$$\frac{5 \text{ meters}}{1.25 \text{ seconds}} \div \frac{1.25}{1.25} = \frac{\text{meters}}{\text{second}}$$

3. **Express regularity in repeated reasoning.** Another way to find the speed of each mousetrap car is to reason this way: "If 5 meters is the distance the car travels in 1.25 seconds, then how many meters does the car travel in 1 second?"

   a. Explain why a proportion can be used to find the speed of the mousetrap car. Then write and solve the proportion.

   b. Write this unit rate using the word *per*.

4. Confirm your prediction from Item 1 by finding the average speed as a unit rate for the other two mousetrap cars. Use one of the methods above. Round to the nearest hundredth.

Lesson 19-3
Calculating Rates of Speed

5. Reason quantitatively. Michela used the tape diagram below to help her predict the speed of her mousetrap car. She knew that the length of the track is 15 feet, and that her car traveled one-fifth of the length of the track in 0.5 seconds.

```
                        15 feet
        ┌──────────────────────────────────────┐
track   │                                      │
        └──────────────────────────────────────┘
        ┌────────┬────────┬───────┬───────┬───────┐
        │ 3 feet │ 3 feet │       │       │       │
        └────────┴────────┴───────┴───────┴───────┘
    sec │  0.5   │  0.5   │  0.5  │  0.5  │  0.5  │
        └────────┴────────┴───────┴───────┴───────┘
```

a. What was the unit speed of Michela's mousetrap car?

b. How can you use the tape diagram to write Michela's mousetrap car as a unit rate?

Check Your Understanding

6. Another car in the Mousetrap Car event raced 12 meters in 5.2 seconds. Is it faster than Michela's car? Explain. Note: 1 ft = 0.305 m.

7. What is the average speed of a mousetrap car that covers 4 meters in 2.5 seconds?

LESSON 19-3 PRACTICE

8. What is the average speed of a mousetrap car that covers 5.25 meters in 1.75 seconds?

9. How can finding the unit rate help you determine the fastest car in the Mousetrap Car event?

10. Reason quantitatively. Michela experimented with filming her toy car as it ran through the racecourse. Her film was made up of 150 photo frames taken in 5 seconds.
   a. What is the unit rate for the frame speed?
   b. If all contestants in the race filmed their cars, how can you use the frame speed to determine which car was the fastest?

My Notes

11. Solve the proportion. Show your work.

$$\frac{7.375 \text{ meters}}{1.475 \text{ seconds}} = \frac{x \text{ meters}}{1 \text{ second}}$$

12. How can you use a proportion to show which mousetrap car is the fastest?

13. Caroline was in charge of buying the mousetraps for the event. She had to choose whether to buy 12 mousetraps in a package that costs $39.99 or 15 mousetraps in a package that costs $45.99.
  a. What is the unit rate for each of the packages of mousetraps?
  b. Which package was a better buy? Explain.
  c. Describe a situation for which Caroline should buy mousetraps in packages of 15.

14. Suppose Caroline needs to buy only 10 mousetraps. Which package should she purchase? Explain.

15. Use appropriate tools strategically. Describe how Caroline could use a tape diagram to help her decide which package to buy in Item 13.

ACTIVITY 19 PRACTICE
Write your answers on notebook paper.
Show your work.

Lesson 19-1

1. A factory can produce mousetraps at a rate of 1,500 traps in 3 hours. What is the unit rate per hour?

2. A factory that produces toy wheels finds that they must discard 3 out of every 100 wheels because they are defective. How many wheels would they expect to discard every day if the factory produces 1,200 wheels per hour in each 8-hour day?

3. A mousetrap car is filmed as it runs the racecourse. The film includes 1,200 photo frames taken in 8 seconds. How many frames were taken in one second? Justify your answer.

4. Last year, one science teacher spent $65.50 to buy materials for the Mousetrap Car event. If 12 students participated in the event, what was the teacher's unit cost per student?
   A. $2.98   **B.** $6.55
   C. $5.46   **D.** $7.86

5. Mr. Walker, the contest sponsor, bought toy wheels in a package of 6 dozen for $81.00. What was the unit cost of each wheel?
   A. $1.125   **B.** $1.50
   C. $6.75   **D.** $13.50

6. Mr. Walker wrote notes about the event that would help him plan for the following year. If he will still purchase 8 traps per person, how many traps will he need to purchase for 25 people in the Mousetrap Car race?
   A. 4   **B.** 8
   C. 200   **D.** 400

7. A meatball recipe has a ratio of 2 cups of breadcrumb mixture to 3 pounds of ground meat. How much breadcrumb mixture is there for 1 pound of ground meat?

Lesson 19-2

8. The table shows rates for the cost of buying model rocket packages. What is the unit rate for each of the models shown?

XYZ Toys	AAA Science Supply
$69.95/5 models	$59.95/4 models

9. PVC pipe used to make the toy rockets is sold by the foot. If 8 feet cost $16.89, what is the cost for 30 feet of pipe sold at the same unit rate?
   A. $2.11   **B.** $4.50
   C. $63.34   **D.** $506.70

10. Write the steps you would use in solving the proportion.

$$\frac{\$12.50}{4 \text{ feet}} = \frac{c}{24 \text{ feet}}$$

11. The height of the Atlas V rocket used for space lifts was 205 feet. What is the height of a model of the Atlas V rocket if the scale factor is 1 ft : 32 ft?
   A. 6.4 ft   **B.** 12.8 ft
   C. 102.5 ft   **D.** 6,560 ft

Lesson 19-3

12. An online seller is offering 30 photo images of mousetraps for $24. Use a tape diagram to predict the unit cost of each image.
    a. $0.72   **b.** $0.80
    c. $1.20   **d.** $1.25

13. Mr. Walker, a runner, asked students to find the unit rate of the winner of the first Boston Marathon in 1897. John J. McDermott ran the marathon in 175 minutes. The length of the course was only 24.5 miles instead of 26 miles as it is today. What was the unit rate?

14. Mr. Walker used proportions and the following example to teach students how to calculate speeds: An F-15 Eagle travels at a speed of 1,875 miles per hour for 3.5 hours. Which distance solves the proportion he used?
    A. 535.7 mi   **B.** 3,750 mi
    C. 4,687.5 mi   **D.** 6,562.5 mi

15. Jackie made a poster for the school advertising the Science Olympiad. She included sample statistics on the speed of the mousetrap cars from the previous years.
    a. If one car raced 8 meters in 1.5 seconds, what was its speed?
    b. How does this compare to the record time of 10 meters in 2.32 seconds?

16. Mr. Walker drove 20 miles to pick up supplies for the Science Olympiad. If the trip to the supply store took 0.75 hours, what was his unit speed for one hour?

17. Bryce, a previous winner of the contest, made a trip of 360 miles in 6.5 hours. At this same average rate of speed, how long will it take Bryce to travel an additional 300 miles so that he can judge the contest? Explain your reasoning.

18. It is about 2,508 miles from a Science Olympiad in Orange County, California, to a Science Olympiad in Orange County, Florida. With an average speed of 70 miles per hour, about how long will it take to drive from one to the other? Use a proportion in determining your answer.

19. One Mousetrap Car contestant researched the speed of actual race cars. He found that when NASCAR drivers race on the Phoenix International Raceway, they make 312 laps. In April 2009, the race that was held there lasted for about 3 hours. What was the approximate rate the racers were traveling?

MATHEMATICAL PRACTICES
Reason Quantitatively

20. On the way to the Mousetrap Car contest, the judge drove from Exit 32 on the highway to Exit 170 in 2 hours. Exits 32 and 170 are 138 miles apart. Did the judge follow the speed limit of 65 mph? Explain how you know using a proportion.

Write your answers on notebook paper. Show your work.

Wendy has a summer job working 5 days per week. She is surprised how many decisions she has to make. Her decisions are shown in the questions below.

1. The two different pay options she may choose from are either $62 per day or $304 per week. Which is the better deal for Wendy? Use unit rates to explain your decision.

2. Using the option you chose in Item 1, determine how much money Wendy will earn by working 4 weeks.

3. To get the right color to paint the house, Wendy must mix 1 gallon of green paint with 3 gallons of white paint.
   a. Write a ratio in 3 different ways to show the relationship between green paint and white paint.
   b. How many gallons of paint will her mixture make?

4. Wendy is told ahead of time that she will need to purchase about 12 gallons of paint in order to cover the entire house.
   a. Write equivalent ratios to determine the amount of green and white paint she will need to purchase.
   b. If there are 4 quarts in 1 gallon, how many quarts of paint does she need to purchase?

5. How many gallons of green paint would be needed if Wendy had 10 gallons of white paint? Explain your reasoning.

6. How many gallons of white paint would Wendy need to mix with 0.5 gallon of green paint? Explain your answer.

7. Suppose that Wendy accidentally mixed 2 gallons of green paint with 3 gallons of white paint.
   a. How would her color change? Would it be darker or lighter? Explain.
   b. Without starting over, how could she fix her mistake to get the right color to paint the house?

Scoring Guide	Exemplary	Proficient	Emerging	Incomplete
	The solution demonstrates these characteristics:			
Mathematics Knowledge and Thinking (Items 1, 2, 3a-b, 4a-b, 5, 6, 7a-b)	• Clear and accurate understanding of ratios, unit rates, and solving proportions. • Effective understanding and accuracy in converting between measurements.	• An understanding of ratios, unit rates, and solving proportions that usually results in correct answers. • Mostly correct conversion between measurements.	• An understanding of ratios, unit rates, and solving proportions that sometimes results in correct answers. • Difficulty converting between measurements.	• Incorrect or incomplete understanding of ratios, unit rates, and solving proportions. • Incorrect conversion between measurements.
Problem Solving (Items 1, 2, 3, 4b, 5, 6, 7b)	• An appropriate and efficient strategy that results in a correct answer. • Accurate interpretation of the solution of a proportion to solve a problem.	• A strategy that may include unnecessary steps but results in a correct answer. • Interpretation of the solution of a proportion to solve a problem.	• A strategy that results in some incorrect answers. • Difficulty interpreting the solution of a proportion to solve a problem.	• No clear strategy when solving problems. • Incorrect or incomplete interpretation of the solution of a proportion to solve a problem.
Mathematical Modeling / Representations (Items 1, 3a, 4a, 5, 6, 7b)	• Accurately representing a problem situation with a ratio, proportion, or unit rate.	• A mostly correct representation of a problem situation with a ratio, proportion, or unit rate.	• Difficulty representing a problem situation with a ratio, proportion, or unit rate.	• An incorrect or incomplete representation of a problem situation with a ratio, proportion, or unit rate.
Reasoning and Communication (Items 1, 5, 6, 7a-b)	• Precise use of appropriate math terms and language to explain solutions using ratios and proportions.	• An adequate explanation of solutions using ratios and proportions.	• A misleading or confusing explanation of solutions using ratios and proportions.	• An incomplete or inaccurate description of solutions using ratios and proportions.

Using Models to Understand Percents

A "Cent" for Your Thoughts

Lesson 20-1 Using Models to Understand Percents

Learning Targets:

- Find a percent of a quantity as a rate per 100.
- Represent ratios and percents with concrete models and decimals.
- Represent benchmark fractions and percents.
- Generate equivalent forms of decimals and percents.

SUGGESTED LEARNING STRATEGIES: Interactive Word Wall, Marking the Text, Visualization, Quickwrite, Create Representations, Simplify the Problem

Another way to represent a part-to-whole relationship is by using another type of ratio called a *percent*. A percent is a ratio that is always a number compared to 100. The symbol % is used to represent the term *percent*.

1. Consider the words *century, cent, centavo,* and *centimeter*. What do these words have in common?

2. What other words do you know that have the base word *cent* in them?

3. Consider the parts of the word *percent*. Why do you think a number out of 100 is called a percent?

4. **Reason quantitatively.** Since you know that there are 100 cents in a dollar and percents are parts of 100, write each of these dollar amounts as a percent.
   a. a penny
   b. 10 cents
   c. $0.25
   d. 5 cents
   e. a dollar
   f. $1.50

My Notes

MATH TERMS

Percent means parts per hundred. A percent can be expressed as a fraction, such as $\frac{87}{100}$, or with a percent sign, 87%.

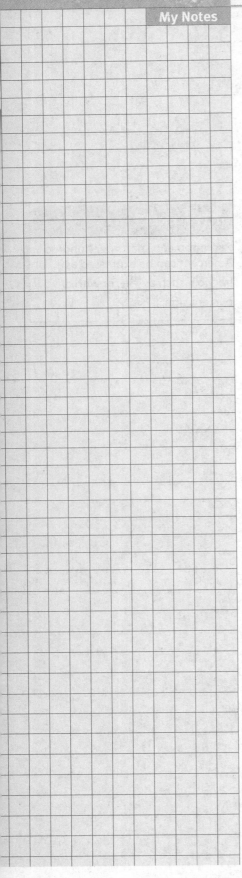

My Notes

5. Use the grid to answer the following questions.

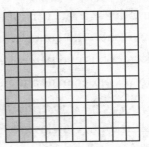

  a. How many squares out of 100 are shaded? _____ out of _____

  b. Replace *out of 100* with the word *percent*:

  c. Replace *percent* with its symbol:

6. Since percents are parts of 100, they can be modeled on a 10-by-10 grid.
  a. Create a design using red, orange, yellow, green, and blue. Be sure to color in all of the squares.

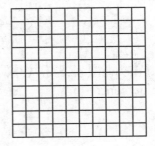

  b. In the table below, write the percent of the grid that is covered by each color.

	Red	Orange	Yellow	Green	Blue
Percent of Grid					

  c. Represent the percent for each color using a strip diagram.

  d. Add together the percents from the table above. What do you notice about the sum?

  e. How is your answer to part c related to what you know about percents?

7. There are some important *benchmark* percents that will be seen often in math class and in everyday life. Use the grids to determine the percent that represents each fraction.

a. $\frac{1}{2} =$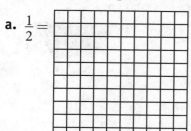

b. $\frac{1}{4} =$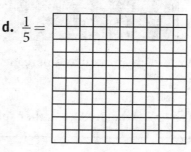

c. $\frac{1}{10} =$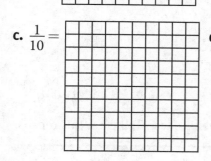

d. $\frac{1}{5} =$

MATH TIP

A benchmark fraction may have a 1 in the numerator. Other benchmark fractions are $\frac{1}{3}$, $\frac{1}{6}$, $\frac{1}{8}$, and $\frac{3}{4}$.

ACADEMIC VOCABULARY

A **benchmark** is a standard or reference point for comparing or evaluating against.

Equivalent forms of decimals and percents can sometimes be used to represent real-world problems.

8. **Make sense of problems.** Out of 100 students in the cafeteria, 42 wanted chicken fingers and 24 wanted salad. Explain how you can represent the number of students who did not want either choice as a decimal and as a percent.

9. A common tip for a restaurant bill is 15%. Explain how much money that adds to the amount you pay.

10. Write a description of a math context that involves money that can be expressed using decimals or percents. Be sure to use appropriate vocabulary, both real-world and mathematical, to describe the situation. Refer to the Word Wall as needed to help you choose words for your description.

My Notes

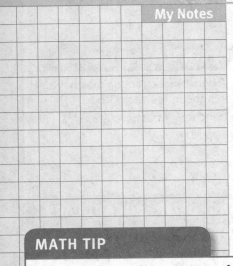

MATH TIP

Other ratios equivalent to 80 out of 100 are 4 out of 5, 16 out of 20, and so on.

Check Your Understanding

11. Write the shaded part of each figure as a percent.

a.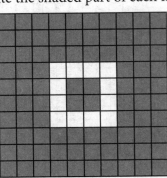

b.

12. Write each amount as a percent.

a. $\dfrac{12}{100}$

b. 79 out of 100

13. Abby received an 80% on her spelling test. Tell what this means.

LESSON 20-1 PRACTICE

14. Copy and complete the table below by filling in missing percents or shading figures to represent given percents.

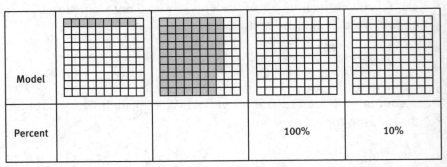

Model				
Percent			100%	10%

15. Describe how you should write a percent for the shaded part of a figure that has 20 equal squares with 8 squares shaded and 12 squares unshaded.

Use a grid to help you write each benchmark fraction as a percent.

16. $\dfrac{1}{5}$ **17.** $\dfrac{1}{4}$ **18.** $\dfrac{3}{4}$ **19.** $\dfrac{1}{8}$

20. Model with mathematics. A typical professional basketball player may make 64 out of 100 free throws. Draw a model to show this ratio. Then write the ratio as a percent.

Lesson 20-2
Percents, Fractions, and Decimals

My Notes

Learning Targets:

● Represent ratios and percents with fractions and decimals.

● Represent benchmark percents such as 1%, 10%, 25%, $33\frac{1}{3}$%, and multiples of these values using number lines and numbers.

● Use percents, fractions, and decimals to show parts of the same whole.

SUGGESTED LEARNING STRATEGIES: Marking the Text, Visualization, Note Taking, Sharing and Responding, Create Representations

1. Color the grid. The table at the right tells how many squares to fill with each color. Make any design you want.

Color	Squares
Red	40
Orange	8
Yellow	13
Green	17
Blue	22

MATH TIP

Recall that one way to convert a fraction to a decimal is by division.

For example, $\frac{3}{4}$ is 3 divided by 4, which gives a quotient of 0.75. This can be written as a percent, 75%.

This gives the same answer as using equivalent fractions:

$\frac{3}{4} = \frac{75}{100} = 0.75 = 75\%$.

2. For each color, write a ratio of the number of squares of that color to the total number of squares using a colon. Then write each ratio in fraction, decimal, and word form and as a percent.

	Red	Orange	Yellow	Green	Blue
Ratio (:)					
Fraction					
Decimal					
Word Form					
Percent					

3. **Reason quantitatively.** Use the table from Item 2 to answer each question.

   a. What is the sum of the percents?

   b. What is the sum of the fractions?

   c. What is the sum of the decimals?

   d. What relationships do you see among your answers to parts a–c?

My Notes

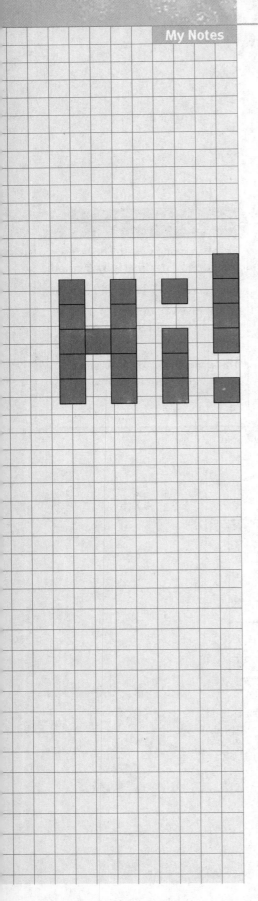

4. Look at the table showing the colors you used in the grid.
   a. List the colors and percents from Items 1 and 2 in order from the color most used to the color least used.

   b. What representations other than the percents could you have used to order the colors?

5. What about the grid in Item 1 made it easy to find the percent?

6. How many tiles make up the message *Hi!* as shown?

7. To find the percent of the tiles in *Hi!* that are in the *H*, first find either the fraction or the decimal that represents the number of tiles in the *H* out of the total number of tiles.
   a. Which is easier to find in this situation, a decimal or a fraction? Explain.

   b. Find the equivalent fraction to your answer in hundredths, since percent is a number out of 100. Then convert the hundredths to a percent.

   c. Write this percent as a decimal.

8. Think about the tiles in the letter *i*.
   a. What percent of the tiles in *Hi!* are in the *i*?

   b. Write this percent as a decimal.

9. Use your answers to Items 7 and 8 to determine what percent of the tiles in *Hi!* are in the *!* without counting them. Explain how you found your answer.

My Notes

10. Write the percent from Item 9 as a decimal and as a fraction.

11. You just learned to write percents using a ratio or a decimal written in hundredths. Convert each fraction, decimal, or ratio below to a percent. If not already in hundredths, first convert to hundredths and then write as a percent.

   a. 0. 45   **b.** $\dfrac{34}{100}$ **c.** 0.9

   d. $\dfrac{7}{10}$ **e.** $\dfrac{11}{25}$ **f.** 0.30

In the last activity you learned that there are some fraction, decimal, and percent conversions that are commonly used and are called benchmarks. Solving problems will be easier if you learn and remember them.

12. a. Express regularity in repeated reasoning. Complete the table below with the fraction, decimal, and percent forms of these commonly used numbers.

Fraction	Decimal	Percent
		1%
$\dfrac{1}{4}$		
$\dfrac{1}{3}$		
	0.5	
		75%
	0.1	
		20%
1		

  b. Place the fractions, decimals, and percents on this triple number line.

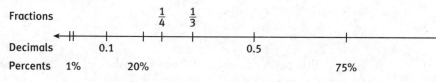

  c. What patterns do you notice in the table and the number line that can help you to remember the different forms of these numbers?

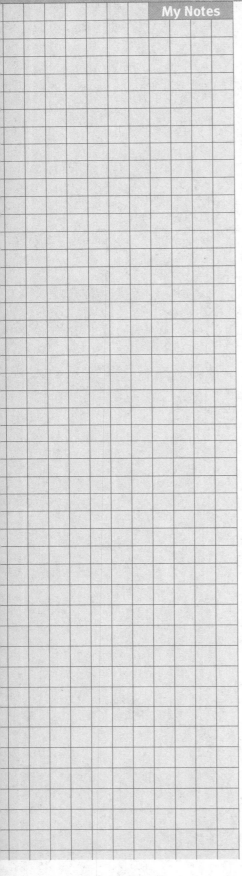

13. Work with your group. Use the grid below. When answering parts a–c below, do not use more than one color in a box. Assign each group member a region to color from parts a–c.

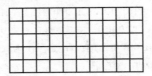

  a. Color 36% of the grid blue. Write the fraction and the decimal that represent the amount of the grid that is now blue.

  b. Color $\frac{2}{5}$ of the grid red. Write a decimal and the percent to represent the number of red boxes.

  c. Color 0.16 of the grid yellow. Write this amount as a fraction and convert your fraction to a percent.

  d. What percent of the grid is now shaded? Write this percent as a decimal and a fraction.

14. Use the squares you colored in on the grid to order 36%, $\frac{2}{5}$, and 0.16 from least to greatest.

15. If you did not have a shaded model to look at, you could use a number line to compare percents, fractions, and decimals. Place 36%, $\frac{2}{5}$, and 0.16 on the number line below.

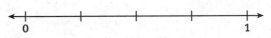

16. Use this figure: ⬤◯◯◯◯◯◯◯

  a. What percent of the figure is shaded? Explain how you determined your answer.

  b. How is this percent different from the other percents you have found in this activity?

  c. How would you read this percent? Write your answer in words below.

Check Your Understanding

17. Write 55% as a decimal and as a fraction.

18. Kate kicked 25 goal shots at soccer practice and scored on 13 of them. What percent of shots did she make?

19. Explain why fractions may represent a quantity better than a percent.

LESSON 20-2 PRACTICE

Replace each bold number in the facts below with a percent.

20. $\frac{1}{4}$ of all the bones in your body are in your feet.

21. About **0.18** of people let their pets sleep in their beds.

22. About $\frac{8}{20}$ of America is wilderness.

23. Pizzerias make up about $\frac{1}{2}$ of all restaurants.

24. **Reason abstractly.** Copy and complete the table below by filling in missing amounts and shading figures. Write ratios using a colon (:) to represent part-to-whole relationships.

Figure	Ratio	Fraction	Decimal	Percent
	3:5			
		$\frac{1}{4}$		
			0.3	
	7:10			
				100%

25. Write each number as a percent.

a. $\frac{2}{3}$ **b.** 0.23   **c.** $\frac{73}{100}$

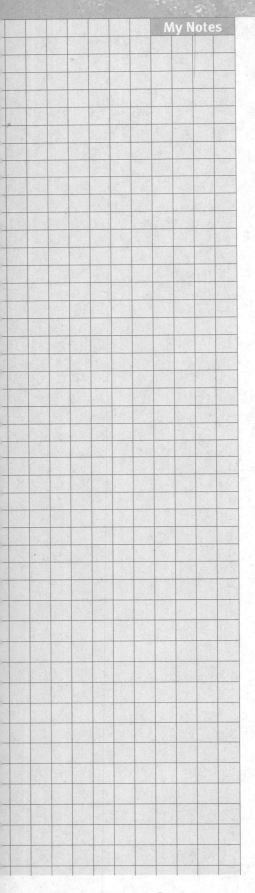

My Notes

Learning Targets:

- Find a percent of a quantity as a rate per 100.
- Generate equivalent forms of fractions, decimals, and percents using real-world problems.
- Represent percents with concrete models, fractions, and decimals.

SUGGESTED LEARNING STRATEGIES: Marking the Text, Note Taking, Think-Pair-Share, Critique Reasoning, Sharing and Responding, Create a Plan, Construct an Argument

To convert percents that include tenths to fractions, the decimal point must be moved within the fraction so that there is no decimal point in either the numerator or the denominator.

1. **a.** Explain how you write a percent as a fraction. What is 51.2% written as a fraction?

    b. Fractions should not have decimal points in the numerator. How can the decimal point be eliminated while still keeping this an equivalent fraction?

    c. What fraction is equivalent to 51.2%?

2. Percents are commonly used in trivia or fun facts. Convert each percentage in the facts below to decimals and fractions.
   a. About 50.8% of the U.S. population is female.

    b. In the U.S., 32.4% of households own a cat.

3. Find four examples of percents used in real life. You may use newspapers, signs, pictures, or another source. Create a poster showing the percents, giving their equivalent decimal and ratio forms, and telling what the percents mean in the situation. Share your poster with your class, and describe how you organized its contents.

4. **Reason quantitatively.** A factory produces stickers at a rate of 4,000 sheets per minute. They know that 1.52% of the sheets of stickers are rejected because at least one sticker is loose on the sheet.

   a. Express the percent rejected as a rate per 100.

   b. Write and solve a proportion to find how many sheets are rejected each minute during production.

   c. How many whole sheets are rejected? Write your answer as a ratio.

5. **Make sense of problems.** In 2012, 40.1% of the population of China, about 1,343,000,000 people, were Internet users.

   a. Express the percent as a rate per 100 people in China.

   b. About how many people in China use the Internet?

   c. If the number in part b represents 22.4% of the Internet users in the world, predict the number of Internet users there were in the world in 2012. Justify your reasoning.

My Notes

Check Your Understanding

6. Use what you have learned about converting percents, decimals, and fractions to each of the different forms. Then compare each amount.

   a. $\frac{5}{7}$ ◯ 71%   b. 0.5625 ◯ 56.4%

   c. 27% ◯ 0.3   d. 10% ◯ 0.01

7. Write 89.6% as a decimal and as a fraction.

8. Put the following amounts in order from greatest to least: 60%, $\frac{2}{3}$, 0.599. Show the form you choose to convert the numbers in order to compare them.

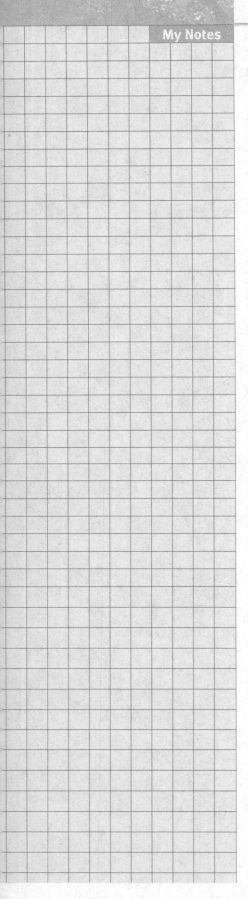

My Notes

LESSON 20-3 PRACTICE

9. Order from greatest to least: 43%, $\frac{3}{7}$, 0.453.

10. What fraction is equivalent to 123.5%?

11. Carlos has $10 more than Jeremy. Jeremy has $5 more than Michele. Altogether they have $80. What part of 100 does Michele have?

12. Explain how you would write $\frac{7}{8}$ as a rate per 100.

13. Reason quantitatively. A factory produces bottled water at a rate of 2,000 cases per hour. They know that 1.14% of the cases must be rejected because at least one bottle was damaged in the production line.
  a. Express the percent as a rate per 100.
  b. Write and solve a proportion to find how many cases are rejected each hour during production.

14. Model with mathematics. In 2012, a survey found that 92% of people in the 18–29 age group used social networking sites.
  a. Express the percent as a rate per 100 people.
  b. What is this percent written as a fraction?

15. Model with mathematics. In 2012, there were about 620,000,000 websites in the world. About $\frac{2}{3}$ of these websites were inactive for various reasons. What percent of the websites were inactive?

ACTIVITY 20 PRACTICE
Write your answers on notebook paper.
Show your work.

Lesson 20-1

1. Write the shaded part of each figure as a percent.
   a. 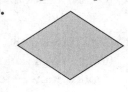 **b.**

2. Write each amount as a percent.
   a. $\dfrac{17}{100}$ **b.** 23 out of 100

3. Marco's mother told him that she would add 25% to his allowance if he saved it all. What fraction is this?

4. In 2012, 75% of the population of India had mobile phones in use. Draw a model to show this percent. Then write the percent as a ratio.

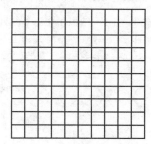

5. A dairy that produces milk cartons for schools finds that they must discard 4 out of every 100 cartons because they are not sealed properly. What percent of the cartons of milk are not discarded?
   A. 2% **B.** 40%
   C. 4% **D.** 96%

6. Three-fourths of the students in sixth grade participate in after-school activities. What percent is this?
   A. 3% **B.** 25%
   C. 50% **D.** 75%

Lesson 20-2

7. Convert each fraction, decimal, or ratio below to a percent. If not already in hundredths, first convert to hundredths and then write as a percent.
   a. $\dfrac{7}{20}$ **b.** 91:100 **c.** 0.34

8. Which letter on the triple number line below corresponds to $\dfrac{1}{2}$?

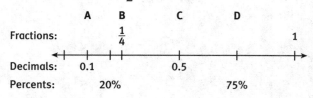

   A. A **B.** B
   C. C **D.** D

9. Order 68%, $\dfrac{3}{5}$, and 0.72 from least to greatest.

10. What fraction of each figure below is shaded? Explain how your determined your answer. Then give the percent for each fraction.
    a. **b.**

11. In 2011, over 82% of the population of Mexico used a mobile phone. What fraction is equivalent to 82%?
    A. $\dfrac{18}{100}$ **B.** $\dfrac{19}{50}$
    C. $\dfrac{41}{50}$ **D.** $\dfrac{83}{100}$

Lesson 20-3

12. What is 68.2% written as a fraction in lowest terms?

A. $\dfrac{8}{25}$ **B.** $\dfrac{159}{500}$

C. $\dfrac{17}{25}$ **D.** $\dfrac{341}{500}$

13. About 78.6% of the population of North America used the Internet in 2012. Convert the percent to a decimal and a fraction in lowest terms.

14. Put the following amounts in order from greatest to least.

54%, $\dfrac{4}{7}$, 0.525

A. $\dfrac{4}{7}$, 54%, 0.525   **B.** $\dfrac{4}{7}$, 0.525, 54%

C. 0.525, 54%, $\dfrac{4}{7}$ **D.** 0.525, $\dfrac{4}{7}$, 54%

15. A factory produces toy dolls at the rate of 400 per hour and has to recycle 3% of them because the clothes are torn.
  a. Express the recycle percent as a rate per 100.
  b. How many dolls are recycled each hour during production?

16. The number of websites in 2012 represented an increase of 28% over 2011. Explain how you write 28% as a rate per 100.

17. In 2012, the number of mobile phones in the United States was 103.9% of the population.
  a. Explain how you write the percent as a fraction.
  b. Give a reason for why this percent can be over 100.

18. Gina traveled 48% of the distance from her home in Maryland to Chicago in one day. Represent the percent using the model below.

19. The surface of the Earth is about 70% water.
  a. What does the percent 30% represent?
  b. Write 30% as a fraction.

MATHEMATICAL PRACTICES
Model with Mathematics

20. Shade in 70% of the counters below. What fraction of the counters are shaded?

○○○○○○○○○○
○○○○○○○○○○

Applying Percents

Feel the Beat

Lesson 21-1 Using Models to Understand Percents

Learning Targets:

- Solve real-world problems to find the percent given the part and the whole.
- Use ratio and rate reasoning to solve real-world and mathematical problems.

SUGGESTED LEARNING STRATEGIES: Marking the Text, Note Taking, Quickwrite, Identify a Subtask

Isaac and his older brother, Nate, both need to find part-time jobs. Nate is considering starting a deejay business and wants Isaac to be his partner. They could share the deejay jobs, advertising, scheduling, and billing.

The brothers did some research and found prices for startup equipment. The items they needed for their business and the cost for each item are shown in the table below.

Item	Cost
Fog machine	$150.00
Controller for MP3 and computer	$280.00
Speakers	$1,000.00
Mirrored ball and light	$70.00
Wireless microphone	$250.00
Lights	$750.00

1. How much money will be needed to start the deejay business? Show your work.

The boys asked their parents for a loan to start the business. Their parents told them that they would consider loaning them the money if they put together a business plan showing their costs and their expected income.

The first step for the boys is to determine what percent each item above is of their total budget. Nate had already learned how to determine percents in school, but Isaac had not learned yet. Nate explained to his brother the process they could use to find these percents.

A proportion can be used to find a percent of a number. When using a proportion to find a percent, information from the problem is used to set up the two ratios that form the proportion.

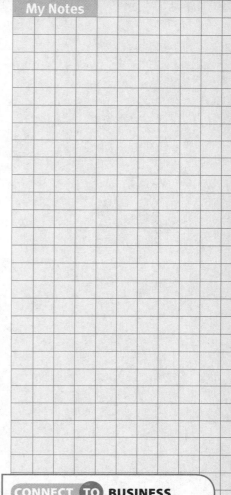

My Notes

CONNECT TO BUSINESS

A business plan tells potential investors, people who loan you money to start your business, what you plan to do and how much this will cost.

MATH TIP

Recall that proportions are "equivalent ratios." One example of a proportion is $\frac{1}{2} = \frac{50}{100}$.

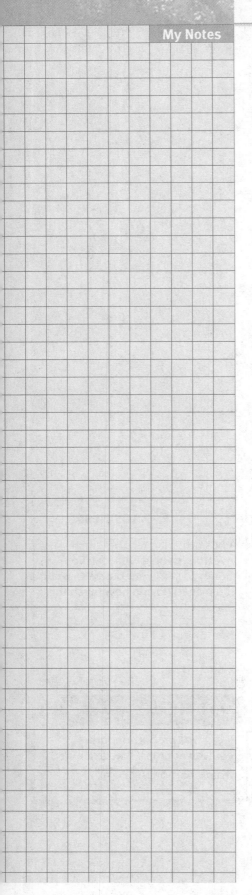

My Notes

This is the example that he showed Isaac.

Example A

25 is what percent of 80?

Step 1: Set up the proportion.

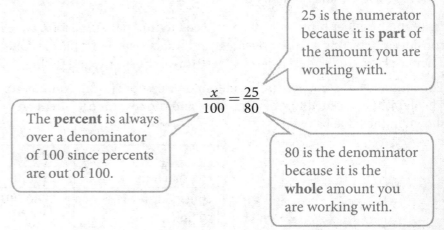

25 is the numerator because it is **part** of the amount you are working with.

$$\frac{x}{100} = \frac{25}{80}$$

The **percent** is always over a denominator of 100 since percents are out of 100.

80 is the denominator because it is the **whole** amount you are working with.

Step 2: Solve the proportion.

$$80x = 25 \cdot 100$$
$$80x = 2{,}500$$
$$\frac{80x}{80} = \frac{2{,}500}{80}$$
$$x = 31.25$$

Solution: When rounded to the nearest whole percent, 25 is 31% of 80.

Try These A

Find the percent the fog machine is of the total budget. Write the proportion used to solve the problem and show any work needed to solve the proportion. Round to the nearest whole percent.

2. Find the percents the other items are of the total budget. Round to the nearest whole percent. What is the sum of the percents?

3. When finding percents, can the answer ever be greater than 100%? Give an example illustrating why or why not.

Check Your Understanding

4. 18 is what percent of 96?

5. Isaac wanted to earn $200 of the startup equipment cost for the deejay business. What percent of $2,500 is this?

6. The boys' aunt wanted to contribute $2,100 toward the cost. What percent of $2,500 is this?

LESSON 21-1 PRACTICE

7. $300 is what percent of $3,200?

8. Construct arguments. Suppose Nate and Isaac wanted to add another item to their list of startup equipment. Use an example to describe how you would find the percent this item's cost is of the total budget.

9. Nate and Isaac decided they also needed a work schedule to accommodate their deejay business. They planned to spend 12 out of 20 work hours per week performing as deejays. What percent is this?

10. Isaac predicted that advertising their business would add an additional $400 out of the $900 the brothers were adding to the equipment cost. What percent is $400 out of the additional amount they were adding?

11. Isaac's parents paid $3,200 per month to rent an office space for their own business. Of this amount, $352 was for utilities. What percent of their rental cost was for utilities?

12. Use a proportion to determine what percent $1,800 of the $2,500 startup cost is.

13. Reason quantitatively. Nate found sound amplifiers online for $150 off the price of $990, although he did not buy them. About what percent would he have saved on the speakers if he had bought them?

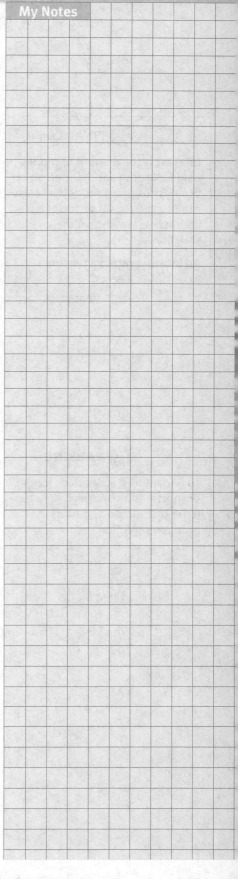
My Notes

Learning Targets:

- Solve real-world problems to find the part, given the whole and the percent.
- Use ratio and rate reasoning to solve real-world and mathematical problems.

SUGGESTED LEARNING STRATEGIES: Marking the Text, Summarizing, Create a Plan, Identify a Subtask

The boys' parents decided the business would be a good investment and loaned them the money. However, Nate and Isaac would have to pay interest when they paid the loan back in one year.

1. When dealing with interest, how can you determine if the interest is going to be paid to you or if it will be paid to someone else?

Simple interest on a loan for one year can be determined using a proportion. If you know the percent and the total, you can find the part. Remember to set up the proportion using the information you know from the problem.

Example A

Find the interest for a 2% interest rate loan of $3,000 for 1 year.

Step 1: Set up a proportion.

> The **part** is the variable because we do not know the interest amount for the loan.

> This time we know the **percent.** It is 2%. The percent is always the numerator over 100 since percents are out of 100.

$$\frac{2}{100} = \frac{x}{3,000}$$

> $3,000 is in the denominator because it is the **whole** amount of the loan.

Step 2: Solve the proportion.

$$100x = 2 \cdot 3,000$$
$$100x = 6,000$$
$$\frac{100x}{100} = \frac{6,000}{100}$$
$$x = 60$$

Solution: The interest is $60 on a $3,000 loan at a rate of 2% for 1 year.

My Notes

CONNECT **TO** **FINANCE**

Interest is the amount of money paid for letting another person or business use your money. Interest can be paid to you or you can pay interest depending on the situation.

An **interest rate** is a percent used to compute interest.

CONNECT **TO** **BANKING**

To find interest for periods longer or shorter than one year, time has to be considered as part of the problem's solution.

Try These A

a. How much will the interest be for a $500 loan at 6% interest for one year?

b. If 40% of 240 minutes of music are slow songs, how many minutes of slow songs will there be?

c. The future deejays know that they cannot expect that all customers will give them a top rating. If 85% of the customers are extremely happy with their work, how many customers out of 120 should they expect to be extremely happy?

d. The loan that Nate and Isaac got from their parents was at 2% interest for one year. How much will the boys pay in interest on their loan of $2,500? Show your work.

Nate and Isaac have now picked out and purchased equipment. Next, they need to set their prices. To do this, they decide to look at advertisements for other deejay businesses and find an average price. They decide to charge $649 for 4 hours of service. In addition, they are going to charge $200 for each hour that they work beyond 4 hours.

2. How much would an event that lasted 6 hours cost the customer? Show your work.

After the first month, the brothers found that they were not getting as many jobs as they thought they would. They decided to offer a summer **discount** to get more business.

Summer Discount
15% off

Let Us Deejay Your Next Event!

3. a. Construct viable arguments. Is a discount added to or subtracted from the total? Explain your thinking and give a real-life example.

MATH TERMS

The **average** price is the mean price. The mean is determined by adding the prices found and dividing this total by the number of prices found.

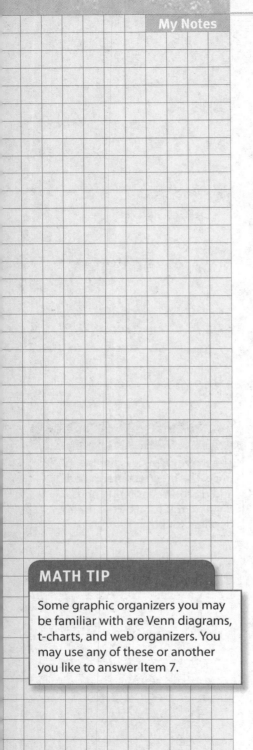

My Notes

b. What is the difference between a $25 discount and a 25% discount?

4. Use a proportion to determine what 15% of the $649 base rate is.

5. Explain how to find the discounted amount they will offer their customers. What is the discounted amount?

Nate and Isaac have gotten quite a few jobs using their discounted price. In fact, with the holiday season approaching, they feel they can raise their price above the original price of $649 for 4 hours.

6. They decide to mark up the price of $649 by 10%.
   a. What is a **markup**?

   b. Give an example of a markup that you have seen on clothing or other items.

   c. Use a proportion to find the amount that the price will be marked up.

   d. Using the original amount and the markup you just found, determine their new price for 4 hours of work.

MATH TIP

Some graphic organizers you may be familiar with are Venn diagrams, t-charts, and web organizers. You may use any of these or another you like to answer Item 7.

7. How are markups and discounts the same and different? You may use a graphic organizer to help show your thinking.

Lesson 21-2
Find the Part Given a Percent and the Whole

Check Your Understanding

8. Find 45% of $649.

9. Isaac found a wireless microphone online at a sale price of 32% off.
  a. What is 32% of $250.00?
  b. What is the final price after the discount?
  c. Describe another way you could calculate the final price using a different percent.

10. Nate's mother wanted to buy some jewelry until she found out it was marked up 400%. If the original jewelry cost $100, what was the final price of the jewelry?

11. Explain why markup is necessary for retail sales.

LESSON 21-2 PRACTICE

12. What is 108% of 112?

13. Draw a group of 15 identical music CDs or other simple figures. Shade 60% of the figures. Explain how you know that you shaded 60%.

14. Isaac played a video game 20 times and won about 70% of the games. How many games did he win?

15. Nate tells his mom that he took a test with 60 questions and scored 85%. How many questions did he answer correctly? Show how you know.

16. Reason abstractly. In a survey of 398 students, 52% said they loved music. Use estimation to explain about how many students loved music.

17. Make sense of problems. Which costs less to buy, a $1,000 computer that is discounted 20% and then offered at an additional 10% off, or a $1,000 computer that is discounted 30%? Explain.

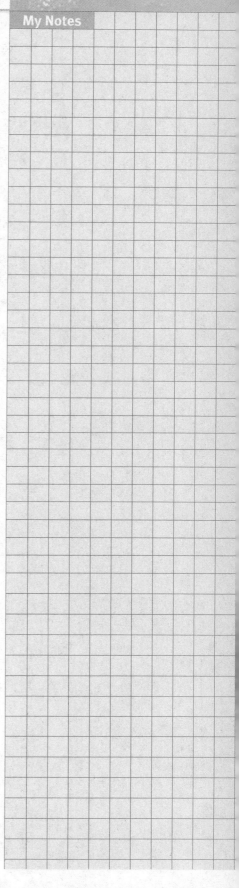

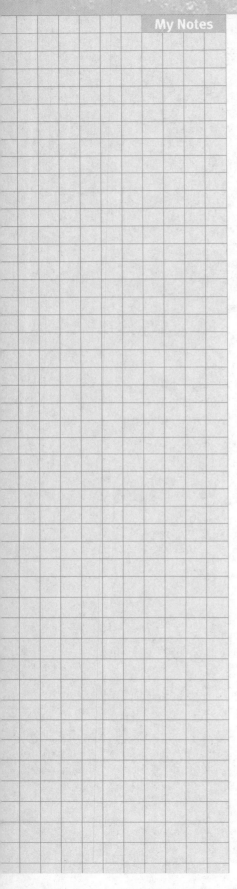

Learning Targets:

- Solve problems to find the whole given a part and the percent.
- Represent ratios and percents with fractions and decimals.
- Represent benchmark percents such as 1%, 10%, 25%, and $33\frac{1}{3}\%$, and multiples of these values using number lines and numbers.
- Use equivalent percents, fractions, and decimals to show parts of the same whole.

SUGGESTED LEARNING STRATEGIES: Marking the Text, Graphic Organizer, Note Taking, Identify a Subtask

Nate and Isaac need to have access to thousands of songs. They both have MP3 players and are using them to create playlists for the business. Nate's MP3 player shows that he has used 53% of the memory. He can't quite remember how much his MP3 player holds, but knows that he can find out using a proportion.

53%

Example A

There are 9.4 hours of music left on Nate's playlist, and this is 47% of the total memory. How much memory does Nate's MP3 player have?

Step 1: Set up a proportion.

> The part is 9.4 because that is the part of the memory remaining.

$$\frac{47}{100} = \frac{9.4}{x}$$

> The variable is in the denominator because we do not know the whole (total) amount of memory of the MP3 player.

Step 2: Solve the proportion.

$$47x = 9.4 \cdot 100$$
$$47x = 940$$
$$\frac{47x}{47} = \frac{940}{47}$$
$$x = 20$$

Solution: Nate's MP3 player can hold 20 hours worth of playlists.

Lesson 21-3
Find the Whole Given a Part and the Percent

Try These A

Make sense of problems. Using a decimal equivalent to the percent, write another equation you could have solved to find the total memory of Nate's MP3 player.

1. Set up and solve a proportion.
   a. Nate worked for 28 hours last week. This is 40% of the total hours he worked this month. How much did he work this month?

   b. Isaac's part of the check at dinner was $18.00 and he was paying 25% of the total bill. How much was the total bill?

   c. The brothers' music project at school was worth 44 points. This is 88% of the total number of points possible. Using a decimal equivalent to the percent, write an equation to find the total number of points possible on the project. Then solve the equation.

Check Your Understanding

2. Are tips added or subtracted from the total bill? Explain.

3. Nate paid $108 for a food bill that included a 15% tip. Using a decimal equivalent to the percent, write an equation to find the total amount of the bill. Then solve the equation.

4. Some of the students at Beats Middle School say that proportions make working with percents easier. Do you agree or disagree? Explain your reasoning.

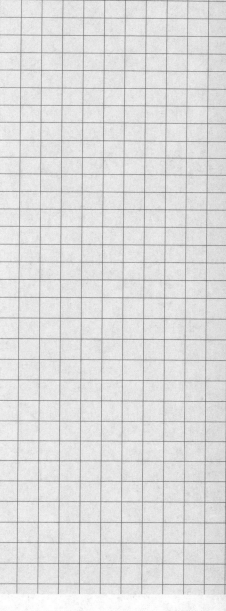

My Notes

CONNECT **TO** **SOCIAL STUDIES**

Sales tax is collected by the local or state government to help pay for services to people who live in the city or state that collects the tax.

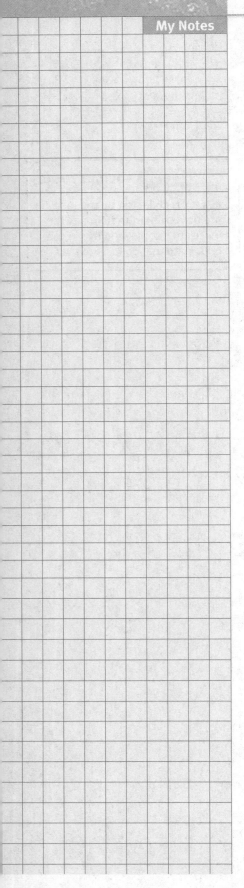

My Notes

LESSON 21-3 PRACTICE

5. An entertainment news reporter stated that "about $33\frac{1}{3}$% of Americans love listening to deejays, which is about 106,000,000 people." At the time the reporter made that statement, about how many people were in the United States?

6. 62% of Nate's class came to see one of his performances. If 186 students saw his performance, how many students are in Nate's class?

7. Isaac and Nate made enough money to pay off their startup loan and go shopping. Nate wants to buy a pair of basketball shoes that are on sale for 35% off. If Nate paid $70, what was the original cost of the shoes?

8. A compact MP3 player costs $52 after 4.5% sales tax. What was the original price?

9. Nate ordered a pizza to be delivered. The bill with 5% tax and 20% tip was $24.00. What was the original cost of the pizza?

10. Isaac's mother gave him a subscription to an entertainment magazine for his birthday. The magazine was offered at 56% off of the cover price. She paid $1.98 an issue. What was the cover price of the magazine?

11. **Reason abstractly.** Explain why the solutions to $\frac{12}{w} = \frac{25}{100}$ and $12 = 25\% \times w$ are the same.

ACTIVITY 21 PRACTICE
Write your answers on notebook paper. Show your work.

Lesson 21-1

1. 54 out of 72 of Isaac's songs in a CD collection are pop songs. What percent of this CD collection are pop songs?

2. Write each amount as a percent.
   a. 23 songs out of 92
   b. $8 of $24 earned as profit

3. Nate tells his mom about a great deal he found on MP3 players. "They were originally $110.60 but now they are on sale for $88.48!" Use percents to determine whether this is a good deal. Explain your answer.

4. At the end of one performance, the total that Isaac received was $750. This included a tip for the usual fee of $649. What percent was the tip?

5. Nate's savings account for the business had $12.10 more at the end of the year than the $252 it had at the beginning of the year. What percent more was in the savings account?
   A. 2.4%   B. 4.6%
   C. 4.8%   D. 48%

6. A subwoofer box for sound costs $260.40 after a price increase. The cost before the price increase was $240.00. What was the approximate percent of the price increase?
   A. 7.8%   B. 8.3%
   C. 8.5%   D. 9%

Lesson 21-2

7. The wholesale price of a special speaker was $64. It was then marked up 85% and sold online. What was the online price?

8. Isaac gave the receipt below to a customer as a bill. The customer was asked to fill in the blanks. What was the amount of the total bill?

> **THANK YOU!**
>
> **IN Deejay Service**
>
> **Fee = $850.00**
>
> **20% Tip = $_____**
>
> **Total Bill = $_____**

   A. $170   B. $680
   C. $708.33   D. $1,020

9. The extra audio parts that would have cost $118 at a supply store increased by 6.75%. What was the new cost of these parts?

10. Which of the pairs of values will give the equivalent final sale price?
    A. a discount of 20% off of $80
    B. a sale of $\frac{1}{4}$ off the original price of $100
    C. a markup of 150% on $30

11. Isaac's father earned 5.2% interest on his investments last year. If he had $40,000 invested, what was the balance in his account at the end of the year?
    A. $2,080   B. $42,000
    C. $42,080   D. $63,840

12. The sales tax on a $120 bill is 7.25%. After a coupon discount of 10% off the total cost with tax, what was the final amount of the bill?
A. $99.30 **B.** $115.03
C. $115.83 **D.** $128.70

13. Complete the table by finding the percent of each number. Describe the relationship you see among the values in each column.

	10%	25%	$33\frac{1}{3}$%
$120			
$240			
$360			

Lesson 21-3

14. How much money must Nate deposit in a savings account that pays 4% simple annual interest to earn $50 the first year?

15. The interest on several accounts is shown below. Each interest rate is simple annual interest. Which account balance was the highest at the beginning of the year?
A. $42 interest earned at 2.8%
B. $48 interest earned at 2.5%
C. $50 interest earned at 2.2%
D. $45 interest earned at 3.1%

16. Nate hears that $33\frac{1}{3}$% of the teen clubs in his area, or 6 clubs, offer discount tickets to students. Write an equation that could be used to determine the total number of teen clubs in the area.

17. Nate estimates that a search for websites about music produces 500,000 websites. If this is a 12% increase over the previous year, explain how you would find the number of websites for the previous year. Then find the approximate number of websites the previous year.

18. Nate knew that most mobile phones also included music players. In 2012, the number of mobile phones in Italy was 147.4% of the population. If the number of mobile phones was 88,600,000 in Italy in 2012, what was the approximate population?

19. Nate is selling a DVD of one performance for $19.99. This is the price after a discount of 25%. What was the original price of the DVD?
A. $14.99 **B.** $25.00
C. $26.65 **D.** $79.96

MATHEMATICAL PRACTICES
Reason Quantitatively

20. People often leave tips between 10% and 25% at the teen clubs where the boys deejay, depending on how well they like the service and music. What was the price range of the original bill if a tip of $22 was given?

Understanding and Applying Percents
AN ICE CREAM TREAT

Write your answers on notebook paper. Show your work.

Every month the Incredible Ice Cream Shop sends a card with a coupon for a free ice cream treat to the members of their ice cream club who were born in that month. The number of members and their birthday month is shown below.

Month	Number of Club Members Born in the Month	Month	Number of Club Members Born in the Month
January	6	July	24
February	12	August	11
March	18	September	18
April	14	October	14
May	10	November	27
June	13	December	33

1. What percent of the total number of coupons are sent out in October through December? Explain your reasoning.

2. Give the fraction, decimal, and percent that represent the number of club member birthdays in January, February, March, April, and June in the table below. Round to the nearest whole percent.

Month	Number	Fraction	Decimal	Percent
January				
February				
March				
April				
June				

3. The manager of the ice cream shop noticed that 90% of all club members brought along a family member who spent an average of $18 in the shop. The tax on their bill was 5.5%.
   a. What was the total amount spent by the family members in one year?
   b. What would each family member have to spend, on average, to generate $5,000 in income before sales tax?
   c. What would each family member's average bill be with sales tax?

Scoring Guide	Exemplary	Proficient	Emerging	Incomplete
	The solution demonstrates these characteristics:			
Mathematics Knowledge and Thinking (Items 1, 2, 3a-c)	• Effective understanding and accuracy in calculating percents and finding a part given a percent.	• Few if any errors in calculating percents and finding a part given a percent.	• Multiple errors in calculating percents and finding a part given a percent.	• Incorrect or incomplete understanding of calculating percents and finding a part given a percent.
Problem Solving (Items 3a-c)	• An appropriate and efficient strategy that results in a correct answer. • Accurate interpretation of a percent to solve a problem.	• A strategy that may include unnecessary steps but results in a correct answer. • Interpretation of a percent to solve a problem.	• A strategy that results in some incorrect answers. • Difficulty interpreting a percent to solve a problem.	• No clear strategy when solving problems. • Incorrect interpretation of a percent to solve a problem.
Mathematical Modeling / Representations (Item 2)	• Clear and accurate understanding of writing a ratio as a fraction, a decimal, and as a percent.	• Writing a ratio as a fraction, a decimal, and as a percent with few or no errors.	• Difficulty writing a ratio as a fraction, a decimal, and as a percent.	• Little or no understanding of writing a ratio as a fraction, a decimal, and as a percent.
Reasoning and Communication (Item 1)	• Precise use of math terms and language to explain calculating a percent.	• An adequate explanation of calculating a percent.	• A misleading or confusing explanation of calculating a percent.	• An incomplete or inaccurate explanation of calculating a percent.

Geometric Concepts

Unit Overview

In this unit you will extend your study of polygons as you investigate properties of triangles and quadrilaterals. You will study area, surface area, and volume of two- and three-dimensional figures.

Key Terms

As you study this unit, add these and other terms to your math notebook. Include in your notes your prior knowledge of each word, as well as your experiences in using the word in different mathematical examples. If needed, ask for help in pronouncing new words and add information on pronunciation to your math notebook. It is important that you learn new terms and use them correctly in your class discussions and in your problem solutions.

Academic Vocabulary

- composite

Math Terms

- theorem
- equiangular
- polygon
- quadrilateral
- consecutive angles
- perimeter
- area
- altitude
- net
- prism
- rectangular prism
- triangular prism
- volume

ESSENTIAL QUESTIONS

? In what ways are geometric figures used in real life?

? Why is it important to understand the characteristics of two- and three-dimensional figures?

EMBEDDED ASSESSMENTS

These assessments, following activities 24 and 26, will give you an opportunity to demonstrate how to find areas and perimeters of triangles and quadrilaterals as well as find the surface area and volume of prisms to solve mathematical and real-world problems.

Embedded Assessment 1:

Geometric Concepts   p. 315

Embedded Assessment 2:

Surface Area and
Volume of Prisms   p. 343

1. Name each of the following geometric figures.

a   b   c   d   e

2. Name the geometric figures in the diagram below.

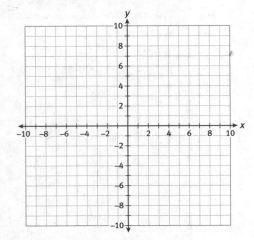

3. Find the perimeter of the figures pictured.

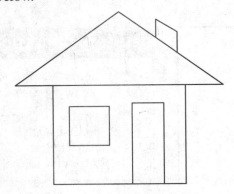

4. Give three characteristics of the following figures.
   a. square   b. rectangle
   c. right triangle d. cube

5. Plot each point on the coordinate plane.

   $A(-2, 3)$ $B(4, 5)$ $C(6, -1)$ $D(-5, -3)$ $E(2, 0)$

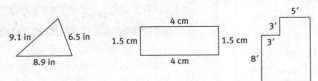

6. State the coordinates of each point.

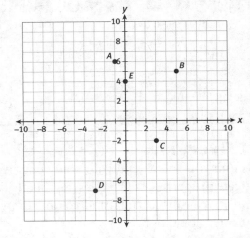

7. Draw a rectangle on the grid below that has a perimeter of 20 units.

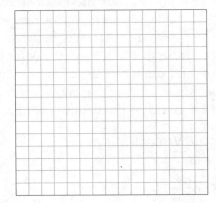

8. Roger is creating designs with pieces of wood. One piece is an equilateral triangle with a perimeter of 24 inches. Another piece is a rectangle with one side the same length as a side of the triangle. The other side of the rectangle is 3 inches shorter than a side of the triangle. Roger places the pieces together so that one side of the triangle touches a side of the rectangle that has the same length.
   a. What are the dimensions of the triangle?
   b. What are the dimensions of the rectangle?
   c. Draw a sketch of the composite figure.
   d. Find the perimeter of the composite figure.

Angles and Triangles

Triangle Trivia
Lesson 22-1 Properties of Triangles and Side Lengths

Learning Targets:

- Determine when three side lengths form a triangle.
- Use the Triangle Inequality Property.
- Classify triangles by side length.

> **SUGGESTED LEARNING STRATEGIES:** Interactive Word Wall, Summarizing, Look for a Pattern, Graphic Organizer

Students in Mr. Mira's math class made up some geometry games. Here are the rules for the game Matt and Allie created.

Triangle Trivia Rules Properties of Triangles—Perimeter Variation	
Players:	Three to four students
Materials:	Three number cubes and a "segment pieces" set of three each of the following lengths: 1 inch, 2 inches, 3 inches, 4 inches, 5 inches, and 6 inches.
Directions:	Take turns. Roll the three number cubes. Find a segment piece to match each number rolled. See whether a triangle can be formed from those segment pieces. The value of the perimeter of any triangle that can be formed is added to that player's score. The first player to reach 50 points wins.

Amir wonders what the game has to do with triangles.

1. Play the game above to see how it relates to triangles. Follow the rules. Record your results in the table.

Player 1		Player 2		Player 3		Player 4	
Numbers	**Score**	**Numbers**	**Score**	**Numbers**	**Score**	**Numbers**	**Score**

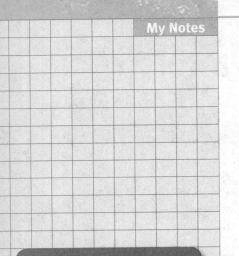

MATH TIP

When sides of a figure have the same length, this can be shown by drawing marks, called tick marks, on those sides. For example, the equal sides of the isosceles and equilateral triangles in the table below right have the same number of tick marks.

2. There is more to the game than just adding numbers. How does the game relate to triangles?

Amir noticed that he could tell whether the lengths would form a triangle even without the segment pieces.

3. Explain how Amir can determine whether a triangle can be formed from three given lengths.

Matt and Allie's game illustrates the following property that relates the side lengths of a triangle.

Triangle Inequality Property

For any triangle, the sum of any two sides must be greater than the length of the third side.

Before students play another game, Mr. Mira wants to review the vocabulary terms *scalene*, *isosceles*, and *equilateral* with the class. He draws the following examples of triangles.

Scalene Triangles	Isosceles Triangles	Equilateral Triangles
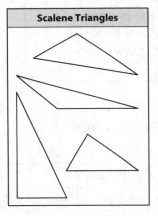	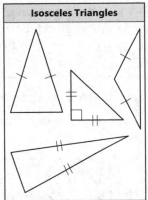	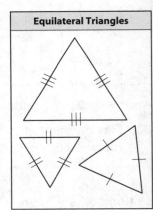

4. Based on Mr. Mira's examples, describe each type of triangle.

    a. scalene triangle

    b. isosceles triangle

    c. equilateral triangle

Amir creates a variation of Matt and Allie's game. Here are the rules for Amir's game.

MATH TIP

A triangle can be identified as scalene, isosceles, or equilateral by the lengths of its sides.

Triangle Trivia Rules - Name the Triangle	
Players:	Three to four students
Materials:	Three number cubes

Directions:	Take turns rolling three number cubes.
	• If you can, form
	    a scalene triangle ....add 5 points
	    an isosceles triangle ....add 10 points
	    an equilateral triangle .....add 15 points
	    no triangle ....add 0 points
	• If you make a mistake, deduct 10 points from your last correct score.
	• The first player to reach 25 points wins.

5. Make use of structure. When playing Amir's variation of Triangle Trivia, suppose that the cubes landed on the following numbers. Tell how many points you would add to your score and why.

    a. 5, 5, 5

    b. 1, 6, 4

    c. 3, 2, 4

    d. 6, 6, 4

    e. 1, 4, 1

Share your responses with your group members. Make notes as you listen to other members of your group. Ask and answer questions clearly to aid comprehension and to ensure understanding of all group members' ideas.

My Notes

Check Your Understanding

6. Can a triangle be formed using the side lengths below? If so, is the triangle scalene, isosceles, or equilateral? Explain.
  a. 4 m, 4 m, and 8 m
  b. 8 ft, 6 ft, and 4 ft

7. If three segments form a triangle, what must be true about the sum of any two side lengths of the triangle?

LESSON 22-1 PRACTICE

For Items 8–14, use the Triangle Inequality Property to determine whether a triangle can be formed with the given side lengths in inches. If a triangle can be formed, classify the triangle by the lengths of its sides. Explain your thinking.

8. $a = 5, b = 5, c = 5$

9. $a = 3, b = 3, c = 7$

10. $a = 7, b = 4, c = 4$

11. $a = 8, b = 4, c = 5$

12. $a = 1, b = 2, c = 8$

13. $a = 8, b = 12, c = 4$

14. $a = 12, b = 5, c = 13$

15. Which of the following are possible side lengths of a triangle?
  A. 12, 20, 15
  B. 33, 20, 12
  C. 12, 20, 11

16. Reason abstractly. Is it necessary to find the sum of all three possible pairs of side lengths to use the Triangle Inequality Property when deciding if the sides form a triangle? Include an example in your explanation.

17. Construct viable arguments. Two sides of a triangle are 9 and 11 centimeters long.
  a. What is the shortest possible length in whole centimeters for the third side?
  b. What is the longest possible length in whole centimeters for the third side?

Learning Targets:

- Classify angles by their measures.
- Classify triangles by their angles.
- Recognize the relationship between the lengths of sides and measures of angles in a triangle.
- Recognize the sum of angles in a triangle.

SUGGESTED LEARNING STRATEGIES: Interactive Word Wall, Summarizing, Visualization, Graphic Organizer

Another way to classify triangles is by their angles. A *right* angle has a measure of 90°. An *acute* angle has a measure of less than 90°. An *obtuse* angle is greater than 90° and less than 180°.

1. Use the angles shown.

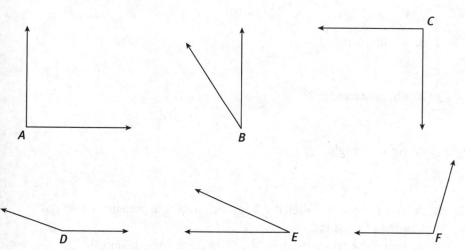

a. Estimate the measure of each angle.

$\angle A \approx$ $\angle B \approx$ $\angle C \approx$

$\angle D \approx$ $\angle E \approx$ $\angle F \approx$

b. Use appropriate tools strategically. Use a protractor to find the measure of each angle to the nearest degree. Then classify each angle as acute, obtuse, or right by its measure.

$\angle A =$ $\angle B =$ $\angle C =$

$\angle D =$ $\angle E =$ $\angle F =$

My Notes

MATH TIP

If the rays are too short to measure with a protractor, extend the length of the sides of the angle.

My Notes

MATH TIP

A box at the vertex of an angle indicates an angle with measure 90°.

Now Mr. Mira draws the following examples of triangles.

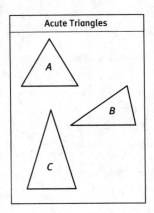

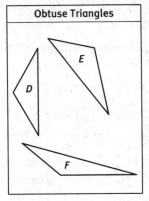

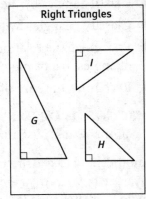

2. Based on Mr. Mira's examples, describe each type of triangle.

   a. acute triangle

   b. obtuse triangle

   c. right triangle

3. A triangle can be labeled using both its angle measures and the lengths of its sides.
   a. Label the triangles that Mr. Mira drew by side length.

   b. Choose one of the triangles and give the two labels that describe it.

   c. Explain how the two labels together provide a better description of the triangle than either one alone. Share your ideas with our group and be sure to explain your thoughts using precise language and specific details to help group members understand your ideas and reasoning.

Lesson 22-2
Properties of Triangles and Angle Measures

Mr. Mira has his class investigate the sum of the measures of a triangle. Students measured the angles of some scalene, isosceles, and equilateral triangles. They recorded their results as shown.

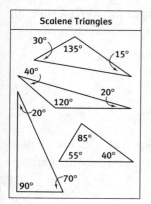

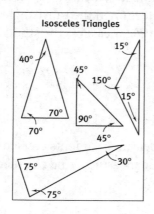

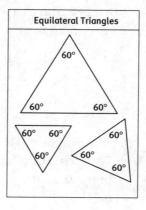

4. a. Find the sum of the angle measures for each triangle.

The **Triangle Sum _Theorem_** states that the sum of the three angle measures in any triangle is always equal to a certain number.

b. What is the sum of the angle measures in any triangle?

> **MATH TERMS**
>
> A **theorem** is a statement or conjecture that has been proven to be true.

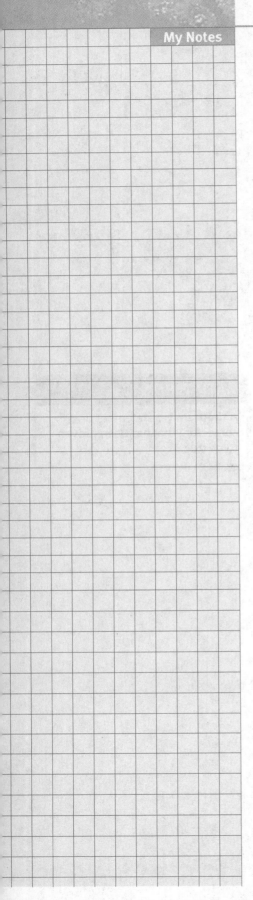

My Notes

The Triangle Sum Theorem allows you to find the measure of the third angle in a triangle when you are given the other two angle measures.

5. Students played a game in which they chose two angle measures of a triangle and then determined the third angle measure. What must be true about the two angle measures the students choose?

6. Some of the angle measures students created for triangles are shown. For each pair of angle measures, find the measure of the third angle in the triangle.
   a. 43°, 94°

   b. 38°, 52°

   c. 57°, 39°

   d. 140°, 12°

   e. 60°, 60°

The angle measures of a triangle can be used to determine if the triangle is scalene, isosceles, or equilateral. Look back at the triangles Mr. Mira drew.

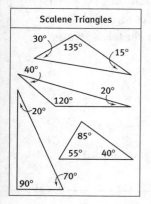

Scalene Triangles

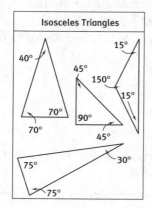

Isosceles Triangles

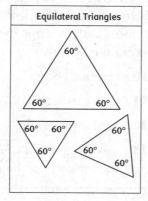

Equilateral Triangles

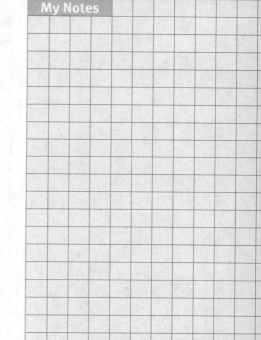

7. Compare the angle measures of the triangles. Look for patterns in Mr. Mira's examples to help you determine if the triangles described below are scalene, isosceles, or equilateral.

   a. a triangle with three different angle measures

   b. a triangle with exactly two congruent angle measures

   c. an *equiangular* triangle

8. Look back at Item 6. Classify each triangle by its side lengths and by its angle measures.

MATH TERMS

A triangle with three equal angles is called **equiangular.**

Another relationship exists between the angles and the sides of a triangle. In a triangle, the side opposite the angle with the greatest measure is the longest side.

9. Compare the angle measure to the side opposite the angle in a scalene triangle. What is true about the side opposite the angle with the least measure?

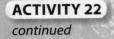

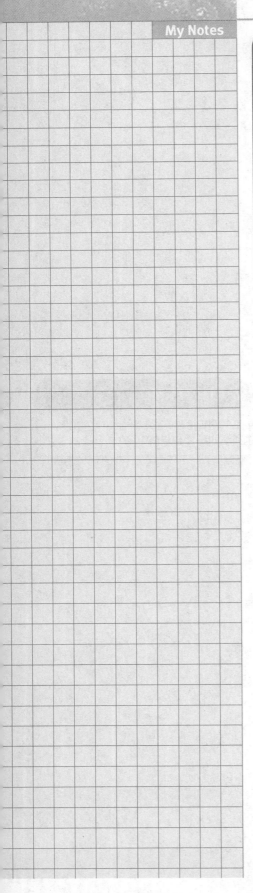

Check Your Understanding

For Items 10–12, sketch a triangle described by each pair of words below or state that it is not possible. Use tick marks and right angle symbols where appropriate. If it is not possible to sketch a triangle, explain why not.

10. scalene, obtuse

11. isosceles, acute

12. equilateral, right

13. Two angles in a triangle measure 35° and 50°. Explain how to find the measure of the third angle.

LESSON 22-2 PRACTICE

For Items 14–19, sketch a triangle described by each pair of words below or state that it is not possible. If it is not possible to sketch a triangle, explain why not.

14. scalene, right

15. isosceles, obtuse

16. equilateral, acute

17. isosceles, right

18. scalene, acute

19. equilateral, obtuse

20. Use appropriate tools strategically. Use a ruler and a protractor to sketch a triangle that is scalene and has an angle that measures 30°. Is the triangle acute, right, or obtuse? Explain.

21. Two angles in a triangle measure 65° each. What is the measure of the third angle?

22. Reason quantitatively and abstractly. Find the missing angle measure or measures in each triangle below. Then classify the triangle by both its angle measures and its side lengths.
  a. The three angles in a triangle have the same measure.
  b. Two angles in a triangle measure 45° each.
  c. Two angles in a triangle measure 25° and 50°.

23. Construct viable arguments. Determine whether each statement below is *always true, sometimes true, or never true*. Explain your reasoning.
  a. The acute angles of an isosceles triangle add up to 90°.
  b. An isosceles triangle has two equal angles.
  c. An equilateral triangle has a right angle.
  d. The largest angle of a scalene triangle can be opposite the shortest side.

ACTIVITY 22 PRACTICE
Write your answers on a separate piece of paper.
Show your work.

Lesson 22-1

1. The side lengths of a triangle are 16 cm, 9 cm, and 16 cm. Classify the triangle using its side lengths.

2. The side lengths of a triangle are 23, 14, and 30 yards. Classify the triangle using these side lengths.

3. Classify the triangles below using their side lengths.
   a. 7 ft, 24 ft, 21 ft
   b. 9 cm, 9 cm, 9 cm
   c. 35 mm, 25 mm, 35 mm

For Items 4–13, use the Triangle Inequality Property to determine whether a triangle can be formed with the given side lengths in centimeters. If a triangle can be formed, classify the triangle using the side lengths.

4. $a = 2, b = 2, c = 5$

5. $a = 6, b = 3, c = 8$

6. $a = 3, b = 5, c = 5$

7. $a = 4, b = 5, c = 9$

8. $a = 11, b = 7, c = 6$

9. $a = 16, b = 16, c = 16$

10. $a = 21, b = 9, c = 21$

11. $a = 32, b = 5, c = 25$

12. $a = 13, b = 13, c = 30$

13. $a = 14, b = 25, c = 19$

14. Which of the following are possible side lengths of a triangle?
    A. 5, 8, 13
    B. 8, 21, 16
    C. 11, 60, 61

15. Two sides of a triangle are 18 and 20 feet long. What is the shortest the third side of the triangle could be? What is the longest the triangle's third side could be? Explain your reasoning.

16. Two sides of a triangle are 4 meters and 12 meters long. Which of the following is **not** a possible length of the third side?
    A. 8 meters   B. 12 meters
    C. 9 meters   D. 15 meters

Lesson 22-2

17. Use a protractor to determine the measure of the angle.

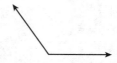

18. Identify Triangle *ABC* by side length and angle measure. Use appropriate measuring tools to justify your answer.

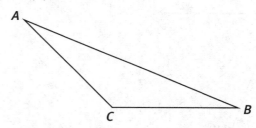

19. Sketch a triangle described by each pair of words below or state that it is not possible and explain why not. Use tick marks and right angle symbols where appropriate.
    a. scalene, acute
    b. isosceles, obtuse
    c. equilateral, right

For Items 20–25, find the measure of the numbered angle in each triangle.

20.

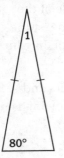

21.

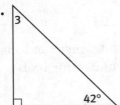

22.

23.

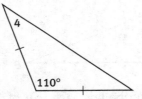

24.

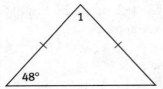

25.

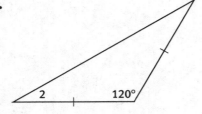

For Items 26–30, two angle measures of a triangle are given. Find the missing angle measure in each triangle. Then classify the triangle by both angle measures and side lengths.

26. 32°; 58°

27. 162°; 9°

28. 60°; 60°

29. 43°, 74°

30. 27°; 63°

31. One of the angle measures of a right triangle is 36°. Which of the following is the measure of one of the other two angles of the triangle?
   A. 36°   **B.** 44°
   C. 54°   **D.** 144°

32. Two of the angles of a triangle measure 42° and 67°. The side opposite which angle of the triangle is the longest side? Explain your reasoning.

33. Explain why it is not possible to draw an isosceles triangle with one angle that measures 52° and a second angle that measures 74°.

34. Remi says that every triangle must have at least two acute angles. Is Remi correct? Explain why or why not.

MATHEMATICAL PRACTICES
Express Regularity in Repeated Reasoning

35. Create a graphic organizer showing how triangles are classified using angle measures and side lengths. Include three labeled examples for angle measure and three examples for side length.

Area and Perimeter of Polygons

Play Area

Lesson 23-1 Recalling Quadrilaterals

Learning Targets:

- Define and classify quadrilaterals based on their properties.
- Use properties of quadrilaterals to determine missing side lengths and angle measures.

SUGGESTED LEARNING STRATEGIES: Interactive Word Wall, Marking the Text, Visualization, Think-Pair-Share, Create Representations, Use Manipulatives

The student council at QUAD Middle School is helping to plan a new playground. The three *polygons* shown are quadrilaterals, structures that will be included on the playground.

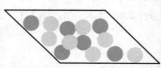

> **MATH TERMS**
>
> A **polygon** is a closed figure formed by three or more line segments that intersect only at their endpoints.
>
> A **quadrilateral** is a polygon with four sides.

The student council members want to understand the special properties of each *quadrilateral* to help them in their design. They did an Internet search and found quadrilaterals are grouped into three categories as shown in the table below.

Types of Quadrilaterals

Quadrilateral with no special name	Trapezoid	Parallelogram
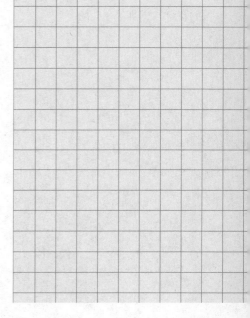		

> **MATH TIP**
>
> The arrowheads along opposite sides of the quadrilaterals indicate that those opposite sides are parallel.

1. Based on the categories in the table, describe the sides and angles in each type of quadrilateral.

    a. quadrilateral with no special name

    b. trapezoid

    c. parallelogram

My Notes

A parallelogram can sometimes be classified as a rectangle, a rhombus, or a square.

2. Model with mathematics. Using the given definitions, mark each diagram to appropriately illustrate the properties.

Rectangle: *Parallelogram with four right angles.*

Rhombus: *Parallelogram with four congruent sides.*

Square: *Parallelogram with four right angles and four congruent sides.*

3. The playground designer investigates the following quadrilaterals.

Quadrilateral 1   **Quadrilateral 2**

a. Use a ruler to measure the length of the sides of each quadrilateral to the nearest quarter of an inch. Label the measures of each side on the diagram.

b. List any patterns you notice about the side lengths in the quadrilaterals.

c. Use a protractor to determine the measure of each of the angles of the quadrilaterals to the nearest degree. Label the measures of each angle on the diagram.

d. List any patterns you notice about the angle measures in the quadrilaterals.

e. Make use of structure. Select the best name for each quadrilateral. Justify your answers.

The opposite sides of a parallelogram have the same length. The opposite angles of a parallelogram have the same measure, and any pair of **consecutive angles** add up to 180°.

4. Write the name of each figure in the Venn diagram below.

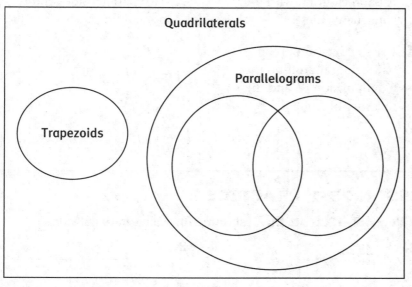

5. Use what you have learned about rhombi to find the missing length and angle measure.

$BT =$
$m\angle T =$

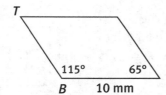

6. **a.** Use the definition of a square or a rectangle. Find the sum of the measures of the four angles of a square or a rectangle.

b. Use what you know about triangles to determine and justify that the sum of the measures of any quadrilateral is 360°.

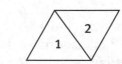

2 triangles times 180° = 360°

7. What is the measure of the fourth angle in a quadrilateral with angles measuring 90°, 70°, and 120°? Explain how you found it.

My Notes

MATH TERMS

Consecutive angles of a polygon are two angles with a side in common that do not overlap.

READING MATH

When referring to more than one rhombus, the terms **rhombuses** or **rhombi** can be used.

WRITING MATH

Write $\overline{AB}$ when you talk about segment AB.

Write AB when you talk about the length of AB.

Write $m\angle A$ when you talk about the "measure of angle A."

Check Your Understanding

For Items 8–9, write the best name for each quadrilateral.

8. A parallelogram with four congruent sides.

9. Two parallel sides and two nonparallel sides

10. Use the diagram of the parallelogram to find the length of side *PL* and the measure of angle *R*.

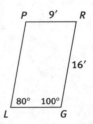

LESSON 23-1 PRACTICE

For Items 11–12, write the best name for each quadrilateral.

11.

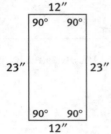

12.

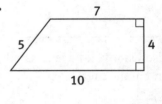

13. Use the diagram of the rectangle to find the length of side *AC* and the measure of angle *A*.

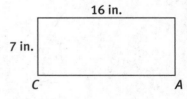

For Items 14 and 15, find the missing angle measure in the quadrilaterals shown.

14.

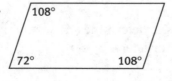

15.

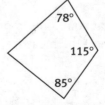

16. Jordan notices that the baseball infield is both equilateral and equiangular. What is the best quadrilateral name for the baseball infield? Explain your reasoning.

17. Construct viable arguments. Jordan claims that all squares can also be classified as either a rectangle or a rhombus, and Reyna claims that all rectangles and rhombuses can be classified as squares. Who is correct? Justify your answer.

Learning Targets:

- Model the area of a parallelogram by decomposing into triangles.
- Find the area of a special quadrilateral by decomposing into triangles.
- Write equations that represent problems related to the area of parallelograms and rectangles.
- Solve problems involving the area of parallelograms and rectangles.
- Find the area of special quadrilaterals and polygons by composing into rectangles or decomposing into triangles and other shapes.

SUGGESTED LEARNING STRATEGIES: Identify a Subtask, Use Manipulatives, Create Representations, Think-Pair-Share, Discussion Group, Sharing and Responding, Interactive Word Wall

Pictured is an *aerial view* of one of the possible playground designs. An aerial view is the view from above something.

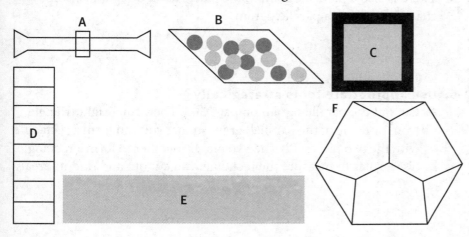

1. Look at the shape of each figure. What piece of playground equipment do you think each figure represents?

2. List all the geometric shapes you can identify in each figure in the playground to complete the table.

Figure	Geometric Shape(s)
A	
B	
C	
D	
E	
F	

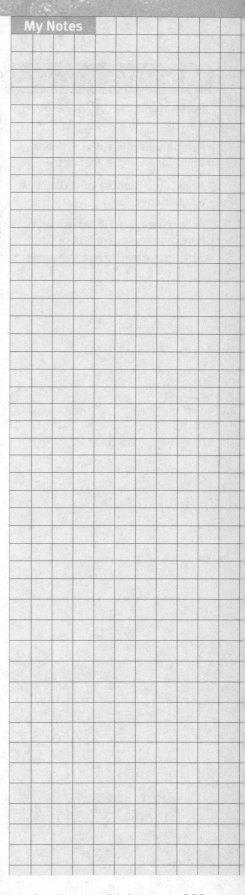

My Notes

My Notes

MATH TERMS

Perimeter is the distance around a figure.

Perimeter is measured in linear units, for example, feet or ft.

Area is the number of square units a figure covers.

Area is measured in square units, for example, square feet or ft^2.

3. The diagram shows the dimensions of Figure *E*.

   What is the **perimeter** of Figure *E*? Explain how you found the perimeter.

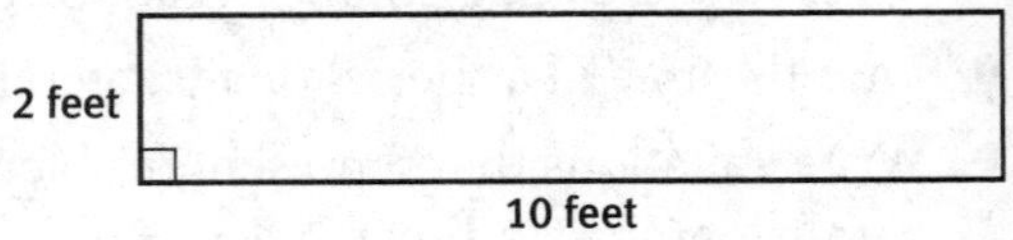

   2 feet

   10 feet

4. What is the **area** of Figure *E*? Explain how you found the area.

5. There is also a parallelogram in the playground design. List some characteristics of a parallelogram.

6. **Use appropriate tools strategically**
   a. Cut out the parallelogram on page 303. Then cut a right triangle from one side of the parallelogram so that you can form a rectangle with the two pieces. Put the two pieces together to form a rectangle.
   b. Use a ruler to measure the rectangle you cut out and find its area.

   c. How do the lengths of the base and the height of the rectangle formed from the parallelogram relate to those of the original parallelogram?

7. What is the relationship between the area of a parallelogram and its base and height? Describe the relationship using words, symbols, or both.

The area, *A*, of a rectangle or a parallelogram is equal to the length of the base, *b*, times the height, *h*: $A = b \times h$.

8. The diagram shows the dimensions of Figure *B*, the ball pit in the playground. What is the area of Figure *B*?

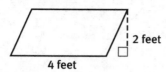

A *composite* figure is a figure that can be decomposed into two or more figures. You can find the area of a figure that can be decomposed, or divided, into rectangles and parallelograms.

9. Persevere in problem solving. The diagram shows the shape of a playground in a park.

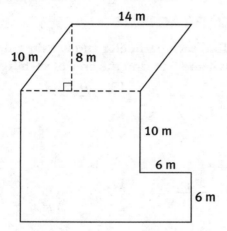

ACADEMIC VOCABULARY

Composite means made up of various separate parts or pieces.

a. Fill in missing dimensions on the playground. Then find the perimeter of the playground.

b. The playground can be decomposed into a parallelogram and two rectangles. Use a colored pencil to draw lines on the diagram to decompose the figure. Explain how to use the shapes you just drew to find the area of the playground.

c. Use the rules or equations you wrote in Items 4 and 7 to find the area of the playground. Justify your answer.

Check Your Understanding

For Items 10 and 11, find the perimeter and area of each figure.

10.
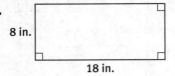
8 in.
18 in.

11.
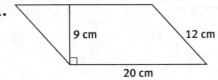
9 cm   12 cm
20 cm

12. Draw the rectangle that would result from rearranging the parallelogram in Item 11. How does the area of this rectangle compare to the area of the parallelogram in Item 11?

13. The area of a rectangle is 100 square feet. If the width is 25 feet, explain how to find the length of the base.

LESSON 23-2 PRACTICE

For Items 14–17, find each perimeter and use the rules or equations you wrote in Items 4 and 7 to find the area of each figure.

14.
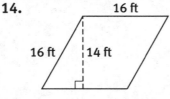
16 ft
16 ft   14 ft

15.
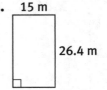
15 m
26.4 m

16.
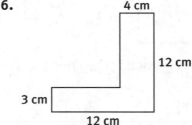
4 cm
12 cm
3 cm
12 cm

17.
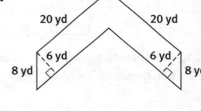
20 yd   20 yd
6 yd   6 yd
8 yd   8 yd

18. **Reason quantitatively.** A square tablecloth has a perimeter of 12 feet. What is the area of the tablecloth?

19. A square field has an area 121 square meters. What is the perimeter of the field?

20. The area of a parallelogram with a height of 6 meters is 126 square meters. What is the base length of the parallelogram?

21. A rectangular pool is 9 feet wide. The pool has an area of 117 square feet. What is the perimeter of the pool?

22. A rectangular floor is 12 feet wide and 18 feet long. How much will it cost to carpet the floor if the carpet costs $1.39 per square foot?

23. **Make sense of problems.** Jamie has to put 2 coats of paint on 6 rectangular walls. Each wall is 9 feet by 15 feet. Each can of paint covers 500 square feet. How many cans of paint should Jamie buy? Explain your thinking.

Learning Targets:

- Model area formulas for parallelograms, trapezoids, and triangles.
- Write equations that represent problems related to the area of trapezoids and triangles.
- Solve problems involving the area of trapezoids and triangles.
- Find the area of triangles, special quadrilaterals, and polygons.
- Model area formulas by decomposing and rearranging parts.
- Find the area of special quadrilaterals and polygons.

SUGGESTED LEARNING STRATEGIES: Identify a Subtask, Look for a Pattern, Discussion Groups, Sharing and Responding, Interactive Word Wall

The diagram shows the aerial view of climbing bars to be included in the playground. To find the area of the figure, decompose the polygon into other shapes. One of these shapes is a triangle.

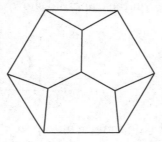

1. Use the congruent triangles on page 303.

- Cut out one of the triangles.
- Label one of its sides *b*.
- Draw the **altitude** of the triangle by drawing a line segment from a vertex perpendicular to side *b*. Label the segment *h*.
- Cut out the second triangle.
- Place the two triangles together to form a parallelogram whose base is the side labeled *b*.

2. How does the area of each triangle compare to the area of the parallelogram? Explain your thinking.

3. Using words, symbols, or both, describe a method for finding the area of a triangle.

My Notes

MATH TERMS

The **altitude** of a triangle is a perpendicular line segment from a vertex to the line containing the opposite side. The measure of an altitude is the *height*.

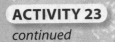
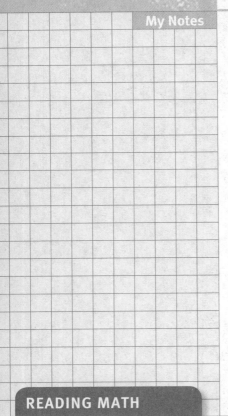

If you know the area of a triangle and the length of its base or its height, you can find the missing measure since the area, A, of a triangle is one-half the length of the base, b, times the height, h: $A = \frac{1}{2} \times b \times h$.

4. The area of a triangular garden near the playground is 12 square feet. The height of the garden is 4 feet. How long is the base of the garden? Explain your thinking.

5. Another shape seen in the aerial view of the playground looks like a trapezoid. The parallel sides of a trapezoid are called the **bases**. The two sides that are not parallel are called the **legs**. Label the bases and legs on the trapezoid shown.

6. Use the congruent trapezoids on page 303.
   - Cut out both the trapezoids.
   - On the inside of each figure, label the bases b_1 and b_2.
   - Draw the height of each trapezoid and label it h.
   - Form a parallelogram by turning one of the trapezoids so that its short base lines up with the long base of the other trapezoid. The long legs of the trapezoids will be adjacent.

7. How does the height of one of the trapezoids compare to the height of the parallelogram?

8. How does the base of the parallelogram relate to the bases of the trapezoid?

9. What is the area of one of the trapezoids? Explain your thinking.

Lesson 23-3
Area of Triangles, Trapezoids, and Polygons

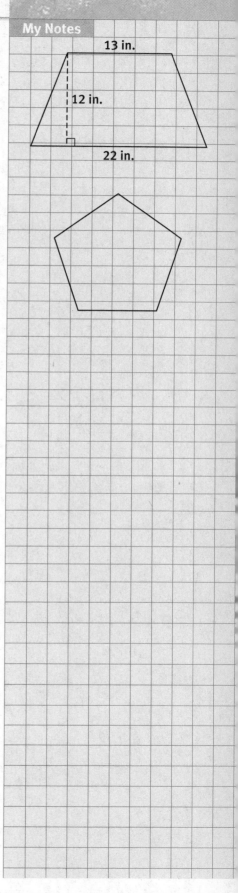

My Notes

The area, A, of a trapezoid is equal to one-half the height, h, times the sum of the bases, b_1 and b_2: $A = \frac{1}{2} \times h \times (b_1 + b_2)$.

10. A planter near the playground has the dimensions shown in the diagram to the right. What is the area of the planter?

You can find the area of a composite figure that can be decomposed, or divided, into rectangles, parallelograms, triangles, and trapezoids.

11. A pentagon is another polygon in the aerial view of the playground. Describe how to find the area of the pentagon using the figure shown.

12. The diagram shows the dimensions of Figure *A* in the aerial view of the playground. Find the area of Figure *A* using the formulas you have learned in this activity. Show your work in the My Notes column.

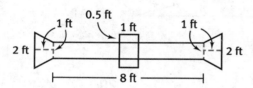

13. Attend to precision. The diagram shows the dimensions of Figure *F* from an aerial view. Find the area of Figure *F*. Explain your thinking.

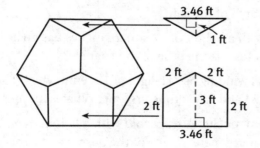

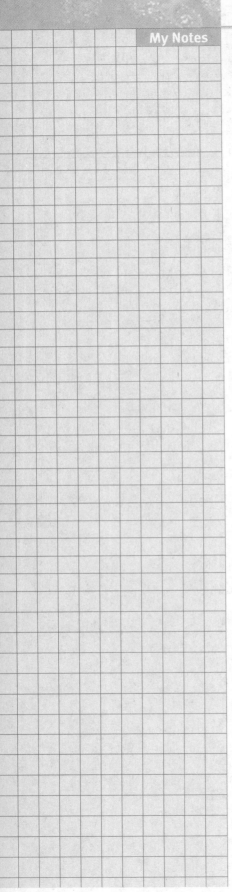

Check Your Understanding

For Items 14 and 15, find the area of each figure.

14.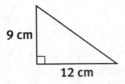
9 cm
12 cm

15.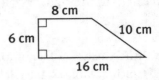
8 cm
10 cm
6 cm
16 cm

16. The area of a trapezoid is 40 square inches. The bases of the trapezoid are 9 inches and 11 inches long. Explain how to find the height of the trapezoid.

LESSON 23-3 PRACTICE

For Items 17–20, find the area of each figure.

17.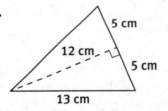
4 ft
5 ft
11 ft

18.
5 ft
8 ft
3 ft

19.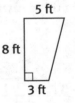
5 cm
12 cm
5 cm
13 cm

20.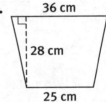
36 cm
28 cm
25 cm

21. A triangular sail with a height of 6 feet has a base that is 9 feet long. What is the area of the sail?

22. A triangle with a height of 12 square inches has an area of 36 square inches. How long is the base of the triangle?

23. A trapezoidal window has a height of 18 centimeters. The bases of the window are 34 and 28 centimeters long. What is the area of the window?

24. **Reason abstractly.** A trapezoid with a height of 6 meters has an area of 36 square meters. One of the bases is twice as long as the other base. How long are the bases of the trapezoid?

25. **Make sense of problems.** The diagram shows an aerial view of a parking lot that needs new concrete. The concrete costs $75 per square yard. How much will the concrete for the parking lot cost? Explain your thinking.

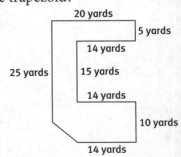
20 yards
5 yards
14 yards
25 yards
15 yards
14 yards
10 yards
14 yards

ACTIVITY 23 PRACTICE
Write your answers on a separate piece of paper.
Show your work.

Lesson 23-1

1. Write the best name for each quadrilateral.

    a.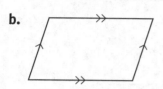

    b.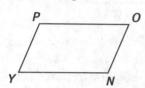

2. *PONY* is a parallelogram.

    a. Label these sides of *PONY*: *PY* = 5 inches and *PO* = 7 inches. What are the lengths of $\overline{ON}$ and $\overline{YN}$?

    b. Label this angle in *PONY*: $m\angle P = 112°$. What are the measures of $\angle O$, $\angle N$, and $\angle Y$?

3. Find the length of each side of a rhombus with perimeter of 40 meters.

4. Complete each statement with *always*, *sometimes*, or *never*.

    a. A square is _____ a rectangle.
    b. A rectangle is _____ a rhombus.
    c. A parallelogram is _____ a square.
    d. A trapezoid is _____ a square.

5. Use the diagram of each parallelogram to find the missing side and angle measures.

    a. square

    $AG =$ _____ and $m\angle A =$ _____

    b. rhombus

    If $m\angle M = 78°$ and $HM = 6$ cm, then $m\angle H =$ _____ and $HT =$ _____.

6. Explain how to determine whether a rectangle is a square. Use an example in your explanation.

7. The measures of three angles in a quadrilateral are 70°, 82°, and 120°. Find the measure of the fourth angle.

8. Identify the quadrilateral. Then find the value of *x*.

    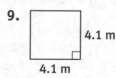

Lesson 23-2
For Items 9 and 10, find the perimeter and area of each figure.

9. 4.1 m

    4.1 m

10.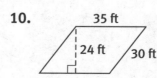

    35 ft

    24 ft   30 ft

For Items 11–13, find the area of each figure.

11.

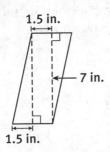

12.

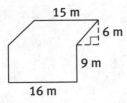

13.

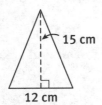

14. The area of a parallelogram with a base of 26 meters is 494 square meters. What is the height of the parallelogram?

15. A square window has a perimeter of 60 inches. What is the area of the window?

16. A rectangular stage that is 9 feet wide has an area of 252 square feet. What is the perimeter of the stage?

Lesson 23-3
For Items 17–21, find the area of each figure.

17.

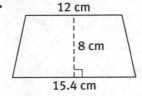

18.

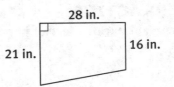

19.

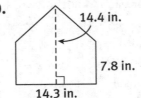

20.

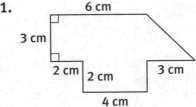

21.

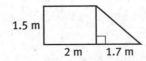

22. Mikel is building a doghouse for his puppy. The diagram shows the shape of the floor. Use the area formula for trapezoids to find the area of the doghouse floor. Confirm your answer by finding the sum of the areas of the rectangle and the right triangle.

23. Describe and model the area formula for trapezoids by breaking up the figure in Item 19 and rearranging the parts.

24. A triangular banner has a base length of 48 inches. The banner has an area of 1,632 square inches. What is the height of the banner?

25. How does knowing how to find the area of a rectangle help you determine the area of other polygons?

MATHEMATICAL PRACTICES
Model with Mathematics

26. Draw and label a triangle, a trapezoid, and a parallelogram that each has an area of 48 square inches. Show your work justifying that each figure has an area of 48 square inches.

Parallelogram Cut out this parallelogram for Item 6 of Activity 23-2.

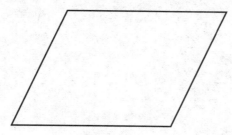

Two Congruent Triangles Cut out these triangles for Item 1 of Activity 23-3.

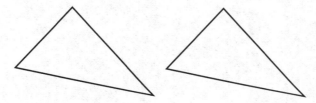

Two Congruent Trapezoids Cut out these trapezoids for Item 6 of Activity 23-3.

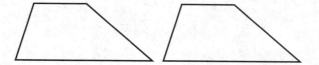

This page is intentionally blank.

Polygons on the Coordinate Plane

Wall Art

Lesson 24-1 Defining Polygons on the Coordinate Plane

Learning Targets:

- Draw polygons in the coordinate plane given vertex coordinates.
- Find the length of a segment joining points with the same first coordinate or the same second coordinate.
- Use coordinate geometry to identify locations on a plane.
- Graph points in all four quadrants.
- Solve problems involving the area on the coordinate plane.

> **SUGGESTED LEARNING STRATEGIES:** Visualization, Think-Pair-Share, Create Representations, Identify a Subtask

Zena is hired to paint a mural on the side of a large building. She creates a scale drawing of her mural, shown on the coordinate grid. She will use the model to plan the painting. Each block on the grid represents 1 foot by 1 foot.

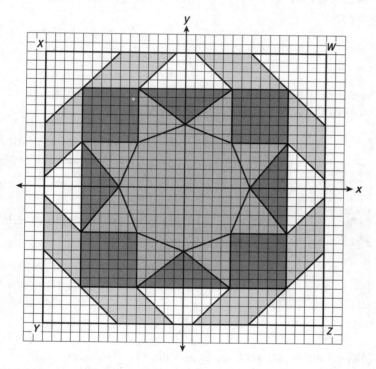

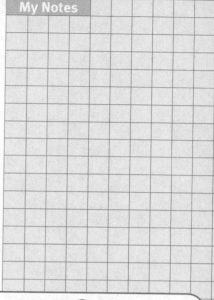

CONNECT TO ART

A mural is a painting or enlarged artwork applied directly to a wall or ceiling.

1. The border of Zena's design forms quadrilateral *WXYZ*.
   a. What are the coordinates of point *W* and point *X*?

   b. What do these coordinates have in common?

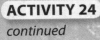

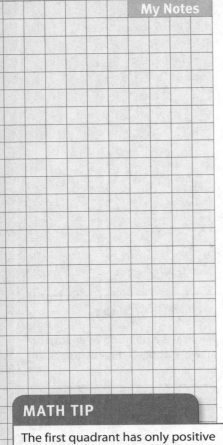

My Notes

MATH TIP

The first quadrant has only positive *x*- and positive *y*-coordinates.

c. What is the length of side $\overline{XW}$ of quadrilateral *WXYZ*? Explain your answer.

d. What are the coordinates of point *Z*?

e. What do the coordinates of points *W* and *Z* have in common?

f. What is the length of side $\overline{WZ}$ of quadrilateral *WXYZ*? Explain your answer.

g. What is the best name for quadrilateral *WXYZ*? Explain your reasoning.

2. Consider only the portion of Zena's design in the first quadrant. The **vertices** of the inner square are labeled *A*, *B*, *C*, and *D*.

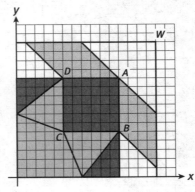

a. The coordinates of point *B* are (11, 5). What are the coordinates of point *A*?

b. What is the length of $\overline{AB}$?

c. What is the area of square *ABCD*?

3. a. Make use of structure. Explain how to find the length of a vertical line segment using the coordinates of the endpoints. Include an example in your explanation.

b. Explain how to find the length of a horizontal line segment using the coordinates of the endpoints. Include an example in your explanation.

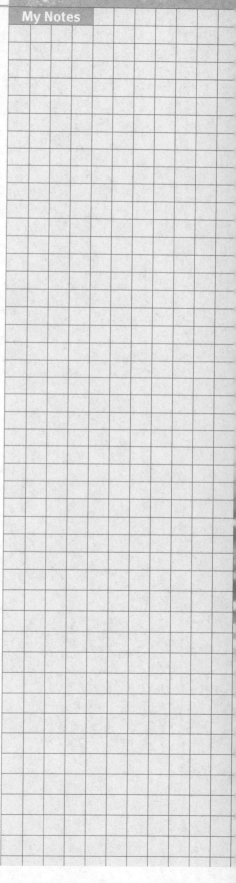

4. The endpoints of a line segment are (−4.5, 6) and (−4.5, −2).
   a. Use the My Notes section to create a coordinate grid. Draw the line segment on the coordinate grid.

   b. What is the length of the line segment? Explain how you determined this length.

5. Look at parallelogram *ADPR* in Zena's first quadrant design.

   a. What is the length of the base of the parallelogram, $\overline{AD}$?

   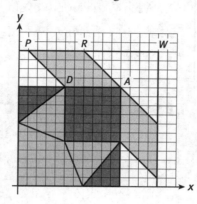

   b. What is the height of the parallelogram? Explain how you determined this.

   c. What is the area of parallelogram *ADPR*? Explain your reasoning.

6. a. What is the total area of the parallelograms in Zena's first quadrant design? Explain your reasoning.

   b. Each of the four quadrants has two of the light blue parallelograms in the mural design. What is the total area of the light blue parallelograms in the mural design?

   c. **Make sense of problems.** Each gallon of light blue paint costs $45 and will cover 75 square feet. How much will the light blue paint cost that is needed to paint the light blue parallelograms in all four quadrants of the mural design? Explain your reasoning.

My Notes

Check Your Understanding

Use the coordinate grid for Items 7–10.

7. The vertices of rectangle *JKLM* are represented by these coordinates: $J(-2.5, 3)$, $K(2, 3)$, $L(2, -1)$, and $M(-2.5, -1)$. Draw rectangle *JKLM*.

8. What is the length of side *JK*?

9. What is the length of side *JM*?

10. What is the area of rectangle *JKLM*?

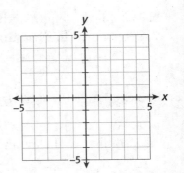

LESSON 24-1 PRACTICE

Use the coordinate grid for Items 11–14.

11. The coordinates $Q(2, 2)$, $R(1, -3)$, $S(-2, -3)$, and $T(-1, 2)$ represent the vertices of parallelogram *QRST*. Draw parallelogram *QRST*.

12. What is the length of the base of parallelogram *QRST*?

13. What is the height of parallelogram *QRST*?

14. What is the area of parallelogram *QRST*?

15. What is the distance between the points $(1, 3)$ and $(1, 7)$? Explain your reasoning.

16. A line segment has the endpoints $(2.25, 5.75)$ and $(-1, 5.75)$. What is the length of the line segment?

Use parallelogram *ABCD* for Items 17 and 18.

17. What are the coordinates of the vertices of the parallelogram?

18. A stained-glass designer will align eight different colored parallelograms of this same size to create a pattern. What is the total area of the designer's pattern if each square on the grid represents 1 square centimeter?

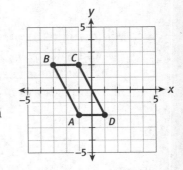

19. **Reason abstractly.** A square has vertices $(1, 7)$, $(1, 2)$, $(6, 7)$, and $(6, 2)$. What is the area of the square? How can you find the area of the square without drawing the square in a coordinate plane? Explain.

Learning Targets:

- Use coordinate geometry to identify locations on a plane.
- Graph points in all four quadrants.
- Solve problems involving the area of parallelograms, trapezoids, and triangles.

> **SUGGESTED LEARNING STRATEGIES:** Visualization, Sharing and Responding, Create a Plan, Create Representations

There are three different types of triangles in the scale drawing of Zena's mural design. They are shown in the first quadrant section of the mural. Remember, each square on the grid represents 1 square foot.

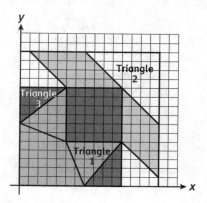

1. Find the area of each triangle. Justify your answers.
   a. gray triangle 1

   b. white triangle 2

   c. dark blue triangle 3

My Notes

MATH TIP

Remember, two sides of a polygon intersect at a vertex. The plural of vertex is vertices.

MATH TIP

Remember, the area, A, of a trapezoid with height h and bases b_1 and b_2 is $A = \frac{1}{2} \times h \times (b_1 + b_2)$.

2. The endpoints of triangle ABC on a coordinate grid plane are $A(-3.5, 4)$, $B(-3.5, -1)$, and $C(2.5, -1)$.
   a. Use the My Notes section to create a coordinate grid. Draw the triangle on the coordinate grid.

   b. What is the area of triangle ABC? Explain.

3. There are four congruent white trapezoids in the original mural design. One of the trapezoids is shown on the grid.

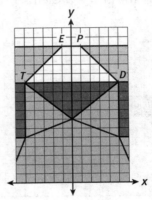

   a. What are the coordinates of the vertices of the trapezoid?

   b. What is the height of the trapezoid in the mural design? What are the lengths of the bases?

   c. What is the area of the trapezoid in the mural design? Explain your reasoning.

   d. How much of the mural area do the four white trapezoids make up?

The complete model of Zena's mural design is shown.

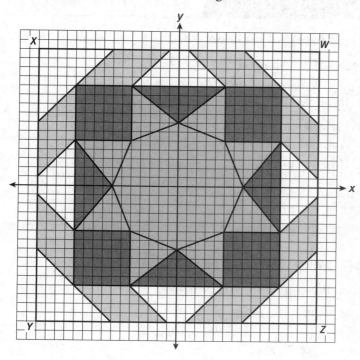

4. Look back at Items 1 and 3.
   a. What is the total area of the four white triangles? Explain your reasoning.

   b. What is the total area of the white trapezoids and the white triangles? Explain your reasoning.

   c. Each can of white paint costs $42.75 and will cover 50 square feet. How much will the white paint cost for the mural? Explain your reasoning.

5. **Construct viable arguments.** There is an octagon in the center of the mural. Use what you know about the area of triangles and rectangles to find the area of the octagon. Explain your reasoning.

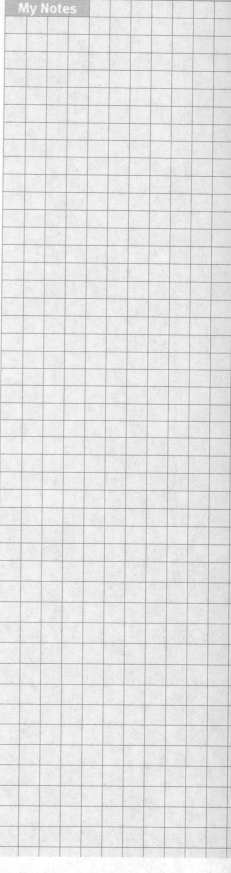

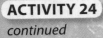

ACTIVITY 24
continued

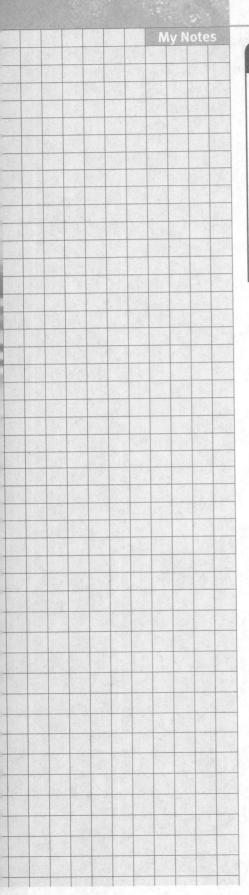

My Notes

Check Your Understanding

Use the coordinate grid for Items 6–9.

6. Trapezoid *ABCD* has vertices at *A*(1, 3), *B*(−2, 3), *C*(−3, −2), and *D*(4, −2). Draw trapezoid *ABCD*.

7. What is the length of the bases of trapezoid *ABCD*?

8. What is the height of trapezoid *ABCD*?

9. Find the area of trapezoid *ABCD*.

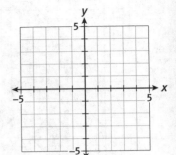

LESSON 24-2 PRACTICE

Use the coordinate grid for Items 10–13.

10. Triangle *PQR* has vertices at *P*(−1, 1), *Q*(−1, −3), and *R*(2.5, −2). Draw triangle *PQR*.

11. What is the length of the base of triangle *PQR*?

12. What is the height of triangle *PQR*?

13. Find the area of triangle *PQR*.

Use trapezoid *CDEF* for Items 14–18.

14. What are the coordinates of the vertices of this trapezoid?

15. What are the lengths of the bases of the trapezoid?

16. What is the height of the trapezoid?

17. Find the area of the trapezoid if each square on the grid represents 1 square meter.

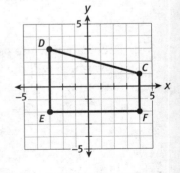

18. **Make sense of problems.** The trapezoid in Items 14–17 is a scale model of a deck that Gayle is planning to build. The material for the deck costs $4.35 per square meter. What will be the cost of the deck?

19. **Construct viable arguments.** A right triangle has vertices at (16.5, 12), (16.5, −8), and (−10, 12). Explain how to find the area of the triangle without drawing the triangle on a coordinate grid.

ACTIVITY 24 PRACTICE

Write your answers on a separate piece of paper.
Show your work.

Lesson 24-1

1. Name another point on the same horizontal line as the point (2, 8).

2. Name another point on the same vertical line as the point (−1, 4).

3. Name another point on the same horizontal line as the point (−6, 3.5).

4. Name another point on the same vertical line as the point (−2.5, −4.25).

5. Find the length of the line segment connecting each pair of points.
   a. (1, 3), (6, 3)   **b.** (−4, 2), (1, 2)
   c. (7, −5), (7, −3) **d.** (−8, −4), (8, −4)

6. The length of the line segment connecting the points (2, 8) and (2, y) is 7. What are the two possible values of y?

For Items 7 and 8, use parallelogram *JKLM*.

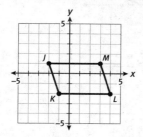

7. What are the coordinates of the vertices of parallelogram *JKLM*?

8. What is the area of parallelogram *JKLM*?

For Items 9–11, find the area of each figure.

9.

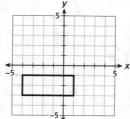

10.

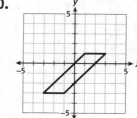

11.

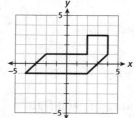

12. On a coordinate grid, draw a rectangle with vertices at (0, 4), (0, 6), (3, 4), and (3, 6). What is the area of the rectangle?

13. On a coordinate grid, draw a square with vertices at (3, 2), (−1, 2), (−1, −2), and (3, −2). What is the area of the square?

14. On a coordinate grid, draw a parallelogram with vertices at (2, 4), (0, −1), (−3, −1), and (−1, 4). What is the area of the parallelogram?

15. On a coordinate grid, draw a rectangle with vertices at (3.5, 8), (−2.5, 8), (−2.5, −6), and (3.5, −6). What is the area of the rectangle?

16. On a coordinate grid, a scale drawing of a banner is shaped like a parallelogram with vertices at (−15, 10), (0, −5), (30, −5), and (15, 10). Each square on the grid represents 1 square inch. What is the area of the banner?

Lesson 24-2

For Items 17 and 18, write the missing coordinates for the vertices of each figure. Then find the area of the figure.

17.

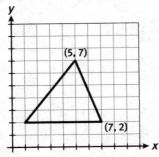

(5, 7)
(7, 2)

18.

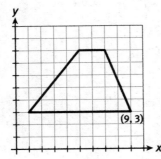

(9, 3)

For Items 19–24, find the area of each figure.

19.

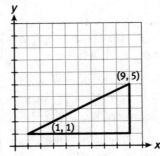

(9, 5)
(1, 1)

20.

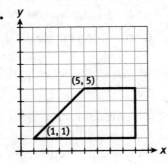

(5, 5)
(1, 1)

21.

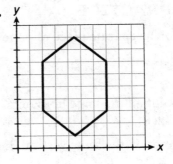

22.

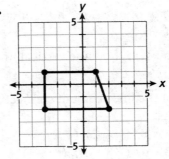

23.

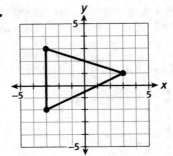

24.

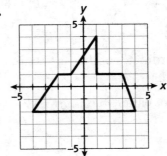

25. What is the area of a triangle with vertices at (−8, 4), (12, 16), and (12, −4)?

MATHEMATICAL PRACTICES
Use Appropriate Tools Strategically

26. On a coordinate grid, a trapezoid has vertices at (−6, 9), (−6, 6), (3, −9), and (3, 12). Each square on the grid represents 1 square foot. Explain how to find the area of the trapezoid.

Write your answers on a separate sheet of paper. Show your work.

Students at STAR Middle School are designing a logo for their astronomy club. They are considering different designs for the logo. The students have decided to use different polygons to create their logo. Before they begin designing, they review some of the properties and characteristics of polygons.

> **CONNECT TO SCIENCE**
>
> Astronomy is the branch of science that studies matter in outer space and the physical universe as a whole system.

1. Some of the shapes they may use in the logo are shown. Identify the best name for each triangle or quadrilateral and explain your reasoning.

   a. 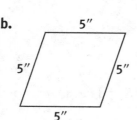   **b.** 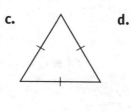   **c.**   **d.**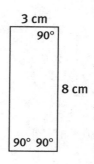

2. Find the missing angle measure in each polygon. Explain your reasoning.

   a. 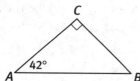   **b.**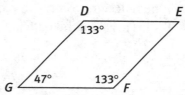

3. Determine whether each statement below is *always true, sometimes true,* or *never true.* Explain why you chose each answer.

   a. A rectangle is a rhombus.

   b. Two angles of a scalene triangle are congruent.

   c. A rhombus is equilateral.

   d. An equilateral triangle is equiangular.

   e. A parallelogram is a rectangle.

   f. An obtuse triangle contains at least two obtuse angles.

   g. A square is a rhombus.

   h. A triangle has side lengths 3 inches, 4 inches, and 8 inches.

After each student designed a logo, the club members voted on their favorite. The two designs that got the greatest number of votes are shown below.

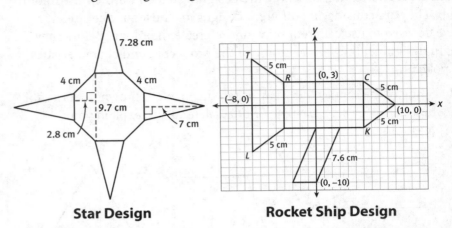

Star Design

Rocket Ship Design

4. Determine the areas and perimeters of both designs. Explain your reasoning.

5. Which design will take up the greatest amount of space on the students' T-shirts? Explain how you made your decision.

6. Which design would you recommend the students use for the T-shirt? Use mathematical reasons to support your decision.

Scoring Guide	Exemplary	Proficient	Emerging	Incomplete
	The solution demonstrates these characteristics:			
Mathematics Knowledge and Thinking (Items 1a-d, 2a-b, 3a-h, 4, 5)	• Clear and accurate understanding of finding angle measures, perimeter, and area of triangles and quadrilaterals.	• An understanding of finding angle measures, perimeter, and area of triangles and quadrilaterals.	• Partial understanding of finding angle measures, perimeter, and area of triangles and quadrilaterals.	• Incorrect or incomplete understanding of finding angle measures, perimeter, and area.
Problem Solving (Items 2a-b, 4)	• Interpreting a problem accurately in order to find angle measures, perimeter, or area.	• Interpreting a problem to find angle measures, perimeter, or area.	• Difficulty interpreting a problem to find angle measures, perimeter, or area.	• Incorrect or incomplete interpretation of a problem.
Mathematical Modeling / Representations (Items 1a-d, 3a-h)	• Clear and accurate understanding of the characteristics of triangles and quadrilaterals.	• Identifying and naming triangles and quadrilaterals correctly.	• Difficulty identifying triangles and quadrilaterals.	• Incorrect or incomplete identification of triangles and quadrilaterals.
Reasoning and Communication (Items 1a-d, 2a-b, 3a-h, 4, 5, 6)	• Precise use of appropriate terms to explain reasoning in geometry concepts.	• Competent use of appropriate terms to explain reasoning in geometry concepts.	• Partially correct use of terms to explain reasoning in geometry concepts.	• An incomplete or inaccurate use of terms to explain reasoning in geometry concepts.

Nets and Surface Area

All Boxed Up

Lesson 25-1 Nets and Surface Area of Cubes

Learning Targets:

- Represent three-dimensional figures using nets.
- Use nets to find the surface area of figures.
- Write equations that represent problems related to the area of rectangles.
- Determine solutions for problems involving the area of rectangles.

SUGGESTED LEARNING STRATEGIES: Visualization, Create Representations, Identify a Subtask, Use Manipulatives

A **net** is a two-dimensional drawing used to represent or form a three-dimensional figure. Nets can be used to form different types of boxes.

The shape in Figure 1 is a net.

1. Use the net of Figure 1 on page 327.
   Cut out the net. Fold it along the dotted lines to form a box. The figure formed is a cube. What are the characteristics that make the three-dimensional figure a cube?

2. The net shown will also form a cube. If face 1 is the bottom of the cube, which numbered face is the top of the cube?

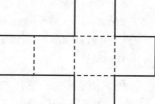

3. **Model with mathematics.** Many other nets can be used to represent a cube.

   a. Use graph paper to draw as many of these other nets as you can find. Cut out each net and fold it to verify that a cube can be formed.

   b. Sketch the nets you found that form a cube in the My Notes space.

   c. Below, sketch two nets made up of six squares that do not form a cube.

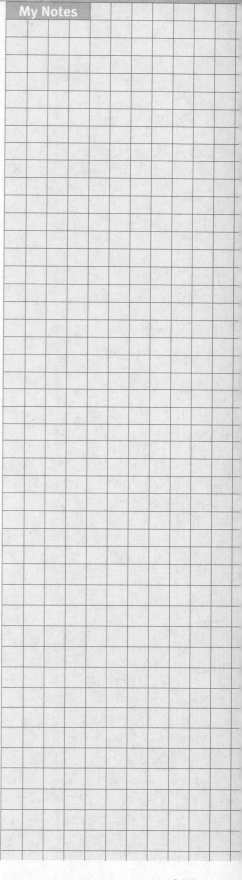

My Notes

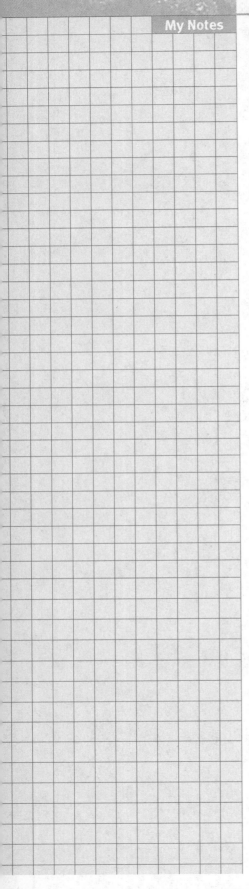

Elaine sells shipping materials, including boxes and packing peanuts, at her business All Boxed Up. Her box supplier charges her $\frac{1}{2}$ cent per square inch of surface area for each box. Elaine can find the **surface area** of a box by adding the areas of the six faces of the box (front, back, top, bottom, left, and right).

Elaine needs to find the surface areas of boxes of many different sizes. She wants to find a pattern that will make it faster to find the surface area.

4. One type of box that Elaine keeps in stock is a cube. For one of the cube-shaped boxes, the length of each edge is 5 inches.

   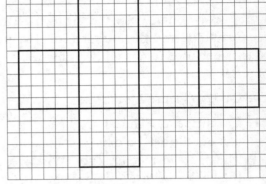

   a. Find the area of each face of the cube.

   b. Find the total surface area of the cube.

5. Elaine makes a table to record the surface areas of the cube-shaped boxes.

   a. Complete the table.

Length of Edge (in.)	Number of Faces	Area of One Face (in.^{2})	Surface Area (in.^{2})
5			
6			
7			
8			
		100	600
			1,350

   b. Describe any patterns you see in the table.

   c. For each box, how does the area of one face relate to the surface area?

6. You can use a variable to represent the
length of the edge of a cube.

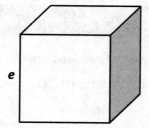

   a. What variable is used to represent the
   length of the edge of the cube in the
   diagram?

   b. What is the area of one face of a cube in terms of the length of
   an edge, *e*?

   c. Make use of structure. Write a rule for finding the surface area,
   SA, of a cube in terms of the length of an edge, *e*.

7. Cube-shaped boxes with 12-inch edges are kept in stock at
All Boxed Up.

   a. Determine the surface area of a box with 12-inch edges.

   b. Attend to precision. The supplier charges Elaine $\frac{1}{2}$ cent per
   square inch of surface area for each box. Determine how much
   profit Elaine will make on a 12-inch cube-shaped box if she sells
   the box for $4.95. Explain your reasoning.

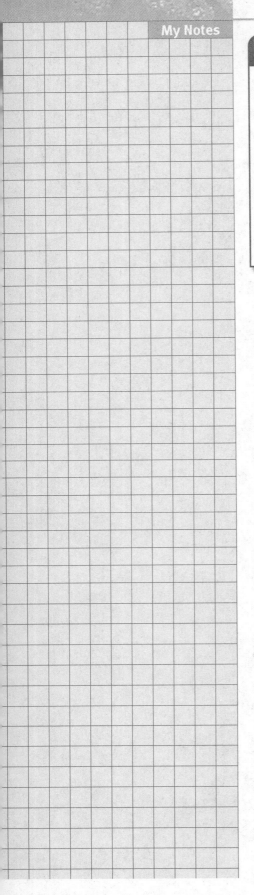

My Notes

Check Your Understanding

Use the net for Items 8–10.

8. What is the length of each edge of the cube?

9. What is the area of each face of the cube?

10. What is the surface area of the cube?

11. Draw a net and use it to find the surface area of a cube with edges that are 9 centimeters long.

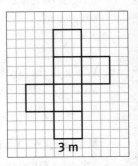

3 m

LESSON 25-1 PRACTICE

Use the net for Items 12 and 13.

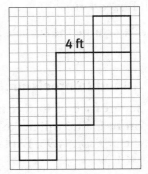

4 ft

12. What is the area of each face of the cube?

13. What is the surface area of the cube?

14. Draw a net and use it to find the surface area of a cube with edges that are 11 meters long.

15. Draw a net and use it to find the surface area of a cube with edges that are 14 feet long.

16. The edges of a cube are 20 millimeters long. Draw a net and use it to find the surface area of the cube.

17. The edges of a cube are 5.2 centimeters long. Draw a net and use it to find the surface area of the cube.

18. What is the surface area of a cube with edges that are $2\frac{1}{2}$ feet long?

19. **Reason quantitatively.** A cube has a surface area of 384 square inches. What is the edge length of the cube? Explain your reasoning.

20. **Make sense of problems.** A cube-shaped box has edges that are 18 centimeters long. The box does not have a top. What is the surface area of the box? Justify your answer.

21. **Critique the reasoning of others.** The edge of a cube-shaped display case is 30 inches long. Drake says that the surface area of the display case is 3,600 square inches. Is he correct? Explain why or why not.

Learning Targets:

- Represent three-dimensional figures using nets.
- Use nets to find the surface area of figures.
- Write equations that represent area problems.
- Solve problems involving the area of rectangles and triangles.

SUGGESTED LEARNING STRATEGIES: Note Taking, Visualization, RAFT, Graphic Organizer, Create Representations

Elaine has boxes in stock at All Boxed Up that are rectangular prisms and triangular prisms.

A **prism** is a three-dimensional figure with parallel congruent bases that are both polygons. The faces (sides) of a prism are rectangles. A prism is named for the shape of its bases. A **rectangular prism** has bases that are rectangles. Its faces are also rectangles.

The net of one of Elaine's boxes is shown. The box is a rectangular prism.

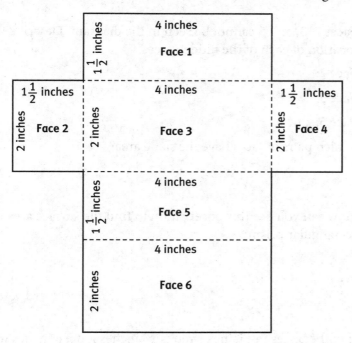

1. **a.** Show the calculation needed to find the area of each face of the rectangular prism.

   Face 1:   Face 2:

   Face 3:   Face 4:

   Face 5:   Face 6:

   b. Find the surface area of the rectangular prism and explain your process.

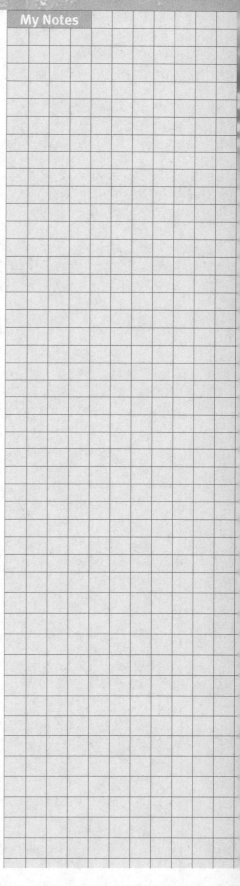

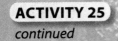

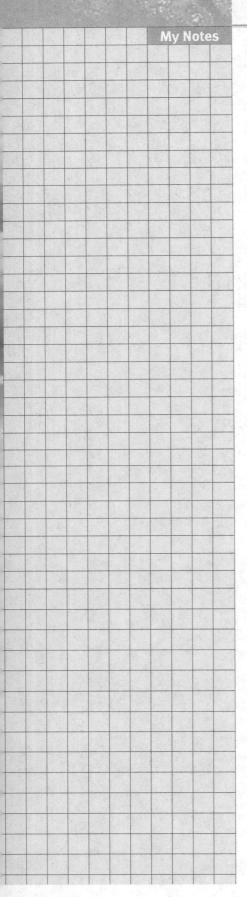

My Notes

You can use a net to find the surface area of a rectangular prism. You can also use congruence to help you find the surface area of a rectangular prism.

2. **a.** Cut out the net (Figure 2) on page 327. Fold it to form a rectangular prism with the measurements on the outside.

   b. Label the length, width, and height of the rectangular prism you formed on this diagram.

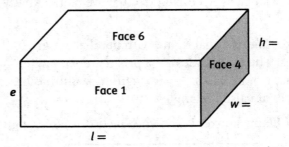

   c. Faces 2, 3, and 5 cannot be seen in the diagram. Describe the location of each of the hidden faces.

   Face 2:

   Face 3:

   Face 5:

   d. Which pairs of faces have the same area?

   e. How can you use this observation to find the surface area of a rectangular prism?

3. One of the boxes in Elaine's shop is 18 inches long, 6 inches wide, and 9 inches tall. Explain how to find the surface area of the box.

4. **Construct viable arguments.**
   Write a rule to determine the surface area, *SA*, of a rectangular prism with length *l*, width *w*, and height *h*. Explain your thinking.

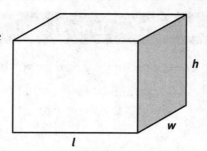

Some of the boxes in stock at All Boxed Up are **triangular prisms**. A triangular prism has two parallel bases that are congruent triangles. The three faces are rectangles.

5. **a.** Cut out the net of Figure 3 on page 329. Identify and label which sides of the prism are the bases and which sides are the faces.

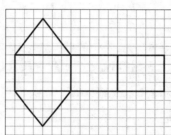

   b. Explain how to find the area of each face of the triangular prism.

   c. Explain how to find the surface area of the triangular prism.

6. Explain how to use a net to find the surface area of the triangular prism shown.

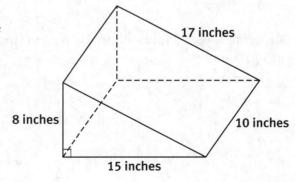

17 inches

8 inches   10 inches

15 inches

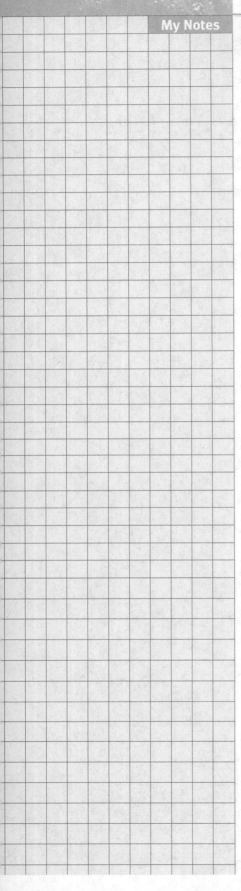

My Notes

Check Your Understanding

Use the rectangular prism for Items 7 and 8.

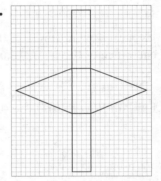

7. Draw and label a net that represents the rectangular prism.

8. Determine the surface area of the rectangular prism.

Use the triangular prism for Items 9 and 10.

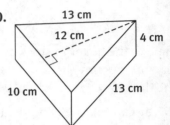

9. Draw and label a net that represents the triangular prism.

10. Determine the surface area of the triangular prism.

LESSON 25-2 PRACTICE

For Items 11 and 12, use the nets to find the surface area of the prisms.

11.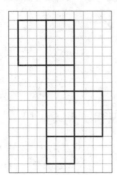

12.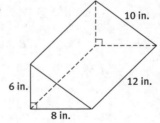

For Items 13 and 14, draw and use nets to find the surface area of each prism.

13.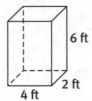

14.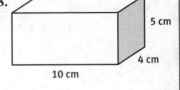

15. A battery shaped like a rectangular prism is 8 inches long, 5 inches wide, and 4 inches tall. What is the surface area of the battery?

16. **Make sense of problems.** Elaine has a new box that is 24 inches long, 12 inches wide, and 10 inches high. Write a proposal to Elaine recommending a price for this size box. Remember that her box supplier charges her $\frac{1}{2}$ cent per square inch of surface area for each box. Be certain to explain how you arrived at your recommendation.

ACTIVITY 25 PRACTICE
Write your answers on a separate piece of paper.
Show your work.

Lesson 25-1

1. Determine whether this net can form a cube.

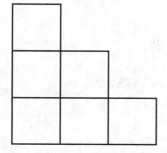

2. Use the net below to find the surface area of the cube.

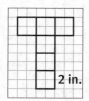

2 in.

3. Use the net below to find the surface area of the cube.

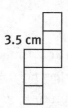

3.5 cm

For Items 4–6, draw a net and use it to find the surface area of each cube.

4.

6 ft

5.

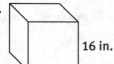

16 in.

6.

4.5 cm

7. Find the surface area of a cube with edges 7 centimeters long.

8. Find the surface area of a cube with edges 19 inches long.

9. Find the surface area of a cube with edges 21 millimeters long.

10. What is the surface area of a cube with edges 6.3 centimeters long?

11. What is the surface area of a cube with edges 40 inches long?

12. A cube has a surface area of 486 square centimeters. How long is each edge of the cube?

13. A cube-shaped block has edges that are 21 millimeters long. All of the faces of the block are painted except for the bottom face. What is the surface area of the painted faces of the block?

Lesson 25-2
Use the rectangular prism for Items 14 and 15.

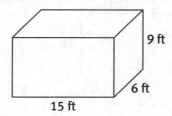

9 ft
6 ft
15 ft

14. Draw and label a net that represents the rectangular prism.

15. What is the surface area of the rectangular prism?

Use the triangular prism for Items 16 and 17.

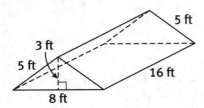

5 ft
3 ft
5 ft
16 ft
8 ft

16. Draw and label a net that represents the triangular prism.

17. What is the surface area of the triangular prism?

18. Use the net of the triangular prism to find the surface area of the prism.

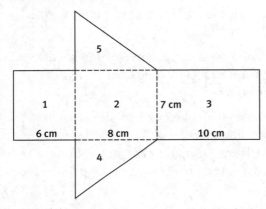

5
1
2
7 cm
3
6 cm
8 cm
10 cm
4

For Items 19–25, draw a net and use it to find the surface area of each prism.

19.

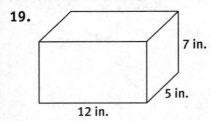

7 in.
5 in.
12 in.

20.

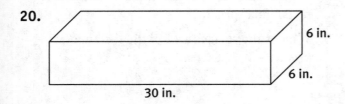

6 in.
6 in.
30 in.

21.

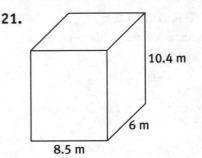

10.4 m
6 m
8.5 m

22.

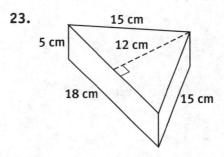

13 cm
12 cm
16 cm
5 cm

23.

15 cm
5 cm
12 cm
18 cm
15 cm

24. A trunk is shaped like a rectangular prism and is 4 feet long, $1\frac{1}{2}$ feet wide, and 2 feet tall. What is the surface area of the trunk?

25. A cereal box is 8 inches long, 3 inches wide, and 12 inches tall. A pasta box is 12 inches long, 1 inch wide, and 2 inches tall. How much greater is the surface area of the cereal box than the pasta box?

MATHEMATICAL PRACTICES
Reason Abstractly

26. Create a graphic organizer comparing and contrasting the methods used to find the surface area of cubes, rectangular prisms, and triangular prisms.

Nets and Surface Area
All Boxed Up

Cut out this net for Item 1 of Lesson 25-1.

Figure 1

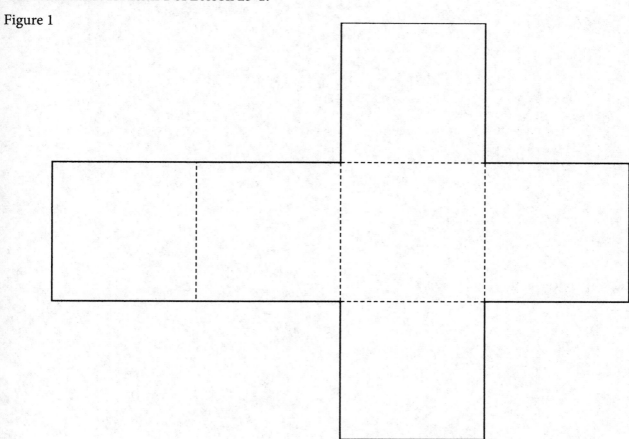

Cut out this net for Item 2 of Lesson 25-2.

Figure 2

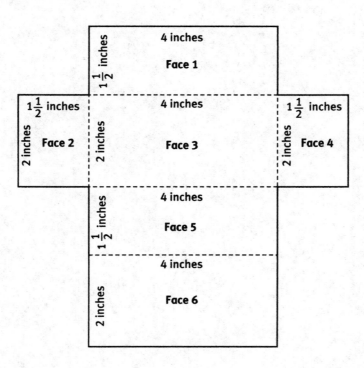

This page is intentionally blank.

Cut out this net for Item 5 of Lesson 25-2.

Figure 3

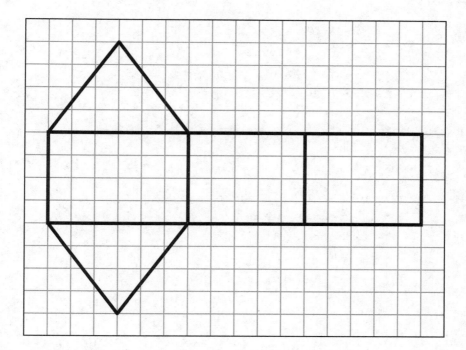

This page is intentionally blank.

Volume
Crystal Collections
Lesson 26-1 Volume of Cubes

Learning Targets:

- Find the volume of a right rectangular prism with fractional edge lengths.
- Write equations that represent problems related to the volume of right rectangular prisms.

> **SUGGESTED LEARNING STRATEGIES:** Close Reading, Paraphrasing, Think Aloud, Visualization, Vocabulary Organizer, Construct Arguments, Create a Plan, Use Manipulatives, Look for a Pattern

Crystals are solids formed by a regular repeated pattern of molecules connecting together. They have a regular shape and flat sides. Some crystals form cubes while others grow into columns with three or more sides. The figures shown below are crystals.

The collected atoms that make up crystals are called unit cells. They are the simplest repeating unit in the crystal and are repeated in exactly the same arrangement throughout the solid. Opposite faces of a unit cell are parallel. A simple cubic unit cell is in the shape of a cube.

Cubes are named for the lengths of their edges:

- A 1-inch cube is a cube with edges that are 1 inch in length.
- A 2-inch cube is a cube with edges that are 2 inches in length.
- A $\frac{1}{2}$-inch cube is a cube with edges that are $\frac{1}{2}$ inch in length.
- Any size cube can be used to build larger cubes.

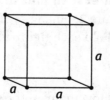

MATH TIP

The cube in the diagram is an a-unit cube. Each edge is a units long.

Volume is a measure of the amount of space a solid occupies. It is measured in cubic units, such as cubic inches (in.^{3}), cubic feet (ft^3), cubic centimeters (cm^3), or cubic meters (m^3).

One way to find the volume of a solid is to fill the solid with cubes. The volume is the total number of cubes needed to fill the solid.

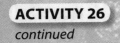
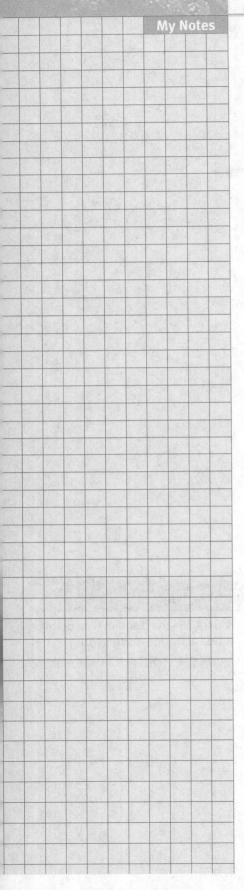

My Notes

1. Halite, or table salt, is a mineral that is made up of cubic crystals. Use unit cubes, provided by your teacher, as models of 1-inch cubes.
   a. Use the unit cubes to build models of 2-inch and 3-inch cubes. Then complete the table.

Length of Edge (in.)	Area of Face (in.^{2})	Volume of Cube (in.^{3})
1		
2		
3		

   b. Describe any patterns you see in the table.

2. **Make use of structure.** Describe how you can use the patterns you found in the table to determine the volume of a cube when you do not have enough unit cubes to build the cube.

3. Let the variable e represent the length of the edge of a cube. Write a rule for finding the volume, V, of a cube in terms of the length of an edge, e.

4. **Model with mathematics.** Cut out the nets of cubes, Figure 1 and Figure 2, on page 341.
   a. Fold each figure to form a cube.

   b. How many of the smaller cubes made from Figure 1 will fit into the larger cube made from Figure 2?

   c. Look back at the table in Item 1. How many cubes with edge length 1 inch will fit into the cube with edge length 2 inches?

5. Consider a cube with edge length 4 inches. How many of these smaller cubes will fit into an 8-inch cube? Explain your thinking.

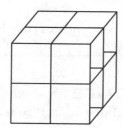

In Items 4 and 5, the ratio of the edge length of the smaller cube to the edge length of the larger cube is $\frac{1}{2}$.

The rule you determined earlier in the activity to find the volume of a cube can also be used to find the volume of a cube with fractional edge lengths.

6. Find the volume of each cube with the given edge length.
   a. $\frac{2}{3}$ foot

   b. $1\frac{1}{4}$ inches

7. A storage shed shaped like a cube has sides that are 3.5 meters long. What is the volume of the storage shed?

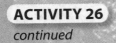
ACTIVITY 26
continued

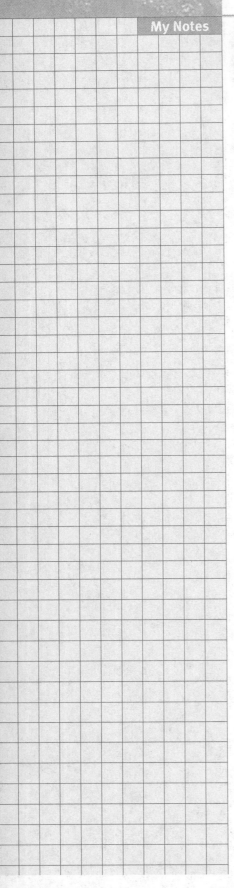
My Notes

Check Your Understanding

8. A cube has an edge length of 5 centimeters. What is the volume of the cube?

9. What is the volume of a cube with an edge length of $\frac{1}{6}$ foot?

LESSON 26-1 PRACTICE

For Items 10–13, find the volume of each cube.

10.

7 in.

11.

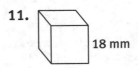
18 mm

12.

$2\frac{1}{3}$ ft

13.

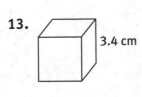
3.4 cm

14. A cube has an edge length of 4.3 meters. What is the volume of the cube?

15. What is the volume of a cube with an edge length of $\frac{1}{4}$ yard?

16. A cube has a volume of 1,000 cubic feet. What is the edge length of the cube?

17. The area of one face of a cube is 36 cubic inches. What is the volume of the cube?

18. How much greater is the volume of a cube with edges that are $2\frac{1}{2}$ feet long than a cube with edges that are 2 feet long?

19. A fish tank shaped like a cube has sides that are 9 inches long. What is the volume of the fish tank?

20. **Reason quantitatively.** A cube has a surface area of 96 square inches. What is the volume of the cube? Explain your thinking.

21. **Make sense of problems.** A tower is made from three cubes stacked on top of each other. The edges of the cubes are 4 inches, 6 inches, and 8 inches. What is the total volume of the tower?

Lesson 26-2
Volume of Rectangular Prisms

Learning Targets:

- Write equations that represent problems related to the volume of right rectangular prisms.
- Apply the formulas $V = lwh$ and $V = bh$ to find volumes of right rectangular prisms.

> **SUGGESTED LEARNING STRATEGIES:** Close Reading, Paraphrasing, Think Aloud, Visualization, Vocabulary Organizer, Construct an Argument, Create a Plan, Use Manipulatives, Look for a Pattern

Some crystals grow into columns in the shape of rectangular prisms. For example, zircon is a tetragonal crystal shaped like a rectangular prism.

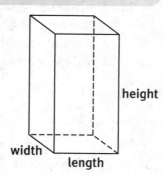

1. Crystals can be stored in display cases. A museum has many different cases. Each display case is shaped like a rectangular prism. The table shows the dimensions of some different cases.

   a. Complete the table. Use unit cubes, provided by your teacher, as models of 1-inch cubes.

Length (in.)	Width (in.)	Height (in.)	Volume (in.³)
2	2	5	
4	3	2	
5	2	3	
3	3	4	

   b. Describe any patterns you see in the table.

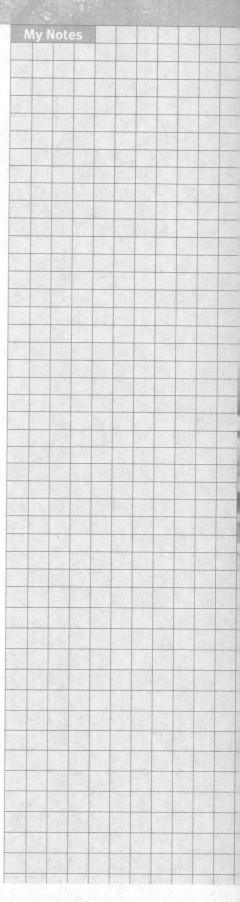

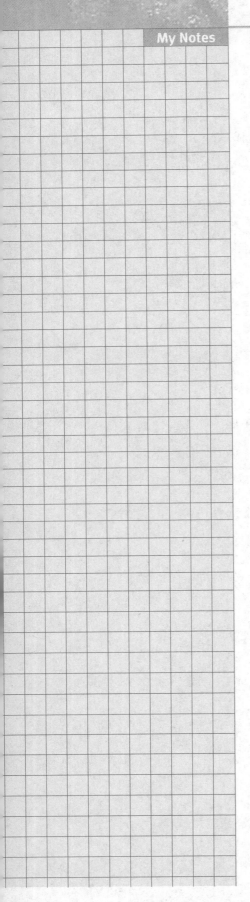

My Notes

2. **Make use of structure.** Look back at the table in Item 1.
   a. Compare the product of the length, width, and height of each prism to its volume. Write a rule for finding the volume, V, of a rectangular prism in terms of its length, l, width, w, and height, h. Explain how this rule follows from the rule you wrote in part b.

   b. Compare the product of the area of the base (length times width) and the height of each prism to its volume. Write a rule for finding the volume, V, of a rectangular prism in terms of the area of the base, B, and the height, h. Explain your thinking.

3. A crystal shaped like a rectangular prism has the dimensions shown.

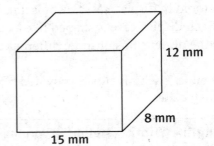

12 mm

8 mm

15 mm

   a. What is the area of the base of the crystal?

   b. What is the volume of the crystal?

4. A crystal shaped like a rectangular prism has a volume of 480 cubic millimeters. The crystal is 10 millimeters long and 8 millimeters tall. How wide is the crystal? Explain your thinking.

Lesson 26-2
Volume of Rectangular Prisms

You can use either of the rules that you determined to find the volume of a rectangular prism with fractional edge lengths.

5. A crystal shaped like a rectangular prism has the dimensions shown.

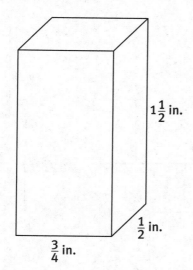

$1\frac{1}{2}$ in.

$\frac{1}{2}$ in.

$\frac{3}{4}$ in.

a. What is the area of the base of the crystal?

b. Use the area of the base in finding the volume of the crystal.

c. Use the rule using the length, width, and height to find the volume of the crystal.

6. A crystal shaped like a rectangular prism has a volume of 2.88 cubic centimeters.
a. The crystal has a square base with an area of 1.44 square centimeters. How tall is the crystal? Explain your thinking.

b. What are the dimensions of the crystal? Explain your thinking.

Check Your Understanding

7. A rectangular prism with a base area of 35 square inches is 12 inches tall. What is the volume of the prism?

8. A rectangular prism is 9 centimeters long, 6 centimeters wide, and 3.5 centimeters tall. What is the volume of the prism?

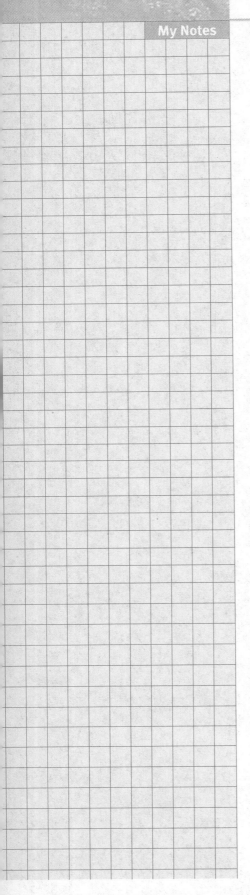

LESSON 26-2 PRACTICE

For Items 9–12, find the volume of each rectangular prism.

9.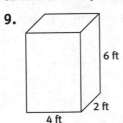

10.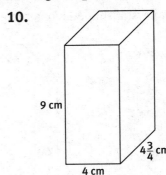

11.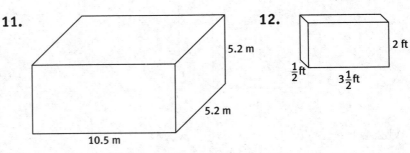

12.

13. A battery shaped like a rectangular prism is 11 inches long, 5 inches wide, and 4 inches tall. What is the volume of the battery?

14. A toy box is $4\frac{1}{2}$ feet long, 2 feet wide, and 2 feet tall. What is the volume of the toy box?

15. A rectangular prism with a volume of 288 cubic inches has a base area of 72 square inches. How tall is the prism?

16. A rectangular prism has a volume of 540 cubic centimeters. The prism is 5 centimeters tall and 18 centimeters wide. How long is the prism?

17. **Reason abstractly.** What is the maximum number of cubes with a side length of 2 inches that can fit inside the box shown?

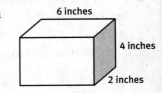

18. **Make sense of problems.** Daniel needs to buy sand to fill the box shown almost to the top. He will leave 6 inches empty at the top of the sandbox. How much sand does Daniel need?

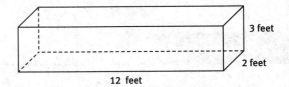

ACTIVITY 26 PRACTICE
Write your answers on a separate piece of paper.
Show your work.

Lesson 26-1
For Items 1–4, find the volume of each cube.

1.

6 ft

2.
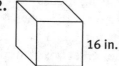
16 in.

3.

4.5 cm

4.
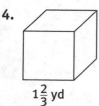
$1\frac{2}{3}$ yd

5. A crystal shaped like a cube has edges that are 8 inches long. What is the volume of the crystal?

6. A cube has a volume of 125 cubic centimeters. What is the edge length of the cube?

7. The area of one face of a cube is 144 square inches. What is the volume of the cube?

8. A cube has a surface area of 294 square inches. What is the volume of the cube?

9. A cube has an edge length of 9.2 centimeters. What is the volume of the cube?

10. What is the volume of a cube with an edge length of $\frac{3}{8}$ foot?

11. What is the volume of a cube with an edge length of $2\frac{1}{2}$ inches?

12. What is the volume of a cube with an edge length of $3\frac{1}{4}$ feet?

13. How much greater is the volume of a cube with edges that are $1\frac{1}{2}$ feet long than a cube with edges that are $\frac{1}{2}$ foot long?

14. A cubical storage box has edges that are 2 feet 4 inches long. What is the volume of the storage box?
    A. 4,704 in.^{3} **B.** 13,824 in.^{3}
    C. 17,576 in.^{3} **D.** 21,952 in.^{3}

Lesson 26-2
For Items 15 and 16, find the volume of each rectangular prism.

15.
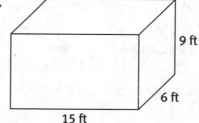
9 ft
6 ft
15 ft

16.
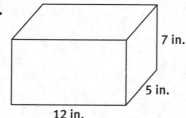
7 in.
5 in.
12 in.

For Items 17–19, find the volume of each rectangular prism.

17.
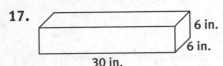
6 in.
6 in.
30 in.

18.
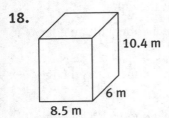
10.4 m
6 m
8.5 m

19.
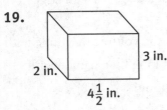
3 in.
2 in.
$4\frac{1}{2}$ in.

20. A rectangular prism with a volume of 720 cubic inches has a base area of 45 square inches. How tall is the prism?

21. A rectangular prism has a volume of 3,220 cubic centimeters. The prism is 20 centimeters tall and 23 centimeters long. How wide is the prism?

22. The dimensions of a brick shaped like a rectangular prism are 23 centimeters by 11 centimeters by 7.6 centimeters. What is the volume of the brick?

23. A party favor box is in the shape of a rectangular prism. The box is 3 inches long, $1\frac{1}{2}$ inches wide, and $\frac{3}{4}$ inch high. What is the volume of the box?

24. A chunk of cheese is cut into the shape of a rectangular prism. The piece is $3\frac{1}{4}$ inches long, $2\frac{1}{2}$ inches wide, and $1\frac{3}{4}$ inches tall. What is the volume of the chunk of cheese?

25. A hole shaped like a rectangular prism is 3 feet wide, 5 feet long, and 3 feet deep. If the hole is made 2 feet deeper, how much will the volume of the hole increase?

26. A cereal box is 10 inches long, 2 inches wide, and 14 inches tall. A pasta box is 15 inches long, 1 inch wide, and 4 inches tall. How much greater is the volume of the cereal box than the pasta box?

27. A trunk is 3 feet long, $1\frac{1}{2}$ feet wide, and 2 feet tall. What is the volume of the trunk?

A. $6\frac{1}{2}$ ft^3 B. $6\frac{1}{8}$ ft^3

C. 9 ft^3 D. $9\frac{1}{8}$ ft^3

MATHEMATICAL PRACTICES
Model with Mathematics

28. Design a box that will hold 24 2-inch cubes, with no empty space left in the box after it is filled with the cubes. Describe two possible designs for the box. Sketch each design and find the surface area and volume of each box.

Cut out these nets for Item 4 of Lesson 26-1.

Figure 1

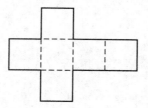

Figure 2

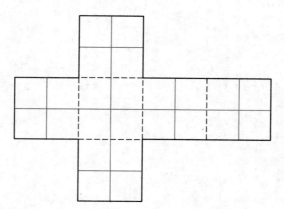

This page is intentionally blank.

Surface Area and Volume of Prisms
COLORING CREATIONS

Write your answers on a separate sheet of paper. Show your work.

Artie is designing crayons and packages for restaurants to give children with their menus.

One part of Artie's marketing plan is to create crayons that will not roll off the tables. He decides to create crayons in the shape of triangular prisms. Each of the crayons that are shaped like triangular prisms will have a paper wrapper around the faces. The crayons have a base edge length of 10 millimeters and the height of each face is 50 millimeters, as shown in the diagram below.

CONNECT TO BUSINESS

A company's *marketing plan* describes specific actions the organization will take to achieve its advertising and marketing goals.

1. Artie must create a paper label that will wrap around the crayon to cover all of the faces.
   a. Sketch each face and include the dimensions of each shape.
   b. Find the total area needed for the paper label. Explain your reasoning.

2. Artie also created a box in the shape of a triangular prism to hold four different color crayons, as shown in the diagram. Find the total surface area of the box.

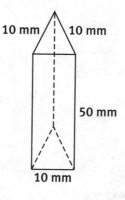

10 mm / 10 mm

50 mm

10 mm

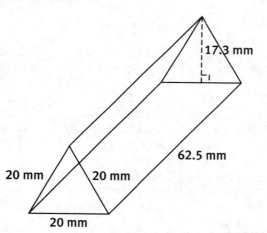

17.3 mm

62.5 mm

20 mm / 20 mm

20 mm

3. Another crayon type the company will make is in the shape of a rectangular prism. The dimensions of each of these crayons is

$10\frac{1}{2}$ mm by $10\frac{1}{2}$ mm by 50 mm.

   a. Sketch a net of one of these crayons.
   b. Find the volume and surface area of one of these crayons and explain what each piece of information tells you about the crayon.

4. A third type of crayon is being created for toddlers. They are referred to as "block" crayons. The dimensions of one of the block crayons is shown in the diagram.

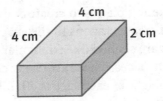

4 cm

4 cm 2 cm

Find the maximum number of these block crayons that can be stacked in a box that is 12 centimeters by 12 centimeters by 6 centimeters. Explain your reasoning.

Scoring Guide	Exemplary	Proficient	Emerging	Incomplete
	The solution demonstrates these characteristics:			
Mathematics Knowledge and Thinking (Items 1a-b, 2, 3a-b, 4)	• Accurately and efficiently finding the surface area and volume of prisms.	• Finding the surface area and volume of prisms with few if any errors.	• Difficulty finding the surface area and volume of prisms.	• No understanding of finding the surface area and volume of prisms.
Problem Solving (Items 1b, 2, 3b, 4)	• An appropriate and efficient strategy that results in a correct answer.	• A strategy that may include unnecessary steps but results in a correct answer.	• A strategy that results in some incorrect answers.	• No clear strategy when solving problems.
Mathematical Modeling / Representations (Items 1a-b, 3a)	• Clear and accurate understanding of how a net represents a three-dimensional figure.	• Relating a net to the surfaces of a three-dimensional figure.	• Difficulty recognizing how a net represents a three-dimensional figure.	• No understanding of how a net represents a three-dimensional figure.
Reasoning and Communication (Items 1b, 3b, 4)	• Precise use of appropriate terms to explain the surface area and volume of solids.	• An adequate explanation of finding the surface area and volume of solids.	• A partially correct explanation of finding the surface area and volume of solids.	• An incomplete or inaccurate explanation of the surface area and volume of solids.

Data Analysis

Unit Overview
In this unit, you will collect data and explore different ways to summarize data and display results as you participate in surveys that involve you and your classmates.

Key Terms
As you study this unit, add these and other terms to your math notebook. Include in your notes your prior knowledge of each word, as well as your experiences in using the word in different mathematical examples. If needed, ask for help in pronouncing new words and add information on pronunciation to your math notebook. It is important that you learn new terms and use them correctly in your class discussions and in your problem solutions.

Academic Vocabulary
- uniform
- range

Math Terms
- statistical question
- variability
- distribution
- bar chart
- mode
- dot plot
- symmetrical
- skewed
- stem plot
- mean

- outliers
- median
- mean absolute deviation
- interquartile range
- quartiles
- five-number summary
- box plot
- histogram
- frequency table
- class intervals

ESSENTIAL QUESTIONS

? How is data organized and presented in real-world situations?

? What are ways you can summarize data both numerically and graphically?

EMBEDDED ASSESSMENTS

These assessments, following activities 28 and 30, will give you an opportunity to demonstrate your ability to summarize data.

Embedded Assessment 1:

Types of Variables and Measures of Center   p. 377

Embedded Assessment 2:

Measures of Variability and Numerical Graphs   p. 407

Write your answers on notebook paper.
Show your work.

1. Write these numbers in order from least to greatest.

   21, 19, 56, 13, 27, 31, 42, 47, 52, 38, 21, 27

2. Write these numbers in order from least to greatest.

   4.2, 5.7, 3.6, 4.9, 5.4, 5.1, 4.3, 3.1, 4.2, 5.4

3. Compute the following:
   a. $45 + 62 + 27 + 38 + 19 + 52$
   b. $625 - 173$
   c. 28×34
   d. $143 \div 22$

4. Which of the following names three graphs?
   A. bar, block, and circle
   B. bar, picture, and circle
   C. picture, block, and circle
   D. bar, rectangle, and picture

5. Carlynn asked 10 friends to name their favorite flavor of ice cream. The results are below.

   vanilla, strawberry, strawberry, vanilla, chocolate, vanilla, vanilla, chocolate, vanilla, chocolate

   a. Construct a bar chart for these data.
   b. What does the bar chart tell you about the friends' favorite flavor?

6. Add these numbers: 13, 28, 12, 42, 65, 88. What is the average?

7. Find the average of these numbers: 24, 9, 27, 14, 15, 7, 19, 21.

Summarizing Data Graphically
Making a Survey
Lesson 27-1 Survey Questions and Variability

Learning Targets:
- Identify statistical questions.
- Interpret the variability of data collected from a survey.

> SUGGESTED LEARNING STRATEGIES: Graphic Organizer, Discussion Groups, Vocabulary Organizer, Sharing and Responding

1. Answer the "Take a Snapshot" survey (on page 349). Do not write your name on the paper. When you have finished, carefully tear out the page and give it to your teacher.

Refer to the questions on the class survey to answer Items 2–4.

2. How do you think your classmates' answers to the survey questions will compare to your answers to the survey questions?

3. Consider the following questions:
   (a) What is your teacher's height?
   (b) How many pets does your teacher have?

   Will these questions have more than one possible answer?

4. How are the "Take a Snapshot" survey questions different from the questions in Item 3?

The answers to *statistical questions* will be different from one person to another. For example, each of your classmates has a different birth date.

5. Which of the questions on the "Take a Snapshot" survey do you think would have student answers with the most *variability*? Explain why you chose this question. Share your answer with your group and list any details you may not have considered before. If you do not know the exact words to describe your ideas, use synonyms or request assistance from group members to help you convey your ideas.

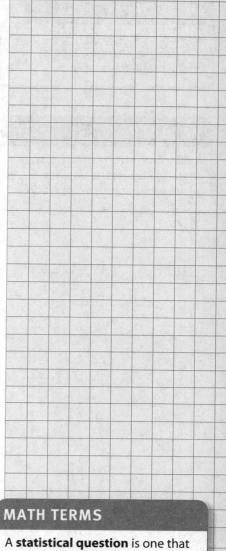

My Notes

MATH TERMS

A **statistical question** is one that produces answers that vary from person to person. **Variability** refers to how many different answers there are to a statistical question.

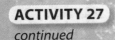

My Notes

MATH TIP

Remember that a *variable* is a number that changes depending on the problem situation.

MATH TERMS

A **distribution** is the collection of all the values for the possible answers to a statistical question.

6. Which of the questions on the "Take a Snapshot" survey do you think would have student answers with the least variability? Explain why you chose this question.

7. Read the following statistical questions. The answers to the questions have **distributions** with different amounts of variability. Would you expect these questions to produce distributions with a lot of variability or very little variability?
   a. How tall are high school students?
   b. What are the scores on a hard math test?
   c. How much actual medicine is in each pill?

8. Suppose that a math test had very little variability. What would that tell you about the distribution of test grades?

Check Your Understanding

9. Decide which questions below are statistical questions. Compare your answers with a partner's answers. Discuss any answers on which you differ and choose one answer.
   a. What day of the week is it today?
   b. What colors of cars do the teachers at this school drive?
   c. How thick are the books in the school's library?
   d. How thick is this SpringBoard math book?

10. How do you recognize questions that will produce answers with a lot of variability?

LESSON 27-1 PRACTICE

Suppose you just watched a basketball game between the Knights and the Tornadoes.

11. Create a question about the game that is NOT a statistical question.

12. Create a question about the game that is a statistical question.

13. Predict a low or a high variability for the following question: Which player had the best game?

14. Create a question about the game that will have a distribution with low variability.

15. **Model with mathematics.** Create a question about the game that will have a distribution with a lot of variability.

My Notes

"Take a Snapshot" Survey

Please answer the following questions about yourself to the best of your ability. This survey is anonymous; **do not** put your name on it.

1. Gender (boy or girl) _____

2. Eye color _____

3. Height (in inches, round to the nearest inch) _____

4. How many people usually live in your home (including yourself) _____

5. Number of the month in which you were born (January = 1, February = 2, and so on) _____

6. Number of pets _____

7. Which of the following superpowers would you most like to have: the ability to read minds, to freeze time, to fly, to be invisible, or to have super strength? _____

8. Room number of your homeroom _____

9. Number of minutes it took you to get ready for school today _____

10. Number of hours you spent on a computer in the last week _____

11. Number of pieces of gum chewed in a typical day _____

12. Your hand span (rounded to the nearest cm) Measure from the tip of your thumb to the tip of your small finger with your fingers spread apart as far as possible. _____

This page is intentionally blank.

Learning Targets:
- Identify types of statistical variables.
- Write statistical questions.
- Construct graphs to represent statistical data.

SUGGESTED LEARNING STRATEGIES: Marking the Text, Create Representations, Sharing and Responding

The answer to each question in your class survey represents a *variable*. Gender and eye color are examples of **categorical variables,** because they place each individual into a category, such as people with blue eyes. Categorical variables can be summarized to show how often each category occurs.

Another type of variable is a **numerical variable.** Numerical variables occur when the data collected results in numbers. Weight and age are examples of numerical variables.

1. Identify each question in your class survey as an example of a *categorical* (C) variable or a *numerical* (N) variable.

Question	C	N
1. Gender		
2. Eye Color		
3. Height		
4. Number of people		
5. Birth month		
6. Number of pets		

Question	C	N
7. Superpower		
8. Room number		
9. Minutes to get ready		
10. Computer hours		
11. Pieces of gum		
12. Hand span		

A variable with values represented by numbers is not automatically a numerical variable. Numerical variables have values for which numerical calculations, such as averages or addition, would make sense. If either of those operations does not make sense, the variable is categorical. For example, a zip code is a number, but it is a categorical variable.

2. Review your answers to Item 1. Should any of your numerical variables be changed to a categorical variable?

3. Write a new question to add to the class survey.

CONNECT TO AP

Key concepts in AP Statistics include summarizing data, creating graphical displays, and recognizing the difference between numerical (also called quantitative) and categorical variables.

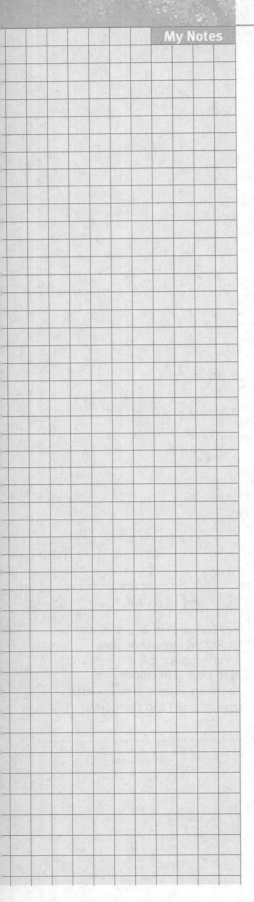

4. Do the answers to your new question produce a categorical or a numerical variable?

Data needs to be organized to analyze it and see patterns. One way to organize data is to create a table. Marshall collected the following categorical data about the eye color of the students in his class.

- Number of students with blue eyes: 6 girls, 7 boys
- Number of students with brown eyes: 9 girls, 6 boys
- Number of students with hazel eyes: 3 girls, 4 boys

Study the table below to see how this data can be organized.

		Gender		Total
		Girls	**Boys**	
Eye Color	**Blue**	6	7	13
	Brown	9	6	15
	Hazel	3	4	7
	Total	18	17	35

With the data organized, you can now use it to make calculations.

Example A

Calculate the percentage of girls with each eye color.

Step 1: The total number of girls is 18, so the fraction of girls with blue eyes is $\frac{6}{18}$, or 33.3%

Step 2: Calculate the percentage of girls with brown and hazel eyes.

	Girls	**Count**	**Fraction**	**Percent**
Eye Color	**Blue**	6	$\frac{6}{18}$	33.3%
	Brown	9	$\frac{9}{18}$	50%
	Hazel	3	$\frac{3}{18}$	16.7%
	Total	18	$\frac{18}{18}$	100%

By looking at the data about eye color for girls, you can quickly see which eye color is the most common for girls in your class.

Lesson 27-2
Types of Variables and Graphs

Try These A

Create a table for boys with each eye color in Marshall's class.

Boys	Count	Fraction	Percent
Blue			
Brown			
Hazel			
Total			

(Eye Color label at left side of table)

My Notes

MATH TERMS

A **bar chart** (also called a bar graph) is used to graph categorical data.

The preceding table of percentages is a *relative frequency chart*. Since it shows what frequencies are calculated, a percent **bar chart** can be created as a visual display of the results. For example, look at the bar chart below.

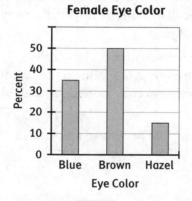

Female Eye Color

The category of brown eyes is the **mode** for the females in the class since that eye color occurred most frequently in this group.

5. Create a percent bar graph for males based on the relative frequency chart and identify the mode.

6. Compare and contrast the eye color distributions for males and females in Marshall's class.

MATH TERMS

The **mode** is the value in the data that occurs most often.

In earlier grades, you used bar charts to graph categorical data. In describing a bar chart, you would discuss which category occurred the most often or the least often. Distributions for numerical data are created using dot plots and stem-and-leaf plots.

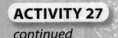
My Notes

Suppose the students in Douglas's class have the following heights.

57 56 58 55 56 60 56 58 57 55 61 54

57 53 58 58 56 57 59 57 59 60 59

7. How might these heights have been measured? In what units were the heights measured?

8. You might wonder what a typical height is or whether height values vary a lot. Could you easily give answers for typical height and variability by looking at a list of values like the one above?

Data needs to be organized to help you analyze it and see patterns. One way to organize data is to show it in a graph. Graphical displays, such as ***dot plots***, help you to easily see how the data are distributed—where the data are centered and how spread out the data are. You can also see the overall shape of the distribution and whether any values appear unusual. To create a dot plot:

• Draw a number line with an appropriate scale.
• Place a dot above the appropriate value on the number line for each piece of data. If the value occurs more than once, stack the dots vertically.

9. Create a dot plot for the heights of students in Douglas's class.

10. Reason abstractly and quantitatively. How would you describe the shape of this distribution? Is the distribution shape easier to see in the dot plot or in the list of numbers?

11. List the heights of students in your class from the class survey.

My Notes

12. Create a dot plot for the heights of students in your class.

13. Describe the shape of the distribution of heights for students in your class.

Another type of graph that can quickly reveal the shape of the distribution for a numerical variable is a *stem plot*.

MATH TERMS

A **stem plot** (also called a stem-and-leaf plot) displays data that is organized by place value. The stem, which is to the left, represents the first digit (or digits) and the leaf represents the last digit of the number. For example, the number 14 is represented by a 1 on the left with a 4 on the right separated by a vertical line: 1 | 4.

Example B

Draw a stem plot for the baseball games won for each of the 20 seasons that Curt Schilling pitched in the major leagues, shown below.

0	0	1	3	14	16	2	7	9	17
15	15	11	22	23	8	21	8	15	9

Step 1: Draw a vertical line. On the left side, write the tens digits of the numbers in the data set.

Step 2: Next to each number in the stem, write the units digit of each corresponding number in the data set. These numbers are the leaf. There will be as many leaves as there are numbers in the data set, which in this example is 20.

```
Stem  Leaf
  0 | 0  0  1  2  3  7  8  8  9  9
  1 | 1  4  5  5  5  6  7
  2 | 1  2  3
```

Try These B

a. Create a stem-and-leaf plot of the recorded low temperatures for the past 15 days.

39	42	38	46	50	43	47	46
51	32	38	42	45	53	50	

b. Create a stem-and-leaf plot for the number of boxes of cookies sold in the fundraiser by each member of the class.

6	0	11	8	3	15	20	17
2	0	21	11	1	16	9	22
13	2	15	1	7	12	30	21

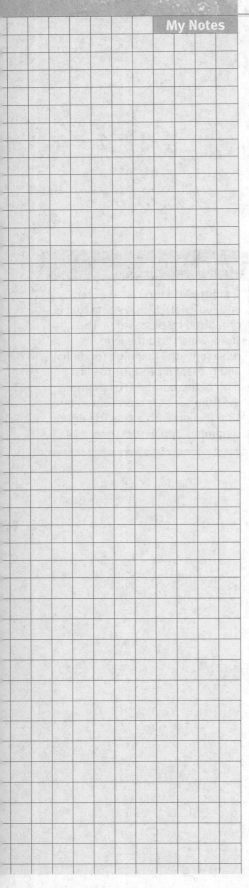

My Notes

Check Your Understanding

14. Write three questions to add to the class survey that lead to categorical variables.

15. Write three questions to add to the class survey that lead to numerical variables.

16. Write a few sentences explaining what a dot plot is and how it helps to organize numerical data.

LESSON 27-2 PRACTICE

17. **Model with mathematics.** Construct a bar chart for the following information: There are 20 students in Mrs. Smith's class, 30 students in Mr. Yu's class, and 40 students in Ms. York's class.

18. Construct a relative frequency chart and percent bar graph for the eye color of all students in Marshall's class. Identify the mode for the eye color distribution of the class.

	Female	Count	Fraction	Percent
Eye Color	Blue	13		
	Brown	15		
	Hazel	7		
	Total	35		

19. Why would it not be appropriate to create a dot plot for Items 17 and 18?

20. Consider the daily high temperatures over the last fifteen days. Create a dot plot to represent this information.

86	90	88	96	90
88	90	92	94	90
90	90	100	92	98

21. Describe the shape of the distribution of temperatures. What conclusions can you draw from the graph?

Learning Targets:

- Organize data from a statistical question.
- Determine appropriate graphical representation of data.
- Describe distributions from graphical representation.

SUGGESTED LEARNING STRATEGIES: Sharing and Responding, Create Representations, Marking the Text, Discussion Groups

1. List the results from the class survey for the number of pets for the students in your class.

2. Determine whether a bar chart or dot plot is appropriate to graph the distribution for the number of pets for the students in your class. Chose an appropriate scale and graph the data.

3. How does the shape of this distribution differ from the shape of the height distribution?

4. Do you see any unusual values in the data for the number of pets? If so, why do you think it is unusual?

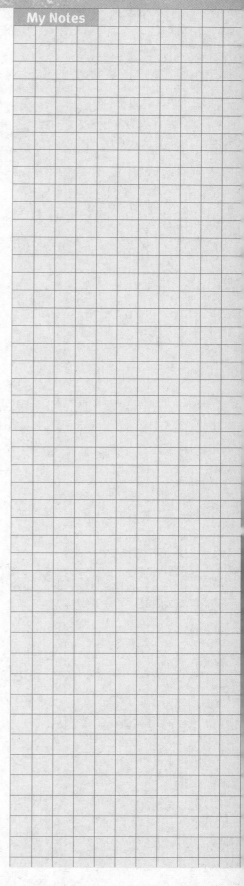
My Notes

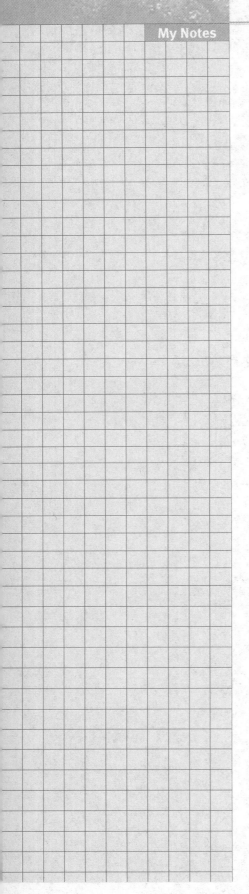

My Notes

5. If you thought values in Item 4 were unusual, why do you think that value for the number of pets may have occurred?

Suppose a teacher recorded the time that it took students to finish a math test. The times, to the nearest minute, are listed below.

| 40 | 30 | 23 | 35 | 28 | 29 | 15 | 37 | 38 | 38 | 36 | 35 |
| 34 | 34 | 35 | 37 | 35 | 36 | 32 | 36 | 35 | 32 | 39 | 34 |

6. How many students are in this class?

7. Determine an appropriate graph to display the distribution for the length of time students took to finish a test. Graph the data.

8. How is the shape of this distribution similar to or different from the shape of the distribution for the number of pets?

9. How is the shape of the distribution for the time to finish a test different from the shape of the distribution for the number of pets?

10. Do you think that 15 minutes is an unusual length of time to finish this test? Why or why not?

Lesson 27-3
Shapes of Distributions

When you graph data, you will notice that the data forms a shape. Look at the examples that follow. When the data extend toward one side or the other, the distribution is **skewed**. A distribution can be skewed either to the right or to the left. Drawing a smooth line above the data helps you see the shape of the distribution.

My Notes

MATH TERMS

The shape of a distribution is **symmetrical** when the two halves are the same. The shape is **skewed** when one side is longer than the other side.

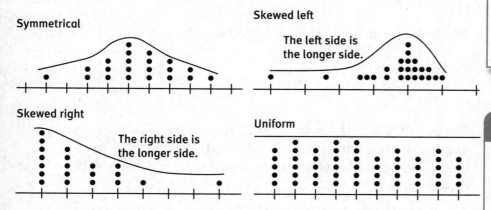

ACADEMIC VOCABULARY

In a **uniform** distribution, the values of the variable occur approximately the same number of times. *Uniform* also has other meanings outside of math; for example, a school uniform.

Now consider the following scenario. Lorelei opens a phone book to a random page, closes her eyes, and puts her finger down on a random spot on the page. She records the last digit of that phone number and the last digit of the next 49 phone numbers.

Last digits of phone numbers:

2	4	4	4	8	1	9	2	9	1
8	2	6	6	3	3	1	2	7	4
7	3	0	0	8	7	5	1	3	2
8	6	3	6	3	0	4	9	0	9
4	8	3	5	5	5	0	1	1	8

11. **Attend to precision.** Create an appropriate graph to study the shape of the distribution for the last digits of phone numbers.

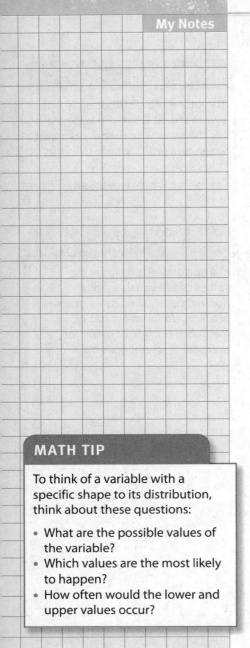

My Notes

MATH TIP

To think of a variable with a specific shape to its distribution, think about these questions:

- What are the possible values of the variable?
- Which values are the most likely to happen?
- How often would the lower and upper values occur?

12. Would you describe the shape of this distribution as skewed right or skewed left?

13. Does the shape of this distribution surprise you? Why or why not?

The distribution of this variable, the last digits of phone numbers, is an example of a uniform distribution. Notice that the number of observations (number of dots) is about the same for each possible value of the variable.

14. What is a statistical question (other than height) that would have answers that have a distribution that is symmetrical?

15. What statistical question from the class survey (other than number of pets) has answers producing a distribution that is skewed? Would the shape of the distribution be skewed left or right?

16. What statistical question (other than digits from a phone book) has answers that produce a distribution with a shape that is uniform?

My Notes

Check Your Understanding

17. What is the shape of the distribution of each of the following dot plots? Explain your reasoning.

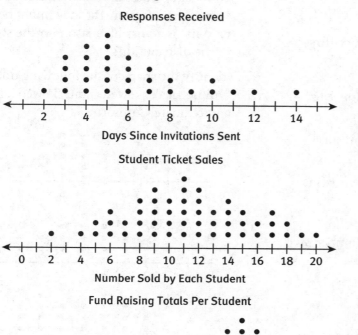

LESSON 27-3 PRACTICE

18. Mr. Clark wants to bring a snack for his class on Friday. He has asked the class about favorite snacks. Their answers are listed below.

Chips	Fruit	Fruit
Chips	Cookies	Chips
Cookies	Chips	Cookies
Fruit	Chips	Fruit
Fruit	Fruit	Chips
Cookies	Cookies	Chips
Cookies	Cookies	Fruit

a. What type of graph can be used to display this data?
b. Create the graph for the class snack data.

19. **Look for and make use of structure.** Does the graph help Mr. Clark decide which snack to bring? Why or why not?

20. Describe the distribution of data for Mr. Clark's class.

21. What would you recommend to Mr. Clark in making his decision about which snack to bring?

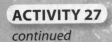

ACTIVITY 27 PRACTICE

Write your answers on notebook paper.
Show your work.

1. Identify the following variables as categorical (C) or numerical (N).
   a. Your favorite flavor of ice cream
   b. The area code in your phone number (first three digits)
   c. Length of your index finger
   d. Time it takes to travel from your house to school each morning

2. For each of the variables listed in Item 1, list three possible observations.

3. For which of the variables listed in Item 1 is it appropriate to create a dot plot?

4. Aidan's class also did the "Take a Snapshot" survey. Below is the data set for the number of pets for students in his class.

   3, 2, 3, 2, 3, 5, 1, 0, 1, 3, 2, 3

   1, 2, 2, 3, 2, 2, 16, 2, 2, 1, 3, 2

   a. Create a dot plot of the number of pets students have.
   b. What shape is this distribution?
   c. Are there any unusual values in this data set? If so, what might be a possible reason for this value?

5. Four candidates are running for the office of Student Council President. Sabina wants to create graphs to show how many votes each homeroom cast for each of the candidates. Should she use a dot plot or a bar graph? Explain.

Use the dot plot below for Item 6.

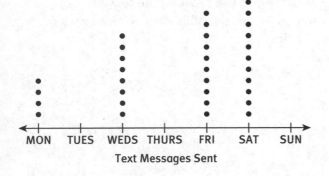

6. The dot plot shows the number of text messages Nguyen sent on four days last week.
   a. What does the shape of the distribution appear to be?
   b. What do you think the number of text messages sent on Tuesday might be? Why?
   c. What is a possible reason for the shape of the distribution?

7. Identify the shape of the following dot plots as symmetrical, skewed right, skewed left, or approximately uniform.

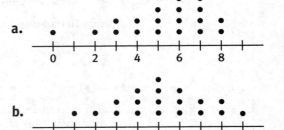

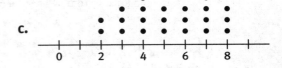

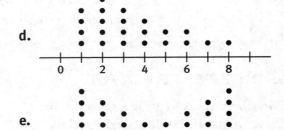

8. Students collected data by counting how many cars passed through the stop light each time it turned green for 16 times. What type of graph could be used to display the data that the students collected? Explain why this graph is appropriate.

MATHEMATICAL PRACTICES
Attend to Precision

9. Explain what a statistical question is in your own words. How can the answers gathered from asking the question be used?

Measures of Center
Bull's Eye
Lesson 28-1 Mean and Outliers

Learning Targets:
- Calculate the mean of a data set.
- Identify outliers of a data set.
- Construct dot plots.

SUGGESTED LEARNING STRATEGIES: KWL Chart, Vocabulary Organizer, Marking the Text, Think-Pair-Share

The distribution of numerical data can be described by discussing its center, spread, and shape. In this activity, you will investigate the center of distributions.

Look at the following heights (in inches) of students on the soccer team.

57	55	60	55	56	60	56	62	57	55	61	54
57	53	58	58	54	56	59	57	61	60	59	

Here is the dot plot for this data.

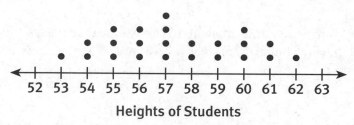

Heights of Students

1. Estimate the center of the distribution for height of students on the soccer team from the information contained in the dot plot.

2. Calculate the **mean** height of students in your class.

   (Round your answer to the nearest tenth of an inch.)

3. How close was your estimate to the actual mean height of students? Explain why your estimate is or is not close to the actual mean. Share your response with your group. As you explain your reasoning, speak clearly and use precise mathematical language.

MATH TIP

To calculate the **mean** (or average) of the values in a distribution, compute the total of the data values by adding all of the values. Then divide this total by the number of observations.

Look at data on the amount of time that several students spent taking a history test. Below is the data set, along with a dot plot of that data.

| 40 | 30 | 23 | 35 | 28 | 29 | 15 | 37 | 38 | 38 | 36 | 35 |
| 35 | 32 | 34 | 39 | 36 | 37 | 32 | 35 | 34 | 34 | 36 | 35 |

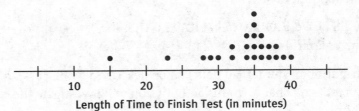

Length of Time to Finish Test (in minutes)

4. Estimate the mean length of time to finish the test for these students by looking at the dot plot.

5. Calculate the mean length of time for these students to finish the test. (Round your answer to the nearest tenth of a minute.)

6. How close was your estimate to the actual mean length of time? Explain why your estimate was (or was not) close to the actual mean.

In this data set, the observations of 15 minutes and 23 minutes appear to be unusual values. Values that are outside the general pattern of data are called *outliers*.

7. **Reason abstractly.** What is a possible reason why someone might finish this test so quickly?

MATH TERMS

Outliers are observations that do not fit the overall pattern of the data set.

Sometimes unusual values like these are correct data values. For example, in the case of height, a data value may look unusual because a student may have reported height in feet rather than in inches. In other cases, these unusual values represent errors—data that was recorded incorrectly or false answers that someone gave to a survey. (For example, suppose a student recorded height as 100 feet or the time to take a test as −4 minutes. These data values would be considered incorrect.)

If an outlier is thought to be an incorrect data value, then it is removed from the data set. However, if an outlier might be a correct data value, it is NOT removed from the data set, although it might need to be corrected. For example, if it were clear that height had been reported in feet rather than in inches, you would convert the measurement to inches and keep it in the data set.

8. Should the observation of 15 minutes or 23 minutes be removed from the data set above? Explain why or why not.

9. Predict what would happen to the mean if these two observations, 15 minutes and 23 minutes, were removed.

10. Remove these two observations and calculate the mean length of time to finish the test for the remaining 22 times.

11. Was your prediction in Item 9 correct? If not, explain why not.

12. State in words what effect these two unusual observations had on the mean length of time to finish the test.

A women's swim team includes ten members who swim relays. Their ages are listed below.

21   19   22   21   22   18   22   20   41   24

13. Create a dot plot of the ages of these relay swimmers.

14. Calculate the mean age for the relay swimmers.

15. Enter each of the 10 ages into the appropriate column in the table below, depending on whether it is above or below the mean age. For example, 21 is below the mean age, so it would be entered into the first column. Once you have entered the 10 ages, complete the rest of the table.

Data Values Below the Mean	Distance from Mean	Data Values Above the Mean	Distance From Mean
Total distance:		Total distance:	

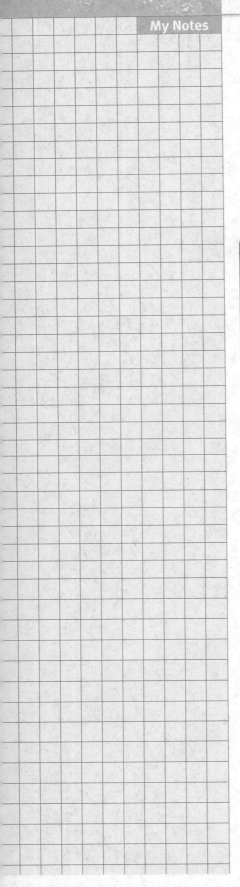

My Notes

16. What do you notice about the total distance from the mean for the values below the mean versus the total distance from the mean for the values above the mean?

17. Do you think this is true for any data set?

18. Is there an outlier in this age distribution? If so, what would be the mean if this value were removed?

Check Your Understanding

19. Explain how to calculate the mean of a data set.

20. What is an outlier?

21. Summarize the effect of outliers on the mean of a distribution.

LESSON 28-1 PRACTICE

22. Alex works in a grocery store after school. Here is his list of hours for a two-week period:

4	3	3	4	4	4	8	3	4	3

 a. Are there any outliers? If so, what are they?
 b. Is the outlier a correct data value?
 c. What might explain the outlier?

23. Calculate the mean.

24. **Construct viable arguments.** Describe the effect of the outlier on the mean.

25. Construct a dot plot representing the hours Alex worked.

26. In a few sentences, describe what the dot plot shows.

Learning Targets

- Find the median.
- Determine relative position of the mean and median in a distribution.

Another measure of center is called the *median*. To find the median, arrange all of the observations in order from least to greatest. Then find the middle value.

- If a list has an odd number of observations, then the median is the middle observation in the list.
- If a list has an even number of observations, then the median is the average of the two middle observations in the list.

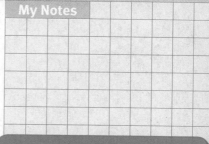

MATH TERMS

The **median** is the middle number in a list of the data that has been ordered from least to greatest.

The following is the list of the ages of the ten members of the women relay swimmers.

21   19   22   21   22   18   22   20   41   24

1. List the ages of the women relay swimmers in order from least to greatest.

2. Find the median age of the relay swimmers.

3. On your dot plot in Item 13 in Lesson 28-1, mark the location of the mean and median. What do you notice about how these two locations compare?

Revisit the data set for the length of time to finish the history test.

40   30   23   35   28   29   15   37   38   38   36   35
35   32   34   39   36   37   32   35   34   34   36   35

4. List the length of times in order from least to greatest.

5. Find the median length of time to finish the test.

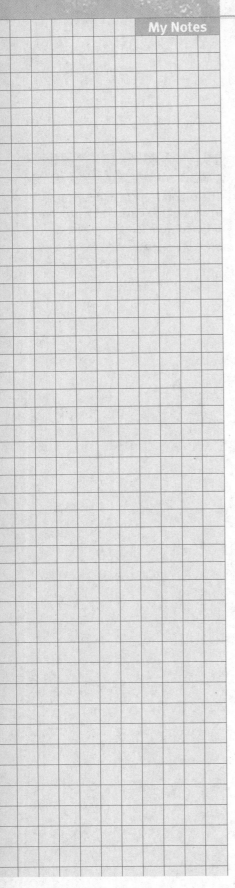

My Notes

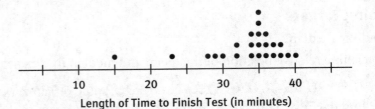

Length of Time to Finish Test (in minutes)

6. On the dot plot, mark the location of the mean and median. What do you notice about how these two values compare?

The heights of students in Douglas's class are shown below.

| 57 | 56 | 58 | 55 | 56 | 60 | 56 | 58 | 57 | 55 | 61 | 54 |
| 57 | 53 | 58 | 58 | 56 | 57 | 59 | 57 | 59 | 60 | 59 | |

7. List the heights of students in order from least to greatest.

8. Find the mean and median height of students in Douglas's class.

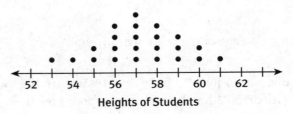

Heights of Students

9. On the dot plot, mark the location of the mean and median. What do you notice about how these two locations compare?

10. **Reason quantitatively.** When do you think the mean and the median will be about the same?

11. When will the mean be greater than the median?

Check Your Understanding

12. Explain how to find the median of a distribution.

13. What does the mean tell us about a distribution?

14. What does the median tell us about a distribution?

15. Explain what might cause the mean and median not to be the same value.

LESSON 28-2 PRACTICE

All the students on your track team are timed as they run one mile. Here are the times rounded to the nearest minute:

7	9	12	11	8	9	18	10	6	11
9	8	7	8	10	8	12	7	7	10

16. Construct a dot plot for the times.

17. List the times in order from least to greatest.

18. Find the median WITH the outlier and WITHOUT the outlier. Explain how the outlier affects the median.

19. What is the mean?

20. **Make use of structure.** The time it takes the average person to run one mile is between 7 and 10 minutes. Is the median for your track team below the average, close to the average, or above the average? Is the mean for your track team below the average, close to the average, or above the average?

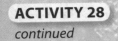

ACTIVITY 28
continued

Learning Targets:

● Construct dot plots.

● Identify whether the mean or the median should be used to summarize the center of a distribution based upon the shape of the distribution.

SUGGESTED LEARNING STRATEGIES: Interactive Word Wall, Predict and Confirm, Visualization, Create Representations

Matthew is a student reporter for the Seven Lakes Middle School newspaper. His assignment for the next issue is to write an article about how much homework is assigned to middle school students. Matthew decides to ask 21 students from each grade (sixth, seventh, and eighth grades) how many minutes they spent on homework the night before. The data for sixth graders is below.

Sixth Grade Homework Times (in minutes)

| 40 | 45 | 42 | 42 | 47 | 38 | 42 | 36 | 44 | 37 | 45 |
| 42 | 40 | 38 | 44 | 49 | 35 | 44 | 50 | 37 | 48 |

1. Create a dot plot for the sixth grade homework times.

2. How would you describe the shape of this distribution?

3. Find the mean and median of the sixth grade homework times.

4. What do you notice about the shape of the distribution for the sixth grade homework times? Explain what this means in terms of the mean and median. Share your response with your group. Speak clearly and use precise mathematical language to describe your reasoning.

Here is the data set for the seventh grade homework times.

Seventh Grade Homework Times (in minutes)

40	45	52	42	47	48	42	56	44	57	45
42	40	44	44	49	55	44	50	60	47	

5. **Model with mathematics.** Create a dot plot for the seventh grade homework times.

6. What shape does this distribution have?

7. Find the mean and median for the seventh grade homework times.

8. What do you notice about the shape of the distribution for seventh grade homework times? Explain what this means in terms of the mean and median.

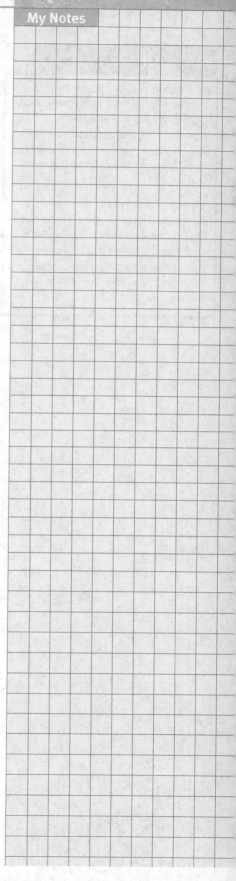

My Notes

MATH TIP

The *mean* is usually reported as a measure of center for *symmetrical* distributions. In a *skewed* distribution, the *median* is usually reported as the measure of center since it is not affected by extreme values.

Measure of center is used to describe what is "typical" for a data set. In the data set (1, 2, 3, 4, 100), the mean would be 22, but the median would be 3. The median best describes the "typical" value of the distribution.

Here is the data set for the eighth grade homework times.

Eighth Grade Homework Times (in minutes)

60	65	62	62	60	56	55	62	58	57	45
64	60	64	58	40	64	62	50	60	57	

9. Create a dot plot and a stem-and-leaf plot for the eighth grade homework times.

10. What shape does this distribution have?

11. Find the mean and median for the eighth grade homework times.

12. What do you notice about the shape of the distribution for the eighth grade homework times? Explain what this means in terms of the mean and median. Share your response with your group. As you discuss your ideas in your group, ask your peers or teacher to clarify any language, terms, or concepts you do not understand.

13. In his article, what can Matthew say about the time spent on homework for middle school students?

14. Summarize how the location of the mean and median compare in relation to the shape of a distribution.

15. For each of the following variables, decide what the shape of the distribution might be. Determine which measure of center would be most appropriate.
    a. the total number of letters in your full name

    b. the age of teachers in your middle school

    c. math scores of all sixth graders on a state achievement test

Check Your Understanding

Students of all ages meet after school to participate in various clubs. The 18 students in the drama club are the following ages:

10	10	11	11	12	13	13	13	13
14	14	14	14	15	15	16	16	17

16. Create a dot plot with the ages of students in the drama club.

17. Compute the mean and the median.

18. Which number is a more accurate reflection of the center of the distribution? Explain your reasoning.

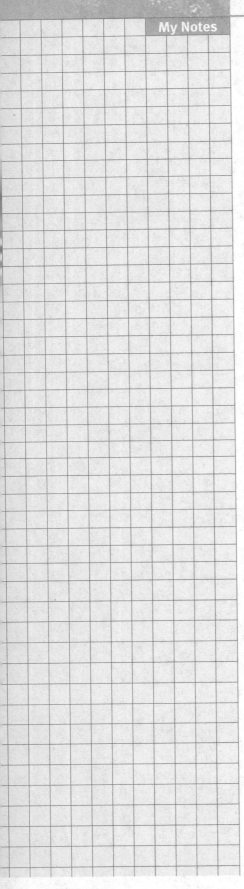

LESSON 28-3 PRACTICE

19. **Reason quantitatively.** Mr. Brown told his class that he would reward the class if students worked hard for a week. Below is a chart of the class data. Should the students use the mean or the median to encourage Mr. Brown to reward the class? Explain your reasoning.

Day	Number of Students Completing Work
Monday	13
Tuesday	15
Wednesday	18
Thursday	26
Friday	27

20. Anna's class wants to go outside during lunch on Friday, but if the average temperature is 50°F or lower then they will have to eat inside. Is mean or median the best measure of central tendency to plead their case? Explain your choice.

Day	Temperature (°F)
Monday	49
Tuesday	50
Wednesday	53
Thursday	60
Friday	48

21. If Karen's test scores are over 90 she will be allowed to go to the dance. Is the mean or median the best measure of central tendency to support her position that she may go? Explain your choice.

Test	Score
1	95
2	84
3	92
4	91
5	83

22. The store manager promised to sell a television for the typical price. To get the best deal, is mean or median the best measure of central tendency? Explain your reasoning.

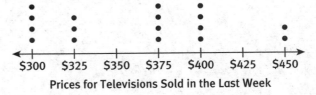

Prices for Televisions Sold in the Last Week

ACTIVITY 28 PRACTICE

Write your answers on notebook paper. Show
your work.

1. The amount of water (in ounces) the sixth
   grade students in Matthew's class drank
   yesterday is shown in the table.

   8   16   20   0   32   24   32   8   16   16   56   48
   0   24   32   28   16   36   72   40   48   24   40   32

   a. Create a dot plot of this data set.
   b. What is the mean amount of water the
      students drank?
      a. 24   c. 30.4
      b. 27.8   d. 48
   c. Identify any outliers.

2. Based on the shape of the dot plot in Item 1a,
   do you think the median will be greater than,
   less than or the same as the mean in 1b?

3. Find the median amount of water students
   drank.

4. Was your prediction in Item 2 correct? Explain.

5. Matthew's class also did the "Take a Snapshot"
   survey. Below is the data set for the number of
   minutes it took students to get ready for school.

   52   12   48   22   20   30   24   25   43   35   78   48
   5   8   25   10   50   20   15   30   30   48   30   35

   a. Create a dot plot of the data.
   b. Predict how the mean and median of this
      data set will compare.
   c. Find the mean and median number of
      minutes it took these students to get ready
      for school.

6. The data represent rainfall from the eleven
   rainiest days of the year. Consider the partial
   dot plot of the data. What needs to be done to
   create a correct dot plot for the data?

   10, 10, 11, 11, 11, 12, 13, 13, 14, 14, 18

   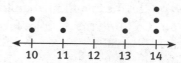

Use the data set for the number of pieces of gum chewed per day by students in Douglas's class to answer Items 7–9.

0	2	3	7	0	0	2	0	0	0
0	1	1	1	1	2	1	3	2	1

7. Compute the mean and median.

8. Identify any possible outliers in the data set.

9. Which is greater: the mean or the median? Explain why.

10. The data set for the minutes needed to get ready for school for students in Douglas's class is shown below.

5	60	25	15	45	15	20	20	20	40
20	15	60	40	28	15	30	80	20	45

 a. Compute the mean and median.

 b. Based on the mean and median in part a, how do you think the dot plot for these data is shaped? Explain.

 c. Identify any possible outliers in the data set.

 d. If there are any outliers, is there any reason to believe that these values are "bad data"?

11. Suppose a data set had a uniform dot plot. How would the mean and median compare? Explain.

MATHEMATICAL PRACTICES
Attend to Precision

12. Determine which measure of center would be more appropriate to use for each of these variables. Explain your reasoning.
 a. Grades on a math test
 b. Number of hours you spent last week watching television or movies or playing video games

Types of Variables and Measures of Center

DRIBBLE, SHOOT, SCORE!

Write your answers on notebook paper or grid paper. Show your work.

At Matthew's school, the basketball team has 14 players. Matthew wants to write an article on the basketball team for his school newspaper. He asked each player the following questions:

- What is Joe's height? (Joe is the center of the basketball team.)
- How many total shots has each player made?
- What is the height of each player?
- What is the shoe size for Sam, the point guard?

1. Which of the questions are statistical questions?

2. Identify each of the following variables as a numerical (N) or a categorical (C) variable.
   a. Jersey number
   b. Height
   c. Number of shots made
   d. Grade level
   e. Number of assists

3. The heights (to the nearest inch) of the 14 players are given below.

68	66	67	70	66	68	67
69	65	67	64	66	63	65

   a. Compute the mean height of these players.
   b. Compute the median height of these players.
   c. Construct a dot plot of the heights of the players.
   d. Describe the shape of the distribution shown in the dot plot.

4. What would happen to the mean height if 70 inches were changed to 75 inches? Explain.

5. What would happen to the median height if 70 inches were changed to 75 inches? Explain.

6. Which value, the mean or the median, best describes the center of this distribution? Explain.

Embedded Assessment 1
Use after Activity 28

Types of Variables and Measures of Center
DRIBBLE, SHOOT, SCORE!

Scoring Guide	Exemplary	Strong	Emerging	Incomplete
	The solution demonstrates these characteristics:			
Mathematics Knowledge and Thinking (Items 1, 2a-e)	• Thorough knowledge of statistical questioning. • Complete understanding of the difference between categorical and numerical variables.	• A working knowledge of statistical questioning. • Adequate understanding of identifying categorical and numerical variables.	• Misunderstanding of the concept of statistical questions. • Incorrect identification of categorical and numerical variables.	• No use or understanding of mathematical knowledge to complete the items.
Problem Solving (Items 3a-d)	• Clear identification of key information needed to create a solution. • Skillful application of math knowledge that results in a reasonable solution.	• Knowledge of most of the key information needed to create a solution. • Application of math knowledge that results in a reasonable solution.	• The misuse of key information for the solution. • An attempt to create a solution, which contains more than one incorrect response.	• The omission of key elements or a missing solution.
Mathematical Modeling / Representations (Item 3c)	• A deliberate choice of scale and how to represent data accurately in a dot plot. • A well-drawn dot plot that is clear and complete.	• A dot plot that represents all data accurately. • A dot plot that is essentially clear and reasonably well drawn.	• A dot plot that is missing some data points. • A dot plot that is confusing or not drawn clearly.	• A representation that is inaccurate, mostly incomplete, or is missing entirely.
Reasoning and Communication (Items 3d, 4, 5)	• Precise use of appropriate math terms and language in describing the distribution. • Thorough explanation of changes in mean and median using precise mathematical language.	• Generally correct use of appropriate math terms and language in describing the distribution. • Explanation of changes in mean and median using correct mathematical language.	• A description of the distribution that is or may be confusing. • An explanation of changes in mean and median that may be incorrect or uses confusing language.	• A description of the distribution that is incomplete or missing entirely.

Measures of Variability

Making the Grade

Lesson 29-1 Range

Learning Targets:

- Compute the range of a distribution as a measure of variability.

> **SUGGESTED LEARNING STRATEGIES:** Graphic Organizer, Marking the Text, Think-Pair-Share, Quickwrite

Mr. Murray teaches science. He has three classes working on group projects. Below are dot plots displaying the grade distributions of the projects for each of the three classes. Work with your group to answer Items 1–3.

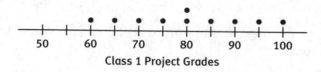

Class 1 Project Grades

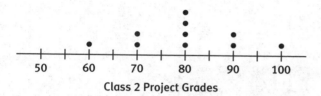

Class 2 Project Grades

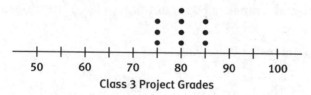

Class 3 Project Grades

1. How do the shapes for each of the three grade distributions compare?

2. Find the mean and median project grade for each class.
   Class 1:
   Class 2:
   Class 3:

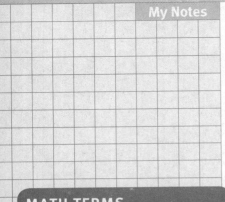

My Notes

MATH TERMS

The **range** of a distribution is the total length of the interval covered by the distribution.
Range = maximum value − minimum value

3. What did you notice about the measures of center for the three classes? What is the same about the three distributions? How do the three distributions differ?

When describing numerical graphs, you should comment on the center, spread, and shape of the distribution in order to give a complete description of the data.

One of the most common measures of spread (or variability) is the *range*. The range is the difference between the least and the greatest observation.

4. Calculate the range for the grade distribution for each of the three classes.
Class 1:
Class 2:
Class 3:

Check Your Understanding

5. What does the range tell us about the spread of the three grade distributions?

6. Find the range for these data sets.

a. 18   17   6   22   21   17   19
   19   18   22   7   20   15   10

b. 62   43   20   91   24   72   22
   31   19   75   51   64   25   33

7. Collect the ages of the students in your group or class. What is the range of the data?

LESSON 29-1 PRACTICE

8. **Construct viable arguments.** Consider the dot plot for the amount of time in minutes that students spent to take a history test.

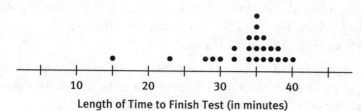

Length of Time to Finish Test (in minutes)

a. What is the range for this set of data?
b. What is the shape of this distribution?
c. Which measure of center would be best to use in this situation?

9. Matthew's class also did the "Take a Snapshot" survey. Below is the data set for the number of minutes it took students to get ready for school. What is the range for this set of data?

| 52 | 12 | 48 | 22 | 20 | 30 | 24 | 25 | 43 | 35 | 78 | 48 |
| 5 | 8 | 25 | 10 | 50 | 20 | 15 | 30 | 30 | 48 | 30 | 35 |

10. Here is the data set for the seventh grade homework times. What is the range for this set of data?

Seventh Grade Homework Times (in minutes)

| 40 | 45 | 52 | 42 | 47 | 48 | 42 | 56 | 44 | 57 | 45 |
| 42 | 40 | 44 | 44 | 49 | 55 | 44 | 50 | 60 | 47 | |

11. Here is the data set for the eighth grade homework times. What is the range for this set of data?

Eighth Grade Homework Times (in minutes)

| 60 | 65 | 62 | 62 | 60 | 56 | 55 | 62 | 58 | 57 | 45 |
| 64 | 60 | 64 | 58 | 40 | 64 | 62 | 50 | 60 | 57 | |

12. The students in Jon's class have the following heights.

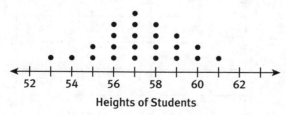

Heights of Students

a. What is the range for this set of data?
b. What is the shape of this distribution?
c. Which measure of center would be best to use in this situation?

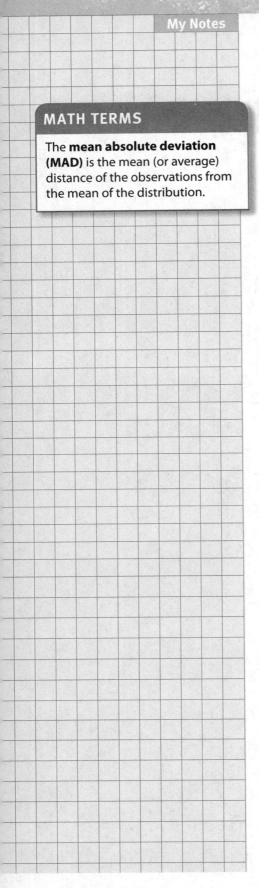

My Notes

MATH TERMS

The **mean absolute deviation (MAD)** is the mean (or average) distance of the observations from the mean of the distribution.

Learning Targets:

● Compute the mean absolute deviation (MAD) of a distribution as a measure of variability.

Another measure of the spread of a distribution is the ***mean absolute deviation (MAD)***. The MAD is the average distance that the observations are from the mean of the distribution.

Investigate the grade distribution for Class 1. The mean project grade is 80. To find how each observation *deviates* from the mean, find the difference between the observation and the mean.

For example, the observation at 90 would have a distance of 10 because the distance between 90 and the mean of 80 is 10 points.

The observation at 70 would also have a distance of 10 because the distance between 70 and 80 is 10 points.

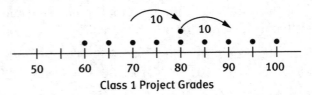

Class 1 Project Grades

1. Complete this table to find the distance from the mean for the grade distribution of Class 1.

Observation	Distance From the Mean
100	
95	
90	
85	
80	
80	
75	
70	
65	
60	
Total =	

2. Now find the mean absolute deviation (MAD) by finding the average or mean of the distances in the table.

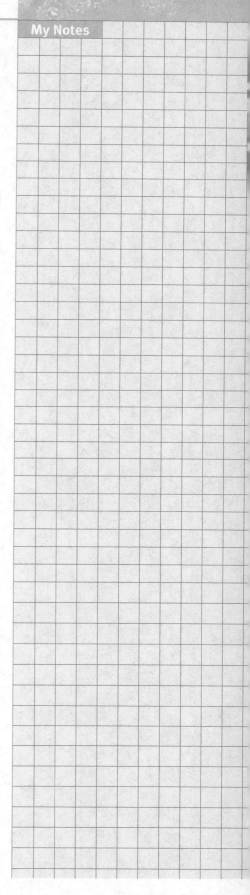

3. Looking back at the dot plot for the grade distribution of Class 1, notice how the observations are spread and relate this to the MAD.

Next, look at the MAD for the grade distribution of Class 2. Here is the dot plot.

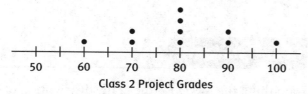

Class 2 Project Grades

4. Predict a value for the MAD of this distribution. Will the MAD of Class 2 be more or less than the MAD of Class 1? Explain.

5. Complete this table to find the distance from the mean for the grade distribution of Class 2.

Observation	Distance From the Mean
Total =	

6. Find the MAD for the grade distribution in Class 2.

7. How did your prediction in Item 4 compare to the actual value of MAD in Item 6? If they were not close, explain why.

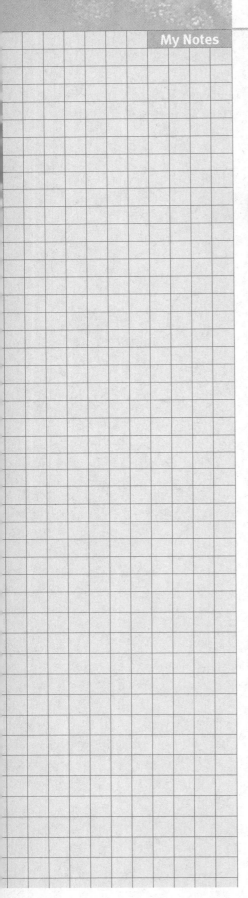

My Notes

Examine the grade distribution for Class 3. The dot plot is shown below.

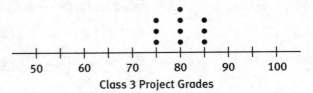

Class 3 Project Grades

Check Your Understanding

8. How do you think the MAD for the grade distribution of Class 3 compares to the MADs for the other two classes?

9. Complete this table to find the distance from the mean for the grade distribution of Class 3.

Observation	Distance From the Mean
Total =	

10. Find the MAD for the grade distribution in Class 3.

11. How did your prediction in Item 8 compare to the actual value of MAD in Item 10? If they were not close, explain why.

LESSON 29-2 PRACTICE

12. In your own words, summarize what MAD tells you about the variability of a distribution.

13. Consider the following three data sets. All of the data values are whole numbers.
   a. Calculate the mean of each data set.
   b. The three data sets have MAD values of 7, 9, and 11. Match the data sets to the appropriate MAD value without actually making a calculation.

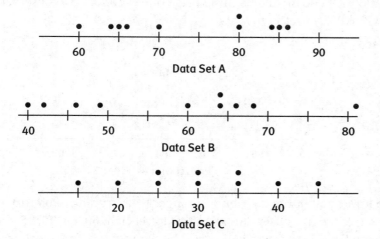

14. Verify the MAD value for one of the data sets in part b.

15. **Attend to precision.** Did you correctly assign the MAD values in part b? If not, explain where your thinking was incorrect.

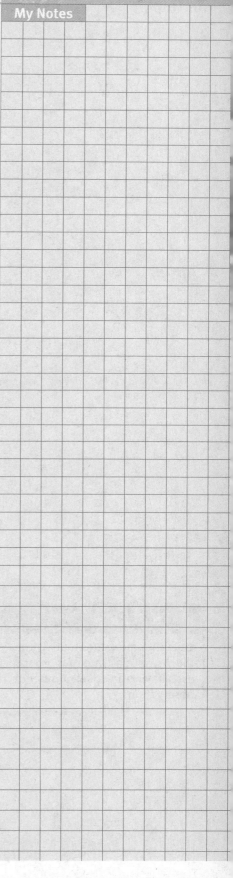

Learning Targets:

- Compute the interquartile range (IQR) of a distribution as a measure of variability.

There are many different measures of variability. The mean absolute deviation (MAD) uses the mean in its calculation. This next measure of variability, **interquartile range**, will use the quartiles.

Look again at the grade distributions of the projects from Mr. Murray's science classes. Recall the medians for the three classes were previously computed. (The median is the average of the middle two observations for the Class 1 data set.)

Class 1

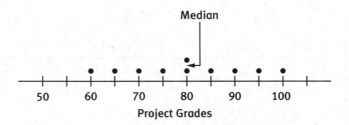

The lower half of the distribution ranges from a grade of 60 to a grade of 80. There are five observations in this lower half: 60, 65, 70, 75, and 80. The median of the lower half would be the middle of these values. The upper half of the data ranges from a grade of 80 to a grade of 100. There are five observations in this upper half: 80, 85, 90, 95, and 100. The median of the upper half would be the middle of these values.

1. Find the median of the lower half of the distribution and the median of the upper half of the distribution.

   Median of lower =

   Median of upper =

MATH TERMS

Quartiles are values that divide the distribution into four groups, each having an equal number of observations.

Mark these values on the dot plot above. Notice that the dot plot is now split into 4 sections with the same number of observations in each section. These sections are called *quartiles*. The median of the **lower** half of a distribution is called the **first quartile (Q1)**. The median of the upper half of a distribution is called the **third quartile (Q3)**.

2. Where do you think second quartile is located?

The *interquartile range (IQR)* is the distance between the first and third quartiles.

3. What percent of the observations in a data set are between first quartile and third quartile?

4. Find the interquartile range of the grade distribution for Class 1.

Indicate the location of the median for Class 2

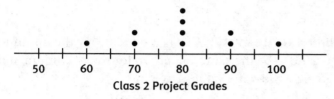

Class 2 Project Grades

5. Find the first and third quartiles. Then find the IQR.
   Q1 =
   Q3 =
   IQR =

Write in the MAD and IQR values for Class 1 and Class 2 below for reference.

Class 1 MAD = _____   Class 2 MAD = _____
Class 1 IQR = _____   Class 2 IQR = _____

6. **Construct viable arguments.** Explain how two distributions can have the same IQR values but different MAD values.

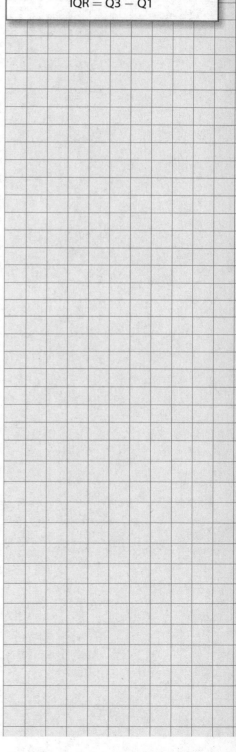

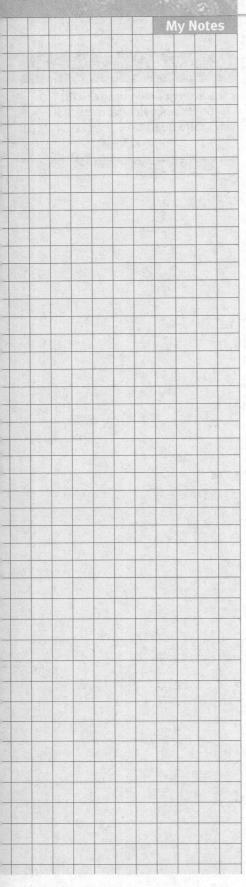

For Class 3 write the median for reference: _____

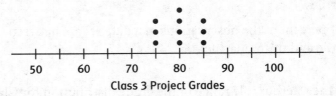

Class 3 Project Grades

7. Find the first and third quartiles. Then find the IQR.
   Q1 =
   Q3 =
   IQR =

8. **Reason quantitatively.** Why is it possible for the minimum and first quartile to be the same value? Or, for the maximum and third quartile to be the same value? Explain.

9. Create a data set with 11 observations that has a median and third quartile of 80.

10. Identify the three measures of variability in this activity. In your own words, state what each one measures.

Check Your Understanding

The data set for hand span (to the nearest half centimeter) of students in Matthew's class is shown below.

18	17	6	7	21	17	19	19	18	22
22	20	21	20	6.5	20	16	20	21	7.5

11. Create a dot plot for the hand span of students in Matthew's class.

12. Do there appear to be any incorrect data values in this data set? Explain.

13. Correct any incorrect data using the conversion factor $2.54 = 1$ inch. Calculate the new values to the nearest centimeter. Then correct your dot plot with the new values.

LESSON 29-3 PRACTICE

Continue working with the corrected data for hand span of students in Matthew's class.

14. **Attend to precision.** Compute the mean, median and range.

15. Compute the mean absolute deviation (MAD).

16. Find the first and third quartile.

17. Compute the interquartile range (IQR).

18. What percent of students in Matthew's class have hand spans that are greater than 17.5 cm?

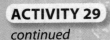

ACTIVITY 29 PRACTICE

Write your answers on notebook paper. Show your work.

1. Aidan's class also did the "Take a Snapshot" survey. Below is the data set for the number of pets for students in his class.

3	4	3	2	3	5	1	0	1	3	2	3
1	2	2	3	2	4	16	2	2	3	3	2

   a. Compute the range of this data set.
   b. Compute the mean and median of this data set.
   c. Determine the first and third quartile.

2. Abby's class took the "Take a Snapshot" survey too. Below is the data set for the number of pets for students in her class.

3	8	4	4	4	3	3	2	5	4	6
3	4	4	4	2	4	1	9	3	4	

   a. Compute the range of this data set.
   b. Compute the mean and median of this data set.
   c. Determine the first and third quartile.

3. Which class, Aidan's or Abby's, will have the largest mean absolute deviation (MAD) value? Explain.

4. Compute the MAD values for the number of pets in both Aidan's class and Abby's class.

5. Which class, Aidan's or Abby's, will have the largest interquartile range (IQR) value? Explain.

6. Compute the IQR values for the number of pets in both Aidan's class and Abby's class.

7. Was your prediction in Item 5 correct? If not, explain why your prediction differed from the computed values.

8. Write several sentences to compare and contrast the distributions for number of pets in Aidan's class and Abby's class.

9. For each of the following values, indicate if it MUST be an actual observation in the data set. (Answer yes or no)
   a. Mean
   b. Median
   c. Minimum
   d. Maximum
   e. Quartile 1
   f. Quartile 3

10. a. For those values in Item 9 that are not always equal to one of the actual observations, give an example of a data set that shows this.
   b. Not all of the values in Item 9 must equal an actual observation in the data set. Give a data set for each to illustrate how this can occur.

MATHEMATICAL PRACTICES
Attend to Precision

11. Explain why it is important to consider measures of variability as well as measures of center when describing a data set.

Summarizing Numerical Data Graphically

Batter Up!
Lesson 30-1 Box Plots

Learning Targets:

- Determine the five-number summary for numerical data.
- Construct a box plot to represent numerical data.
- Describe numerical data sets using comparative language.

SUGGESTED LEARNING STRATEGIES: Interactive Word Wall, Marking the Text, Discussion Groups, Create Representations

Henry "Hank" Aaron and Harmon Killebrew are among the all-time leaders in home runs in Major League Baseball. As a tribute to their outstanding performance during their careers, both were elected to the Baseball Hall of Fame in the 1980s. The table below lists the total number of home runs hit per year for Aaron and Killebrew.

Year	Aaron	Killebrew	Year	Aaron	Killebrew
1954	13	0	1966	44	39
1955	27	4	1967	39	44
1956	26	5	1968	29	17
1957	44	2	1969	44	49
1958	30	0	1970	38	41
1959	39	42	1971	47	28
1960	40	31	1972	34	26
1961	34	46	1973	40	5
1962	45	48	1974	20	13
1963	44	45	1975	12	14
1964	24	49	1976	10	
1965	32	25			

To better understand this data, it can be summarized both numerically and graphically.

1. **Model with mathematics.** To summarize graphically, create two dot plots for the number of home runs, one for each player's data.

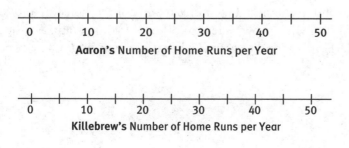

MATH TERMS

The **five-number summary** consists of the values for the minimum, first quartile, median, third quartile, and maximum.

CONNECT TO AP

Describing the distributions of data is a key skill in AP Statistics.

MATH TIP

Comparative language would be words like *greater, smaller, larger, more, less,* and so on.

2. To summarize numerically, compute the mean and the **five-number summary** for each player's data.

	Aaron	Killebrew
Mean:		
Minimum:		
First Quartile:		
Median:		
Third Quartile:		
Maximum:		

To describe a graph of numerical data, you should comment on the **center** (mean or median), **spread** (range, MAD, or IQR), and **shape** of the distribution (symmetrical or skewed).

3. Write a few sentences describing the distribution of number of home runs per year for Hank Aaron.

4. Write a few sentences describing the distribution of number of home runs per year for Harmon Killebrew.

Notice that the same scale was used for both dot plots in Item 1.

5. **Reason quantitatively.** Why is it important for the scales to be the same?

When asked to compare two or more numerical data distributions, you should comment on the center, spread, and shape of the distributions using comparative language.

6. Write a few sentences comparing the number of home runs per year for Hank Aaron and the number of home runs per year for Harmon Killebrew. Discuss your response with your group. As you listen to the group discussion, take notes to aid comprehension and to help you describe your own ideas to others in your group. Ask questions to clarify ideas and to gain further understanding of key concepts.

Below is the dot plot for the number of home runs per year hit by Hank Aaron.

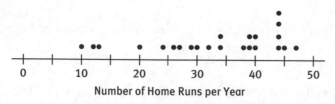

Number of Home Runs per Year

7. Circle the dots that represent the median, first quartile, and third quartile.

8. Count how many dots are in the following intervals. (If dots are stacked on top of each other, then count up from the bottom.)

Less than Q1: _____

Between Q1 and median: _____

Between median and Q3: _____

Greater than Q3: _____

9. What do you notice about the number of dots in each of the intervals above? Explain why this is happening.

Another type of graphical display for numerical data is a box plot. A **box plot** is created using the five-number summary.

The steps to create a box plot are:
- Draw a number line with an appropriate scale.
- Locate the minimum, Q1, median, Q3, and the maximum.
- Draw a box (rectangle) from Q1 to Q3.
- Draw a vertical line inside the box at the median.
- Draw a horizontal line from Q1 to the minimum and a horizontal line from Q3 to the maximum.

Below, the box plot for the number of home runs hit per year by Hank Aaron appears above the dot plot. Follow the steps above to see how the box plot was constructed. Just like the dot plot, where dots are placed above the number line, the box plot also is drawn above a number line.

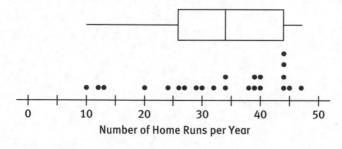

Number of Home Runs per Year

MATH TERMS

A **box plot** (also called a box-and-whisker plot) summarizes the data by showing graphically how it would be divided into four equal parts. The five-number summary is used to create the box plot.

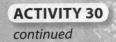

ACTIVITY 30
continued

10. What value does the width of the box represent?

11. What percent of the years did Aaron hit more than 26 home runs?

Below is the dot plot for the number of home runs per year hit by Harmon Killebrew.

12. Circle the dots that represent the median, first quartile and third quartile. If any of these values falls between two data values, circle the space between those numbers.

13. Draw the box plot above the dot plot.

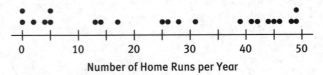

Number of Home Runs per Year

14. Reason abstractly. The box is fairly wide. What does this tell you about this distribution?

15. What percent of the years did Killebrew hit less than 27 home runs?

In a previous activity, you saw the following data set on the time that it took students to finish a math test.

40	30	23	35	28	29	15	37	38	38	36	35
34	34	35	37	35	36	32	36	35	32	39	34

16. Find the median, first quartile, and third quartile.

17. Model with mathematics. Draw a box plot for this distribution above the dot plot below.

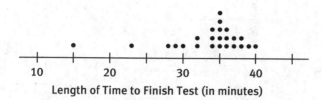

Length of Time to Finish Test (in minutes)

18. Based on the box plot, write a few sentences describing the distribution of length of time it took to finish the test.

Check Your Understanding

Look back at the dot plots and their accompanying box plots for the Number of Home Runs Hit per Year and Length of Time to Finish Test. Use these graphs to help you answer the questions.

19. What feature of a distribution is easier to see in a dot plot than a box plot?

20. What features of a distribution are easier to see in a box plot than a dot plot?

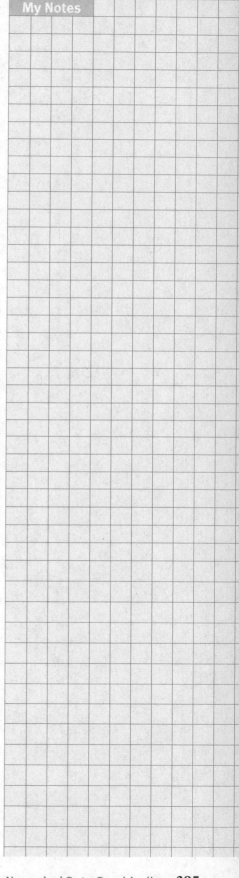

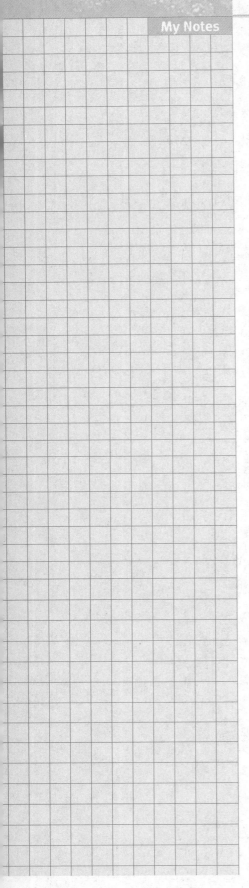

LESSON 30-1 PRACTICE

The dot plot shows the ages of students in the drama club.

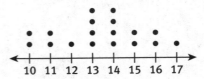

21. Determine the five-number summary.

Minimum	
First Quartile	
Median	
Third Quartile	
Maximum	

22. Write a few sentences about the distribution of students in the drama club.

Compare the two box plots.

A.

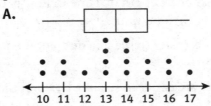

B.

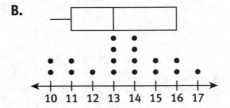

23. Which box plot more accurately reflects the data from Item 21?

24. Reason quantitatively. Explain what is incorrect about the box plot you did not choose.

25. Using the five-number summary, which two numbers represent the starting point and ending point of the following portions of the distribution?
   A. Lowest 50% of the values in the distribution
   B. Highest 25% of the values in the distribution
   C. Middle 50% of the values in the distribution

Learning Targets:

- Summarize data using frequency tables.
- Construct histograms to represent numerical data.

> **SUGGESTED LEARNING STRATEGIES:** KWL Chart, Think-Pair-Share, Create Representations, Note Taking

Numerical data can also be displayed in a ***histogram***. Histograms are drawn differently for numerical data that are *counts* than for numerical data that are *measurements*.

1. In the table below, identify whether the numerical variable is a count or a measurement.

Numerical Variable	Count	Measure
Student's height		
Number of pets		
Amount of time to finish test		
Number of pairs of shoes owned		
Length of index finger		

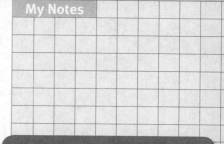

MATH TERMS

A **histogram** is a graph of numerical data that shows the data distribution. Note that a histogram is used to describe numerical data, while a **bar chart** (also called a **bar graph**) is used to describe categorical data. The bars in a histogram always touch, but the bars in a bar chart never touch.

Aoife took a survey of her class. She asked each student how many pieces of gum they chewed per day. The data set is shown below.

4 1 1 5 2 3 4 1 3 0 3 1

1 2 3 0 0 0 1 1 2 0 1

2. **Make sense of problems.** What type of variable is the number of pieces of gum chewed per day?

3. Construct a dot plot for these data.

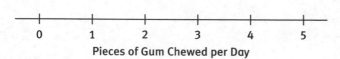

Pieces of Gum Chewed per Day

A *frequency table* can be used to summarize data for a count variable. This table is also the first step in making a histogram.

MATH TERMS

A **frequency table** displays the possible values of the variable along with the frequency or number of times that value occurs.

ACTIVITY 30
continued

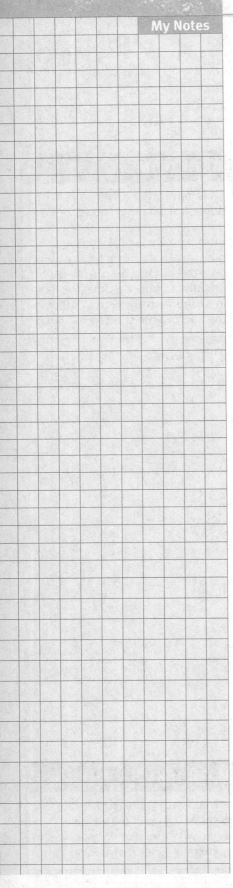

4. Complete the frequency table below for the pieces of gum chewed per day.

Pieces of Gum Chewed	Frequency
0	
1	
2	
3	
4	
5	

To construct a histogram for a numerical count variable:
- Draw a number line for the appropriate values of the variable.
- Draw a vertical line that includes all the values of the frequency.
- Draw a rectangle above each value of the count variable. The rectangle height is the appropriate frequency. This rectangle should be centered over the value.
- Be sure to label each axis.
- Be sure that the rectangles touch.

Below is the dot plot with a vertical scale added that includes the frequency of each value in the frequency table.

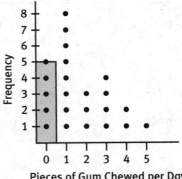

Notice that a rectangle has been drawn over the value 0. The height is the frequency, or number of zeros that occurred in the data set.

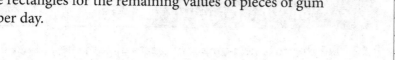
My Notes

5. Draw the rectangles for the remaining values of pieces of gum chewed per day.

6. How do the histogram and dot plot compare?

7. Looking at the histogram, is it easy to see that the median number of pieces of gum chewed is one piece of gum?

8. Write a few sentences describing the histogram for pieces of gum chewed per day.

9. With the help of your teacher, record the number of pieces of gum that students in your class chew per day.

10. Model with mathematics. Construct a histogram for number of pieces of gum chewed per day for students in your class.

11. Write a few sentences describing the histogram for the number of pieces of gum that students in your class chew per day.

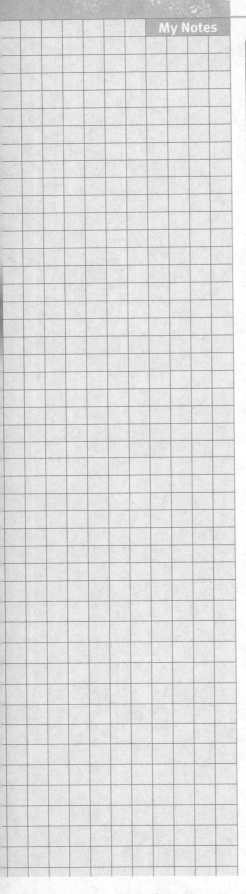

Check Your Understanding

12. For the variable, number of pieces of gum chewed per day, one possible value is "2." Where does the bar for the value "2" begin on the horizontal axis and where does it end?

13. What is one feature of a distribution of a count variable that a histogram shows that a box plot does not show?

LESSON 30-2 PRACTICE

The data represent the number of stairways in the homes of twenty students. Use this data to answer Items 14–18.

4	0	0	4	2	2	3	2	1	2
4	5	3	4	2	2	3	2	2	2

14. Complete a frequency table for the data.

15. **Model with mathematics.** Construct a dot plot for the data.

The histogram for this distribution is partially completed.

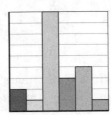

16. Label each axis.

17. Title the histogram.

18. Use several sentences to describe this distribution.

Learning Targets:

● Create class intervals.

● Construct histograms using class intervals.

Histograms for numerical variables that are measurements are constructed differently than histograms of data that came from counting. For measurement variables, we group the possible values into *class intervals*.

There is no rule for the number of class intervals to use, but generally the range of the distribution is divided into anywhere from 5 to 20 class intervals. For a small data set, you can use 5 to 10 intervals.

The data below show the times it took students to finish a math test. The times to the nearest minute are listed below.

40	30	23	35	28	29	15	37	38	38	36	35
34	34	35	37	35	36	32	36	35	32	39	34

This data set is spread from 15 minutes to 40 minutes. We will use 6 class intervals to construct a frequency table. Because the smallest value in the data set is 15, the first interval must include 15. The last interval must include the largest value of 40.

Since time can be measured in parts of minutes, we also want to include all fractional values in the interval.

Notice that the first interval below is from 15 to 20 minutes. This includes 15 minutes and all values up to but not including 20 minutes. The next interval includes 20 minutes and all values up to but not including 25 minutes.

1. Fill in the frequency table for the time to finish a math test data.

Class Interval	Frequency
15 to <20	
20 to <25	
25 to <30	
30 to <35	
35 to <40	
40 to <45	

To construct a histogram for a numerical measurement variable:
• Draw a horizontal line and mark off the class intervals.
• Draw a vertical line that includes all the values of the frequency.
• For each class interval, draw a rectangle above the interval with a height that corresponds to the appropriate frequency. Be sure to label each axis.
• Make sure the rectangles touch.

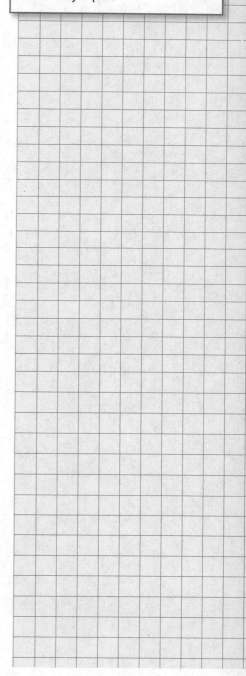

ACTIVITY 30
continued

My Notes

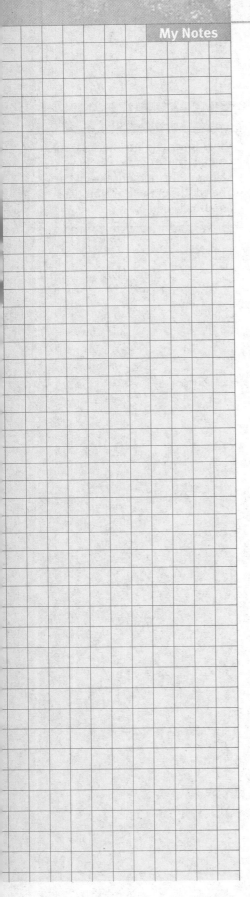

2. Use the frequency table to construct a histogram for the number of minutes needed to finish the test.

In a previous activity, the median time to finish the test was calculated as 35 minutes.

3. **Make sense of problems.** Write a few sentences about the distribution of times to finish the math test in minutes.

Another question on Aoife's class survey was the length of time it took each student to get ready for school that morning (to the nearest minute). The data set is shown below.

38   26   45   37   38   29   33   12   52   22   21   17
32   25   33   21   29   31   6   43   24   30   25

4. Create a frequency table for the length of time to get ready for school. Start by deciding what your class intervals will be. Use between 5 and 7 class intervals.

Class Interval	Frequency

5. Using your frequency table, construct a histogram for the time needed to get ready for school. Be sure to number and label the vertical and horizontal axes.

6. Write a few sentences to describe the distribution of time needed to get ready for school.

7. Compare your histogram with those made by members of your group and other classmates. Are they identical? Why or why not? As you listen to your group's discussion, take notes to aid comprehension and to help you describe your own ideas to others in your group. Ask questions to clarify ideas and to gain further understanding of key concepts.

8. Construct viable arguments. If every student in your class constructed a box plot for the time needed to get ready for school, would your box plots be identical? Why or why not?

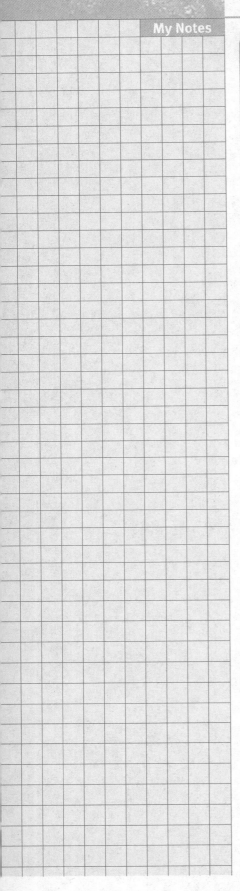

Check Your Understanding

9. Create a frequency table for the histogram.

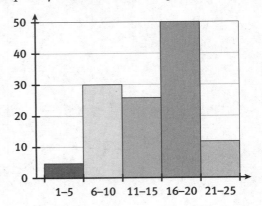

10. Describe the histogram.

11. What quantities might this histogram represent?

LESSON 30-3 PRACTICE

Twenty people attend a family reunion. Their ages are shown below.

10	15	24	36	38
42	54	53	52	64
11	22	35	38	37
37	54	55	55	65

12. Construct a frequency table with a class interval of 10.

13. Construct a histogram based on the frequency table with a class interval of 10.

14. **Model with mathematics.** Construct a frequency table with a class interval of 15.

15. **Model with mathematics.** Construct a histogram based on the frequency table with a class interval of 15.

16. **Construct viable arguments.** Compare the frequency tables and the histograms. How are the shapes different? Which do you think gives a more accurate summary of the ages of the family members who attended the reunion? Why?

ACTIVITY 30 PRACTICE
Write your answers on notebook paper.
Show your work.

Below is the data set for the number of pets for students in Aidan's class and in Abby's class.

Aidan's class:

3 4 3 2 3 5 1 0 1 3 2 3

1 2 2 3 2 4 16 2 2 3 3 2

Abby's class:

3 8 4 4 4 3 3 2 5 4 6

3 4 4 4 2 4 1 9 3 4

1. Construct two box plots for the number of pets (one for each class) using the same scale.

2. Write a few sentences comparing the distribution of number of pets for the two classes.

3. Construct a histogram for the number of pets in Abby's class.

The amounts of time (in hours) that students in Lorelei's class spent on a computer last week are given below. The times were rounded to the nearest half hour.

11   16   3.5   10   8   6.5   6   2.5   9

7   9   13   7   5.5   9   4.5   1   8

10   8   8   4   8   14   7.5

4. Construct a histogram for the time spent on a computer last week.

5. Write a few sentences describing the histogram.

6. Use the histogram to answer the items that follow.

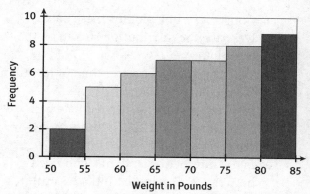

a. What does the height of the bars represent?
b. What does the width of the bars represent?
c. How many intervals have the frequency value of 7?
d. Create a frequency table.
e. Write several sentences describing the histogram and distribution.

7. The data set for the minutes needed to get ready for school for students in Douglas's class is shown.

   5 60 25 15 45 15 20 20 20 40
   20 15 60 40 28 15 30 80 20 45

   a. Construct a box plot for these data.
   b. Describe the distribution shown by the box plot.
   c. Will the mean be greater than or less than the median? Explain.
   d. How many students needed between 17.5 minutes and 22.5 minutes to get ready for school?
   e. Is the number of students who need between 22.5 minutes and 42.5 minutes to get ready for school greater than or less than the number who need between 17.5 and 22.5 minutes (see part d)?

8. Construct a box plot for the minutes needed to get ready for school for students in your class.

9. Write a few sentences comparing the distribution for the minutes needed to get ready for school for students in your class and the distribution for students in Douglas's class.

10. In a survey of her class, Lorelei asked students to record the number of TV's in their homes. The data set appears in the table below.

2	2	7	1	3	3	3	1	1	2
4	5	2	5	4	4	3	2	3	2

   a. Construct a histogram for the number of TVs in homes of the students in Lorelei's class.
   b. What is the mean?
      A. 2   B. 2.5
      C. 2.95   D. 6
   c. What is the range?
      A. 2   B. 3
      C. 6   D. 7
   d. Write a few sentences describing the distribution for the number of TVs in homes of students in Lorelei's class.

MATHEMATICAL PRACTICES
Reason Abstractly and Quantitatively

11. For the graphs studied in this activity, explain what each graph tells you about the distribution of the data set.

Write your answers on notebook paper or grid paper. Show your work.

1. Write a statistical question (similar to those on the "Take a Snapshot" survey) that is of interest to you. The variable resulting from your question must be numerical.

2. Gather data by surveying your classmates. Make a list of their answers.

Use your data to answer Items 3–5.

3. Compute the following values. Be sure to show your work.
   a. mean
   b. five-number summary
   c. range
   d. MAD
   e. IQR

4. On grid paper, construct three separate graphs of your data set: dot plot, box plot, and a histogram.

5. Use the graphs to write a few sentences describing the distributions.

6. Create a poster to display your statistical question and what you learned from your data.

Scoring Guide	Exemplary	Strong	Emerging	Incomplete
	The solution demonstrates these characteristics:			
Mathematics Knowledge and Thinking (Items 1, 3a-e)	• Clear understanding in writing an effective statistical question. • Effective knowledge of the terms describing measures of variability.	• A working knowledge of how to write statistical questions. • Understanding of each measure of variability and how to use that understanding to calculate values.	• Inaccurate knowledge of the concept of statistical questions. • Incorrect understanding of one or more of the measures of variability.	• A question that is not a statistical question or no question at all. • Misunderstanding or no understanding of most of the measures of variability.
Problem Solving (Items 3a-e)	• Clear and accurate computation of each measure of variability.	• Accurate computation of each measure of variability.	• One or more inaccurate calculations.	• Several inaccurate calculations or missing calculations.
Mathematical Modeling / Representations (Items 4, 6)	• Accurate and well-drawn graphs with appropriate scales and labels. • An effective poster that includes all elements and presents a well-reasoned conclusion about the data collected.	• Accurate graphs with appropriate scales and labels. • A poster that includes all elements and adequately explains the data collected.	• One or more graphs that are missing data or graphs that are difficult to read. • A poster that is missing one or more elements or inaccurately describes the data collected.	• Graphs that are mostly incomplete or missing entirely. • A poster that is missing several key elements or no poster at all.
Reasoning and Communication (Items 5, 6)	• Precise use of appropriate math terms and language in describing the distribution. • Thorough explanation of the data using precise mathematical language.	• Generally correct use of appropriate math terms and language in describing the distribution. • Explanation of data using correct mathematical language.	• A confusing description or correct use of few math terms in the description of the distribution. • An explanation of the data that may be incorrect or uses confusing language.	• An incorrect description of the distribution or no description at all. • A confusing or missing explanation of the data collected.

Personal Financial Literacy

7

Unit Overview

Being financially literate means taking responsibility for learning how to manage your money. In this unit, you will learn about banking services that can help you make choices about which financial institution is right for you. You will learn about managing money, using credit wisely, and planning for the future through savings. All those skills are part of personal financial literacy. You will discover how to apply your knowledge of mathematics to help you make wise decisions. As you continue through the unit, you will apply what you have learned to solve real-world financial problems.

Key Terms

As you study this unit, add these and other terms to your math notebook. Include in your notes your prior knowledge of each word, as well as your experiences in using the word in different mathematical examples. If needed, ask for help in pronouncing new words and add information on pronunciation to your math notebook. It is important that you learn new terms and use them correctly in your class discussions and in your problem solutions.

Academic Vocabulary

- savings account
- checking account
- debit card
- deposit
- withdrawal
- transfer
- credit card
- credit report

? How can you build a good credit history?

? How can being financially literate help you plan for college and your future?

Write your answers on notebook paper.
Show your work.

1. Add or subtract.
   a. $\frac{2}{3} + \frac{1}{3}$
   b. $\frac{2}{3} - \frac{1}{3}$
   c. $\frac{5}{8} + \frac{3}{8}$
   d. $\frac{7}{8} - \frac{5}{8}$

2. Multiply.
   a. $4 \times \frac{1}{8}$
   b. $3 \times \frac{1}{3}$
   c. $5 \times \frac{7}{10}$

3. Write the letter for the fraction that is equivalent to $\frac{3}{4}$.
   A. $\frac{3}{8}$ B. $\frac{6}{4}$ C. $\frac{6}{8}$

4. Multiply.
   a. 0.45×75
   b. $6\% \times 180$
   c. $8\% \times 1500$

5. Multiply. Describe any pattern you notice.
   a. 6×20
   b. 6×200
   c. 6×2000

6. Divide. Describe any pattern you notice.
   a. $7000 \div 10$
   b. $7000 \div 100$
   c. $7000 \div 1000$

7. Round each number to the nearest hundred. Explain the rounding rules you used.
   a. 26   b. 349
   c. 457   d. 650

8. Compute. Use what you know about order of operations.
   a. $0.07 \times 840 + 40$
   b. $50 + 8\% \times 720$

Using Financial Services

You Can Bank on It

Lesson 31-1 Understanding Bank Accounts

Learning Targets:

- Examine the features and costs of different types of bank accounts.
- Understand and use a bank account check register.

> **SUGGESTED LEARNING STRATEGIES:** Close Reading, Marking the Text, Summarizing

Learning to manage your money is a skill that you will use throughout life. Many different financial institutions offer banking and other financial services, such as savings and investing accounts. Good money management is all about three things: earning money, saving money, and borrowing wisely.

Having a *savings account* or a *checking account* is a good way to learn about managing money. It pays to check your local financial institutions, because one may pay more or less interest than the other or charge higher fees for their services. Local financial institutions may be branches of national companies or smaller community banks, credit unions, or savings and loans.

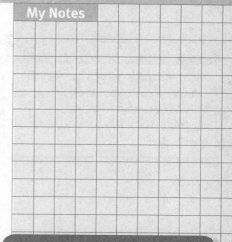

ACADEMIC VOCABULARY

A *savings account* pays interest on the amount of money in the account. A *checking account* may or may not pay interest, depending on the bank or financial institution.

Services	Local Credit Union	Local Bank	Local Savings & Loan
Checking account minimum to open, monthly fees	$100; $10 per month	$150; $5 monthly fee	$50; $5.95 per month
Number of free checks per month	No limit	$0.10 charge per check	Limit of 10 free checks/month; $0.15 thereafter
Interest paid on checking account	0.35%	No	0.4% with combined balances (savings and checking) of $500
Debit card	No fee	No fee	No fee
ATM fees outside network	No fee	$2.50	$2
Overdraft fee	$30	$20	$25

1. Which financial institution has the highest monthly costs for a checking account?

2. Which financial institution has the lowest requirement for opening a checking account?

3. **Apply mathematics in everyday life.** If you wrote 20 checks a month, what fees would you pay to each financial institution?

My Notes

ACADEMIC VOCABULARY

A *debit card* allows customers to withdraw cash from their accounts at ATM (automated teller machines) and pay for purchases at stores.

ACADEMIC VOCABULARY

A *deposit* is money added to an account. A *withdrawal* is money taken out of an account. A *transfer* moves money from one account to another; for example, from a savings account to a checking account.

Most financial institutions offer free *debit cards* to their customers. A debit card works much like a check in that money is taken from the account to pay for the withdrawal or purchase immediately. While the debit card is usually free, fees may be charged if a withdrawal is made from another bank's ATM, called an out-of-network withdrawal.

4. **Communicate reasoning.** Look back at the table on the previous page. Which debit card would you be likely to choose? Why?

5. Compare the features of debit cards offered by each financial institution.

6. Overall, which bank would you be likely to choose? Explain why.

Most financial institutions allow you to open both a checking and a savings account. You can transfer money back and forth between them. You will receive a monthly statement that shows your beginning and ending balances. It also shows *deposits*, checks written on the account, *withdrawals*, and *transfers*. Interest earned will also appear on the statement.

To keep track of how much money you have in your checking account during the month, you would use a check register. Keeping track of your deposits and withdrawals helps you make sure you do not write a check without enough money in the account to cover it. This is known as an *overdraft* for which most banks charge high fees.

7. Use the information in the following check register to calculate the new account balance with each transaction.

Check Number	Date	Description	Check Amount/ Withdrawal	Deposit	Balance
					$287.95
	Mar 1	Allowance		$12.00	
201	Mar 8	Class trip	$15.00		
	Mar 12	High Five Sports (debit card)	$26.77		
	Mar 18	Babysitting		$24.00	
	Mar 21	Transfer to savings	$15.00		
	Mar 24	ATM withdrawal	$20.00		
202	Mar 28	Pet supplies	$8.46		
203	Mar 30	School supplies	$12.40		

8. How many deposits were made in this month? What was the total amount deposited?

9. How many checks were written? What was the total amount?

10. What was the balance at the beginning of the month? At the end?

11. **Analyze mathematical relationships.** What mathematical operations do you use to balance a check register?

Check Your Understanding

12. What facts would you consider in choosing where to open a bank account?

13. Suppose Janice has a beginning bank balance of $467. She makes one ATM withdrawal for $30 and writes 4 checks for $16.80, $22.74, $12.38, and $14. What is her ending balance?

14. How does using a check register help you manage money?

LESSON 31-1 PRACTICE

15. Give examples of the types of fees that banks and other financial institutions charge for using their banking services.

16. **Use a problem-solving model.** If you have a beginning balance of $121.40 and you write checks for $23.50, $12.80, and $97.26, what will be your ending balance? What fees might the bank charge?

17. Complete the following check register.

Check Number	Date	Description	Check Amount/ Withdrawal	Deposit	Balance
					$282.94
	June 3	ATM withdrawal	$20.00		
	June 10	Yard work		$30.00	
412	June 15	T-Shirt Shop	$18.56		
413	June 20	Jeans Store	$22.28		
	June 25	ATM withdrawal	$20.00		
	June 26	Transfer to savings	$25.00		
414	June 30	Books & More	$12.44		

Learning Targets:
- Identify the benefits and costs of credit cards.
- Understand credit history and how it applies to a personal credit score.

SUGGESTED LEARNING STRATEGIES: Close Reading, Marking the Text, Create Representations, Discussion Groups

Using a **credit card** for a purchase is a form of borrowing. The card holder does not pay for the purchase until the card issuer sends a bill, which happens once a month. Credit cards offer convenience in buying items. For example, you may not have enough cash with you or you want to buy something and pay for it over a period of months.

Credit cards, however, carry very high interest rates, often 18 to 19% as an annual percentage rate. You will need to consider the interest you pay as part of the cost of what you're buying. However, if you pay off your total balance each month, there is no interest to pay.

1. Suppose you want to buy new shoes, but you do not have enough money saved. Your older brother agrees to buy the shoes and put them on his credit card. You plan to use part of your allowance each month to repay him.
   a. The shoes cost $35. If you pay your brother $8 when the credit card statement arrives, how much will you still owe him?

   b. **Select appropriate techniques.** Estimate how many months it will take you to repay your brother if you pay $9 per month after the first month.

   c. Calculate the total cost of your shoes, including simple interest of 18% for the number of months it will take you to repay your brother.

Anyone who wants to use credit needs a good credit history. Almost everything you do involving money goes on record somewhere. That record is a **credit report**, which is used to assign a credit score. A credit score is usually a number between 300 and 850. Scores of 700 and higher are considered good. Scores of 580 and lower are "poor" or "very poor."

If you have a high credit score, you can borrow money at the lowest interest rates. Lenders will consider you a good credit risk who will repay on time. If you have a low credit score, lenders will charge higher interest rates for loans or may be unwilling to loan money because you have a history of late payments. People with very low credit scores may not be able to get a credit card.

ACADEMIC VOCABULARY

A **credit card** allows the user to postpone paying for purchases until receiving a monthly bill.

MATH TIP

Remember that the formula for simple interest is $I = R \times T$ (Interest = Rate times Time).

ACADEMIC VOCABULARY

A **credit report** contains a detailed list of a person's credit history prepared by a credit bureau and used by a lender to determine a loan applicant's creditworthiness.

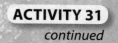

Three nationwide agencies report on consumer credit. Everyone is entitled to a free credit report once a year. Information on the report includes the following:

- Public records, such as any fines remaining unpaid or late payments on utility bills, taxes, or city/local fees
- Late payments on loans, such as car loans or home mortgages
- Past-due or unpaid credit card payments, which might include payments to local stores or for items ordered online
- Accounts in good standing, which includes credit accounts for which all payments are up to date

Here are some ways to build a good credit record:

- Always pay bills on time. Even your monthly utility bill affects your credit score.
- Do not borrow or charge more than you can afford. Paying high interest rates on credit card balances can quickly increase the amount owed.
- Open a bank account before trying to get a credit card.
- Have different types of credit, such as a cell phone contract, credit card, and bank account.

2. What information in your credit report would be especially important to a lender?

3. Working in groups, create a short presentation that reflects your understanding of the information that goes on a credit report. Create a visual to support your presentation.

4. Why is your credit score important to you as a borrower?

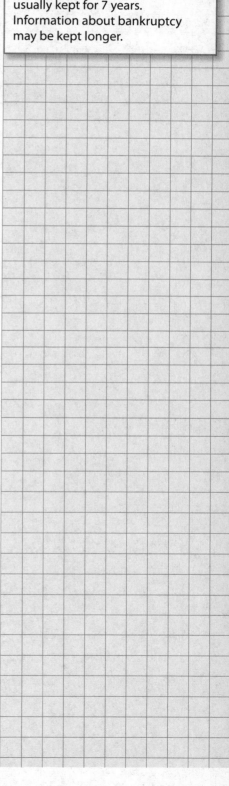

My Notes

MATH TIP

Information on a credit report is usually kept for 7 years. Information about bankruptcy may be kept longer.

Check Your Understanding

5. How long is information kept on a credit report?

6. How does your credit score affect the interest rates on a loan?

7. What can you do to build a good credit history?

LESSON 31-2 PRACTICE

8. Communicate reasoning. Explain why credit reports are valuable to both borrowers and lenders.

9. You have a credit card balance of $188, and you pay annual interest on the unpaid balance of 18%. If you pay $50 on your balance, how much interest will you pay for the next month on the remaining balance?

10. Compare the features of debit and credit cards.

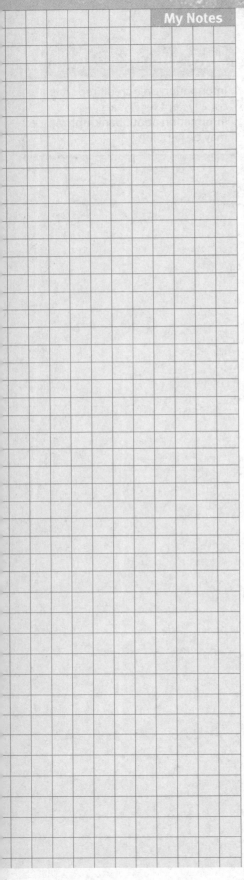

My Notes

Learning Targets:

- Explain various ways to pay for a college education.
- Compare the annual salary of several occupations that require education or training beyond high school.
- Calculate the effects of different annual salaries on lifetime income.

> **SUGGESTED LEARNING STRATEGIES:** Close Reading, Marking the Text, Create a Plan

As you dream about your future, what kind of job or career do you think you will want? Probably you will change your mind several times before deciding. One decision that will affect the kind of job you have and how much you earn is whether you go to college.

College costs can vary greatly depending on the type of school, such as public or private college, community college, university, or trade school. There are several ways to help pay for college.

- *Savings:* Many parents start saving for college when their children are small. Children also can start saving early by putting some of their allowance or cash gifts into savings. There are many types of college savings accounts. Some are offered by local banks or government agencies. Others are private, through insurance or investment companies.
- *Grants and scholarships:* Grants and scholarships are available from several different sources. The federal government provides Pell grants based on financial need, costs to attend school, and status as a full-time or part-time student. Other grants or scholarships may be available from the college itself or from alumni or community groups. Many are available for students with a special talent, such as sports or music. Others are given for high grades. Others may be based on financial need. Unlike student loans, grants and scholarships do not have to be repaid.
- *Student loans:* Like other kinds of borrowing, student loans must be paid back, with interest. Like any loan, it is important to "shop around" for low interest and other terms.
- *Work-study:* Once you are in school, many colleges offer work-study jobs. These jobs can give you experience in a field you are interested in. They may be on campus or in private companies. At the same time, the money you earn helps pay your costs.

1. What factors can earn you a grant or scholarship to help pay college costs?

My Notes

2. Explain the difference between taking out a student loan and paying with savings, work-study, and other options.

3. Assume that you are ready for college. You plan to go to a local college while living at home. The annual cost for tuition, fees, and books is $14,500. Also assume that you qualify for a Pell grant of $5,500 and scholarships of $1,500.
   a. If the rest of your cost must come from savings, how much savings do you need to pay for your first year?

   b. If fees and tuition increase by 4% each year, how much money would you need for four years of college? Round to the nearest whole dollar for each year's calculation before adding all years.

4. **Use a problem-solving model.** Assume that you work 12 hours a week through a work-study program and earn $7.50 per hour.
   a. How much would you earn per week?

   b. How much would you earn for two semesters of 16 weeks each?

   c. If you work 12 weeks during the summer and earn $9.50 per hour for a 40-hour week, how much would you earn during the summer?

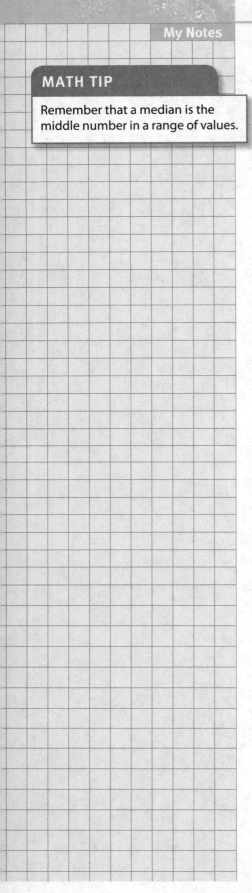

My Notes

MATH TIP

Remember that a median is the middle number in a range of values.

5. The following table shows the median weekly earnings for people with different levels of schooling. Complete the table by calculating the increase in weekly income with each additional level of education.

Education Level	Median Weekly Income (2011)	Increase (in dollars)
Less than high school diploma	$451	--
High school graduate	$638	
Some college, no diploma	$719	
Associate degree	$768	
Bachelor's degree	$1053	
Master's degree	$1263	
Doctoral or professional degree	$1551–1665	

6. **Use representations.** What is the median increase in weekly income between a high school degree and a college (bachelor's) degree?

According to the U.S. Census Bureau, someone with a college degree will earn about $1 million more in a lifetime than someone with only a high school diploma. Consider the following statistics:

• The average total earnings for all people with a bachelor's degree is $2.4 million.
• Those with a professional degree, such as a doctor or lawyer, may earn about $4 million.

Actual income also depends on many other factors, especially the field in which one works. Graduates in business, science, and engineering earn higher incomes than those with other degrees.

7. What is the percentage difference between the lifetime incomes of people with a high school education and those with a bachelor's degree?

8. Research two or three jobs that interest you. Find out the education that is required as well as the salary ranges you can earn. Use the data to create a table.

Lesson 31-3
Planning for the Future

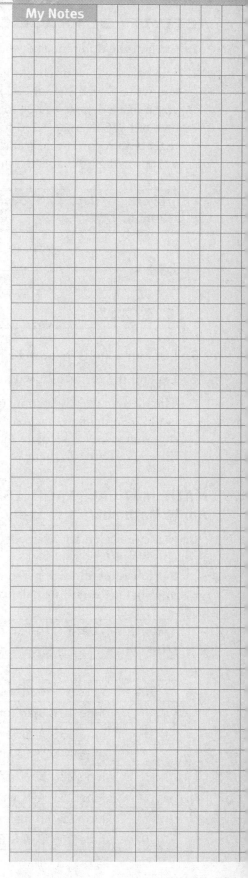

Check Your Understanding

10. Why is starting a college fund early a good idea?

11. Identify ways of paying for college without borrowing.

12. What are the drawbacks of taking out student loans?

13. How does additional education affect your earnings over a lifetime?

LESSON 31-3 PRACTICE

14. **Communicate reasoning.** Describe how work-study can help you both pay college costs and learn a profession.

Education Level	Median Weekly Income (2011)
Less than high school diploma	$451
High school graduate	$638
Some college, no diploma	$719
Associate degree	$768
Bachelor's degree	$1053
Master's degree	$1263
Doctoral/professional degree	$1551–1665

15. Use the weekly figures in the table above to calculate the median yearly incomes of these workers:
    a. High school graduate
    b. Bachelor's degree
    c. Professional degree

16. Compare the expected lifetime earnings for someone with a college degree versus someone with a high school degree.

ACTIVITY 31 PRACTICE

1. Explain the difference between a debit card and a credit card.

2. The balance in your checking account is $342.20. On September 3, you write Check 204 for $33.99 to a clothing store. Three days later you make a deposit of $24 for babysitting. On September 12, you take out $20 from an ATM to go to the movies. Fill in this check register to record those transactions. On September 25, you transfer $25 to savings. What is the new balance?

Check Number	Date	Description	Check Amount/ Withdrawal	Deposit	Balance
					$342.20

3. List four actions that can help you build a good credit history.

4. Explain the various ways that a family can pay for college without borrowing.

5. The median weekly income of someone who drops out of high school is $451. Someone with a bachelor's degree from college earns $1053 in that same week. Calculate each person's yearly income and then the difference between them.

MATHEMATICAL PRACTICES
Apply Mathematics to Everyday Life

6. Make the calculations needed to balance the account shown in this check register.
   a. How often did this person use a debit card? An ATM machine?
   b. What is the ending balance in this account?

Check Number	Date	Description	Check Amount/ Withdrawal	Deposit	Balance
					$420.75
300	June 6	Guitar lesson	$25.00		
	June 10	Bike repair (debit card)	$11.00		
	June 15	Allowance		$25.00	
	June 21	Ms. Soto (babysitting)		$22.00	
	June 22	Shoe Shoppe (debit card)	$19.99		
	June 25	ATM withdrawal	$20.00		
	June 25	Transfer to savings	$25.00		
301	June 30	B & B Books	$9.40		

Symbols

$<$	is less than
$>$	is greater than
$\leq$	is less than or equal to
$\geq$	is greater than or equal to
$=$	is equal to
$\neq$	is not equal to
$\approx$	is approximately equal to
$\lvert a \rvert$	absolute value: $\lvert 3 \rvert = 3$; $\lvert -3 \rvert = 3$
$\sqrt{}$	square root
$\%$	percent
$\perp$	perpendicular
$\parallel$	parallel
(x, y)	ordered pair
$\overset{\frown}{AB}$	arc AB
$\overleftrightarrow{AB}$	line AB
$\overrightarrow{AB}$	ray AB
$\overline{AB}$	line segment AB
$\angle A$	angle A
$m\angle A$	measure of angle A
$\triangle ABC$	triangle ABC
π	pi; $\pi \approx 3.14$; $\pi \approx \dfrac{22}{7}$

Formulas

Perimeter	
P	= sum of the lengths of the sides
Rectangle	$P = 2l + 2w$
Square	$P = 4s$
Circumference	$C = 2\pi r$

Area	
Circle	$A = \pi r^2$
Parallelogram	$A = bh$
Rectangle	$A = lw$
Square	$A = s^2$
Triangle	$A = \frac{1}{2}bh$
Trapezoid	$A = \frac{1}{2}h(b_1 + b_2)$

Surface Area	
Cube	$SA = 6e^2$
Rectangular Prism	$SA = 2lw + 2lh + 2wh$
Cylinder	$SA = 2\pi r^2 + 2\pi rh$
Cone	$SA = \pi r^2 + \pi rl$
Regular Pyramid	$SA = B + \frac{1}{2}pl$
Sphere	$SA = 4\pi r^2$

Volume	
Cylinder	$V = Bh$, $B = \pi r^2$
Rectangular Prism	$V = lwh$
Triangular Prism	$V = Bh$, $B = \frac{1}{2}bh$
Pyramid	$V = \frac{1}{3}Bh$
Cone	$V = \frac{1}{3}\pi r^2 h$
Sphere	$V = \frac{4}{3}\pi r^3$

Linear function	
Slope	$m = \dfrac{y_2 - y_1}{x_2 - x_1}$
Slope-intercept form	$y = mx + b$
Point-slope form	$y - y_1 = m(x - x_1)$
Standard form	$Ax + By = C$

Quadratic Equations	
Standard Form	$ax^2 + bx + c = 0$
Quadratic Formula	$x = \dfrac{-b \pm \sqrt{b^2 - 4ac}}{2a}$

Other Formulas	
Pythagorean Theorem	$a^2 + b^2 = c^2$, where c is the hypotenuse of a right triangle
Distance	$d = \sqrt{(x_2 - x_1)^2 + (y_2 - y_1)^2}$
Direct variation	$y = kx$
Inverse variation	$y = \dfrac{k}{x}$

Temperature	
Celsius	$C = \frac{5}{9}(F - 32)$
Fahrenheit	$F = \frac{9}{5}C + 32$

Properties of Real Numbers

Reflexive Property of Equality	For all real numbers a, $a = a$.
Symmetric Property of Equality	For all real numbers a and b, if $a = b$, then $b = a$.
Transitive Property of Equality	For all real numbers a, b, and c, if $a = b$ and $b = c$, then $a = c$.
Substitution Property of Equality	For all real numbers a and b, if $a = b$, then a may be replaced by b.
Additive Identity	For all real numbers a, $a + 0 = 0 + a = a$.
Multiplicative Identity	For all real numbers a, $a \cdot 1 = 1 \cdot a = a$.
Commutative Property of Addition	For all real numbers a and b, $a + b = b + a$.
Commutative Property of Multiplication	For all real numbers a and b, $a \cdot b = b \cdot a$.
Associative Property of Addition	For all real numbers a, b, and c, $(a + b) + c = a + (b + c)$.
Associative Property of Multiplication	For all real numbers a, b, and c, $(a \cdot b) \cdot c = a \cdot (b \cdot c)$.
Distributive Property of Multiplication over Addition	For all real numbers a, b, and c, $a(b + c) = a \cdot b + a \cdot c$.
Additive Inverse	For all real numbers a, there is exactly one real number $-a$ such that $a + (-a) = 0$ and $(-a) + a = 0$.
Multiplicative Inverse	For all real numbers a and b where $a \neq 0$, $b \neq 0$, there is exactly one number $\frac{b}{a}$ such that $\frac{b}{a} \cdot \frac{a}{b} = 1$ and $\frac{a}{b} \cdot \frac{b}{a} = 1$.
Multiplication Property of Zero	For all real numbers a, $a \cdot 0 = 0$ and $0 \cdot a = 0$.
Addition Property of Equality	For all real numbers a, b, and c, if $a = b$, then $a + c = b + c$.
Subtraction Property of Equality	For all real numbers a, b, and c, if $a = b$, then $a - c = b - c$.
Multiplication Property of Equality	For all real numbers a, b, and c, if $a = b$, then $a \cdot c = b \cdot c$.
Division Property of Equality	For all real numbers a, b, and c, $c \neq 0$ if $a = b$, then $\frac{a}{c} = \frac{b}{c}$.
Zero Product Property of Equality	For all real numbers a and b, if $a \cdot b = 0$ then $a = 0$ or $b = 0$ or both a and b equal 0.
Addition Property of Inequality*	For all real numbers a, b, and c, if $a > b$, then $a + c > b + c$.
Subtraction Property of Inequality*	For all real numbers a, b, and c, if $a > b$, then $a - c > b - c$.
Multiplication Property of Inequality *	For all real numbers a, b, and c, $c > 0$, if $a > b$, then $a \cdot c > b \cdot c$. For all real numbers a, b, and c, $c < 0$, if $a > b$, then $a \cdot c < b \cdot c$.
Division Property of Inequality*	For all real numbers a, b, and c, $c > 0$ if $a > b$, then $\frac{a}{c} > \frac{b}{c}$. For all real numbers a, b, and c, $c < 0$ if $a > b$, then $\frac{a}{c} < \frac{b}{c}$.

*These properties are also true for $<, \leq, \geq$.

Table of Measures

Customary	Metric
Distance/Length	
1 foot (ft) = 12 inches (in.) 1 yard (yd) = 3 feet (ft) = 36 inches (in.) 1 mile (mi) = 5280 feet (ft)	1 centimeter (cm) = 10 millimeters (mm) 1 meter (m) = 100 centimeters (cm) 1 kilometer (km) = 1000 meters (m)
Volume	
1 cup (c) = 8 fluid ounces (fl oz) 1 pint (pt) = 2 cups (c) 1 quart (qt) = 2 pints (pt) 1 gallon (gal) = 4 quarts (qt)	1 liter (L) = 1000 milliliters (mL)
Weight/Mass	
1 pound (lb) = 16 ounces (oz)	1 gram (g) = 1000 milligrams (mg) 1 kilogram (kg) = 1000 grams (g)
Time	
1 minute (min) = 60 seconds (sec) 1 hour (hr) = 60 minutes (min) 1 day (d) = 24 hours (hr) 1 week (wk) = 7 days (d)	1 year (yr) = 365 days (d) 1 year (yr) = 52 weeks (wk) 1 year (yr) = 12 months (mo)

SpringBoard Learning Strategies
READING STRATEGIES

STRATEGY	DEFINITION	PURPOSE
Activating Prior Knowledge	Recalling what is known about a concept and using that information to make a connection to a new concept	Helps students establish connections between what they already know and how that knowledge is related to new learning
Chunking the Activity	Grouping a set of items/questions for specific purposes	Provides an opportunity to relate concepts and assess student understanding before moving on to a new concept or grouping
Close Reading	Reading text word for word, sentence by sentence, and line by line to make a detailed analysis of meaning	Assists in developing a comprehensive understanding of the text
Graphic Organizer	Arranging information into maps and charts	Builds comprehension and facilitates discussion by representing information in visual form
Interactive Word Wall	Visually displaying vocabulary words to serve as a classroom reference of words and groups of words as they are introduced, used, and mastered over the course of a year	Provides a visual reference for new concepts, aids understanding for reading and writing, and builds word knowledge and awareness
KWL Chart (Know, Want to Know, Learn)	Activating prior knowledge by identifying what students know, determining what they want to learn, and having them reflect on what they learned	Assists in organizing information and reflecting on learning to build content knowledge and increase comprehension
Marking the Text	Highlighting, underlining, and /or annotating text to focus on key information to help understand the text or solve the problem	Helps the reader identify important information in the text and make notes about the interpretation of tasks required and concepts to apply to reach a solution
Predict and Confirm	Making conjectures about what results will develop in an activity; confirming or modifying the conjectures based on outcomes	Stimulates thinking by making, checking, and correcting predictions based on evidence from the outcome
Levels of Questions	Developing literal, interpretive, and universal questions about the text while reading the text	Focuses reading, helps in gaining insight into the text by seeking answers, and prepares one for group and class discussions
Paraphrasing	Restating in your own words the essential information in a text or problem description	Assists with comprehension, recall of information, and problem solving
Role Play	Assuming the role of a character in a scenario	Helps interpret and visualize information in a problem
Shared Reading	Reading the text aloud (usually by the teacher) as students follow along silently, or reading a text aloud by the teacher and students	Helps auditory learners do decode, interpret, and analyze challenging text
Summarizing	Giving a brief statement of the main points in a text	Assists with comprehension and provides practice with identifying and restating key information
Think Aloud	Talking through a difficult text or problem by describing what the text means	Helps in comprehending the text, understanding the components of a problem, and thinking about possible paths to a solution
Visualization	Picturing (mentally and/or literally) what is read in the text	Increases reading comprehension and promotes active engagement with the text
Vocabulary Organizer	Using a graphic organizer to keep an ongoing record of vocabulary words with definitions, pictures, notes, and connections between words	Supports a systematic process of learning vocabulary

SpringBoard Learning Strategies
COLLABORATIVE STRATEGIES

STRATEGY	DEFINITION	PURPOSE
Critique Reasoning	Through collaborative discussion, respond to the arguments of others; question the use of mathematical terminology, assumptions, and conjectures to improve understanding and to justify and communicate conclusions	Helps students learn from each other as they make connections between mathematical concepts and learn to verbalize their understanding and support their arguments with reasoning and data that make sense to peers
Debriefing	Discussing the understanding of a concept to lead to consensus on its meaning	Helps clarify misconceptions and deepen understanding of content
Discussion Groups	Working within groups to discuss content, to create problem solutions, and to explain and justify a solution	Aids understanding through the sharing of ideas, interpretation of concepts, and analysis of problem scenarios
Group Presentation	Presenting information as a collaborative group	Allows opportunities to present collaborative solutions and to share responsibility for delivering information to an audience
Jigsaw	Reading different texts or passages, students become "experts" and then move to a new group to share their information; after sharing, students go back to the original group to share new knowledge	Provides opportunities to summarize and present information to others in a way that facilitates understanding of a text or passage (or multiple texts or passages) without having each student read all texts
Sharing and Responding	Communicating with another person or a small group of peers who respond to a piece of writing or proposed problem solution	Gives students the opportunity to discuss their work with peers, to make suggestions for improvement to the work of others, and/or to receive appropriate and relevant feedback on their own work
Think-Pair-Share	Thinking through a problem alone, pairing with a partner to share ideas, and concluding by sharing results with the class	Enables the development of initial ideas that are then tested with a partner in preparation for revising ideas and sharing them with a larger group

WRITING STRATEGIES

Drafting	Writing a text in an initial form	Assists in getting first thoughts in written form and ready for revising and refining
Note Taking	Creating a record of information while reading a text or listening to a speaker	Helps in organizing ideas and processing information
Prewriting	Brainstorming, either alone or in groups, and refining thoughts and organizing ideas prior to writing	Provides a tool for beginning the writing process and determining the focus of the writing
Quickwrite	Writing for a short, specific amount of time about a designated topic	Helps generate ideas in a short time
RAFT (Role of Writer, Audience, Format, and Topic)	Writing a text by consciously choosing a viewpoint (role of the writer), identifying an audience, choosing a format for the writing, and choosing a topic	Provides a framework for communicating in writing and helps focus the writer's ideas for specific points of communication
Self Revision / Peer Revision	Working alone or with a partner to examine a piece of writing for accuracy and clarity	Provides an opportunity to review work and to edit it for clarity of the ideas presented as well as accuracy of grammar, punctuation, and spelling

SpringBoard Learning Strategies
PROBLEM-SOLVING STRATEGIES

Construct an Argument	Use mathematical reasoning to present assumptions about mathematical situations, support conjectures with mathematically relevant and accurate data, and provide a logical progression of ideas leading to a conclusion that makes sense	Helps develop the process of evaluating mathematical information, developing reasoning skills, and enhancing communication skills in supporting conjectures and conclusions
Create a Plan	Analyzing the tasks in a problem and creating a process for completing the tasks by finding information needed for the tasks, interpreting data, choosing how to solve a problem, communicating the results, and verifying accuracy	Assists in breaking tasks into smaller parts and identifying the steps needed to complete the entire task
Create Representations	Creating pictures, tables, graphs, lists, equations, models, and /or verbal expressions to interpret text or data	Helps organize information using multiple ways to present data and to answer a question or show a problem solution
Guess and Check	Guessing the solution to a problem, and then checking that the guess fits the information in the problem and is an accurate solution	Allows exploration of different ways to solve a problem; guess and check may be used when other strategies for solving are not obvious
Identify a Subtask	Breaking a problem into smaller pieces whose outcomes lead to a solution	Helps to organize the pieces of a complex problem and reach a complete solution
Look for a Pattern	Observing information or creating visual representations to find a trend	Helps to identify patterns that may be used to make predictions
Simplify the Problem	Using "friendlier" numbers to solve a problem	Provides insight into the problem or the strategies needed to solve the problem
Work Backward	Tracing a possible answer back through the solution process to the starting point	Provides another way to check possible answers for accuracy
Use Manipulatives	Using objects to examine relationships between the information given	Provides a visual representation of data that supports comprehension of information in a problem

Glossary
Glosario

A

absolute value (p. 85)   The distance of a number from zero on a number line.

valor absoluto (pág. 85)   Distancia entre un número y el cero en una recta númerica.

additive inverse (p. 94)   A number and its opposite are additive inverses. The sum of any number and its additive inverse is zero.

inverso aditivo (pág. 94)   Un número y su opuesto son inversos aditivos. La suma de cualquier número y su inverso aditivo es cero.

algebraic expression (p.136)   A mathematical phrase that contains one or more numbers, one or more variables, and one or more arithmetic operations. For example: $x + 5$ or $5x$.

expresión algebraica (pág. 136)   Una frase matemática que contiene uno o más números, una o más variables, y una o más operaciones aritméticas. Por ejemplo $x + 5$ o $5x$.

algorithm (p. 8)   A set of steps or a procedure used to carry out a computation or solve a problem.

algoritmo (pág. 8)   Conjunto de pasos o procedimiento que se usa para hacer un cálculo o resolver un problema.

altitude of a triangle (p. 297)   The perpendicular line segment from a vertex to the line containing the opposite side.

altura de un triángulo (pág. 297)   Segmento recto perpendicular desde un vértice hasta la recta que contiene el lado opuesto.

annex (p. 4)   To attach or to add something.

anexar (pág. 4)   Unir o agregar algo

area (p. 294)   Area is the number of square units a figure covers. The measure, in square units, of the interior region of a plane figure.

área (pág. 294)   Medida, en unidades cuadradas, de la region interior de una figura plana.

average (p. 265)   An amount found by adding two or more numbers, and then dividing by n. For example, the average price is the mean price; the mean is determined by adding the prices found and dividing this total by the number of prices found.

promedio (pág. 265)   Cantidad encontrada al sumar dos o más números y luego dividida entre n. Por ejemplo: el precio promedio es la media del precio; la media se determina sumando los precios encontrados y dividiendo el total entre el número de precios encontrados.

B

bar chart (p. 353)   A graph used to display categorical data. Every bar represents a different category. The vertical scale for heights is labeled with the count or percent for each category.

gráfica de barras (pág. 353)   Gráfica que usa barras para mostrar datos por categoría. La escala vertical para las alturas de las barras se rotula con el conteo o percentaje para cada categoría.

benchmark (p. 249)   A benchmark is a standard or reference point for comparing or evaluating against.

punto de referencia (pág. 249)   Un punto de referencia es un punto estándar o marco de referencia con el cual comparar o contra el cual evaluar.

box plot (p. 393)   A data display organized into four sections, each representing 25% of the data. Also known as a **box-and-whisker plot**.

gráfica de frecuencias acumuladas (pág. 393)   Representación de datos organizados en cuatro secciones, en que cada una representa un 25% de los datos. También se le conoce como **gráfica de cuadrículas.**

C

checking account (p. 411)   An with a financial institution in which money is deposited and from which a person makes payments.

cuenta corriente (de cheques) (pág. 411)   Una cuenta con una institución financiera en la cual se deposita dinero y desde la cual una persona hace pagos.

class intervals (p. 401)   Class intervals are groups into which the possible values of a range of data are divided; for example, the division of data on a bar chart or histogram.

intervalos de clase (pág. 401)   Intervalos de clase son grupos en los que se dividen los valores posibles de un rango de datos; por ejemplo: la división de datos en una gráfica de barras o un histograma.

coefficient (pp. 136, 178)   A number by which a variable is multiplied. For example, in the term $6x$, 6 is the coefficient.

coeficiente (págs. 136, 178)   Número por el cual se multiplica una variable. Por ejemplo, en el término $6x$, 6 es el coeficiente.

commutative property of addition (p. 143)   The property that states that changing the order of addends does not change the sum and that changing the order of factors does not change the product.

propiedad conmutativa de la suma (pág. 143)   Propiedad que establece que el orden en que se suman dos números no altera la suma y que el orden en que se multiplican los factores no altera el producto.

compare and contrast (p. 145)   To compare and contrast means to point out similarities and differences between two or more things.

comparar y contrastar (pág. 145)   Comparar y contrastar significa señalar similitudes y diferencias entre dos o más cosas.

composite figure (p. 295)   A figure made up of two or more separate parts or pieces.

figura compuesta (pág. 295)   Una figura formada por dos o más partes o piezas separadas.

composite number (p. 27)   A composite number is one that can be divided evenly by numbers other than itself or 1; for example, 15 is a composite number because it can be divided evenly by 3 and 5.

número compuesto (pág. 27)   Un número compuesto es aquel que se puede dividir en partes iguales entre números que no sean el 1 y sí mismos; por ejemplo, 15 es un número compuesto porque se puede dividir en partes iguales entre 3 y 5.

consecutive angles (p. 291)   Consecutive angles of a polygon are two angles with a side in common that do not overlap.

ángulos consecutivos (pág. 291)   Los ángulos consecutivos de un polígono son dos ángulos que comparten un lado en común sin traslaparse.

constant rate of change (p. 202)   If the rate of change remains the same in a problem situation, it is a constant rate of change.

tasa de cambio constante (pág. 202)   Si la tasa de cambio permanece igual en un problema, es una tasa de cambio constante.

conversion factor (p. 224)   A ratio relating a number of units to a unit measure. For example, the ratio 12 to 1 is the conversion factor relating inches to feet, and 1 to 12 is the conversion factor relating feet to inches.

factor de conversión (pág. 224)   Razón que relaciona un número de unidades con una medida unitaria. Por ejemplo, la razón 12 a 1 es el factor de conversión de pulgadas a pies y 1 a 12 es el factor de conversión de pies a pulgadas.

coordinate plane (p. 109)   A coordinate plane is a two-dimensional system for graphing ordered pairs, formed by two perpendicular number lines intersecting at their zero points and creating four quadrants.

plano de coordenadas (pág. 109)   Un plano de coordenadas es un sistema bidimensional para graficar pares ordenados, formado por dos rectas numéricas perpendiculares que se intersecan en sus puntos cero y que generan cuatro cuadrantes.

credit card (p. 414)   A card used to make purchases on credit, allowing the user to postpone paying for purchases until receiving a monthly bill.

tarjeta de crédito (pág. 414)   Tarjeta que se usa para hacer compras a crédito, permitiendo al usuario posponer el pago por las compras hasta que recibe una factura mensual.

credit report (p. 414)   A credit report is a detailed list of a person's credit history prepared by a credit bureau and used by a lender to determine a credit applicant's creditworthiness.

informe de crédito (pág 414)   Un informe de crédito es una lista detallada del historial crediticio de una persona preparado por una entidad crediticia y utilizada por un prestamista para determinar la solvencia de una persona que solicita crédito.

D

debit card (p. 412)   A card issued by a financial institution that allows customers to withdraw cash from their accounts at ATM (automated teller machines) and to pay for purchases at stores.

tarjeta de débito (pág. 412)   Una tarjeta emitida por una institución financiera que permite a los clientes retirar dinero en efectivo de sus cuentas usando cajeros automáticos (ATM) y pagar por las compras en tiendas.

deposit (p. 412)   An amount of money added to a checking or savings account.

depósito (p. 412)   Una cantidad de dinero que se agrega a una cuenta de cheques o de ahorros.

dependent variable (p. 204)   The variable whose value is determined by the input or value of the independent variable.

variable dependiente (pág. 204)   Variable cuyo valor queda determinado por la entrada o valor de la variable independiente.

dimensional analysis (p. 224)   A problem-solving method that uses the multiplicative identity property of one. It states that any number or expression can be multiplied by one without changing its value.

análisis dimensional (pág. 224)   Un método de resolución de problemas que usa la propiedad de identidad multiplicativa del uno. Establece que cualquier número o expresión se puede multiplicar por uno sin alterar su valor.

distribution (p. 348)   The collection of all the values for the possible answers to a statistical question.

distribución (pág. 348)   El conjunto de todos los valores para las respuestas posibles a una pregunta de estadística.

distributive property (p. 145)   The property that states that the result of multiplying a number by the sum of two numbers is the same as the result of multiplying each addend by the number; for example, $4 \times (3 + 5) = (4 \times 3) + (4 \times 5)$.

propiedad distributiva (pág. 145)   Propiedad que establece que el resultado de multiplicar un número por la suma de dos números es igual al resultado de multiplicar cada sumando por el número y luego sumar los productos; por ejemplo, $4 \times (3 + 5) = (4 \times 3) + (4 \times 5)$.

dot plot (p. 354)   A graphic display of data arranged in columns above a horizontal number line, using a single dot to represent each data item. A dot plot is similar to a line plot.

diagrama de puntos (pág. 354)   Representación gráfica de datos dispuestos en columnas sobre una recta numérica horizontal, usando un solo punto para representar cada dato. Un diagrama de puntos es similar a un diagrama lineal.

E

elevation (p. 104)   A distance above orbelow a point of reference, such as ground level or sea level.

elevación (pág. 104)   Distancia por encima o por debajo de un punto de referencia, como el nivel del suelo o el nivel del mar.

equation (p. 149)   A statement showing that two numbers or expressions are equal, such as $4 + 3 = 7$ or $x + 5 = 9$.

ecuación (pág. 149)   Enunciado que muestra que dos números o expresiones son iguales, como $4 + 3 = 7$ o $x + 5 = 9$.

equiangular (p. 285)   A polygon with all angles congruent.

equiángulo (pág. 285)   Polígono con todos sus ángulos congruentes.

equivalent ratio (p. 218)   A ratio that names the same number, just as equivalent fractions do. Equivalent ratios are found by multiplying or dividing both terms of a ratio by the same number.

razón equivalente (pág. 218)   Razón que usa el mismo número, como lo hacen las fracciones equivalentes. Las razones equivalentes se encuentran multiplicando o dividiendo los dos términos de una razón por/entre el mismo número.

equivalent ratio (p. 218)   A ratio that names the same number, just as equivalent fractions do. Equivalent ratios are found by multiplying or dividing both terms of a ratio by the same number.

razón equivalente (pág. 218)   Razón que usa el mismo número, como lo hacen las fracciones equivalentes. Las razones equivalentes se encuentran multiplicando o dividiendo los dos términos de una razón por/entre el mismo número.

evaluate (p. 30)   To find the value of an expression.

evaluar (pág. 30)   Hallar el valor de una expresión.

F

factor (p. 27)   One number is a factor of another number if it divides that number with no remainder. Also, one of the numbers that is multiplied to get a product.

factor (pág. 27)   Un número es factor de otro número si divide a ese número sin que quede residuo. Además, es uno de los números que se multiplican para obtener un producto.

five-number summary (p. 392)   This summary includes the minimum, first quartile, median, third quartile, and maximum. The information in a five-number summary is used in making and interpreting box-and-whisker plots.

resumen de cinco números (pág. 392)   Este resumen incluye el mínimo, el primer cuartil, la mediana, el tercer cuartil y el máximo. La información de un resumen de cinco números se usa para hacer e interpretar una gráfica de frecuencias acumuladas.

frequency table (p. 397)   A table that displays the possible values of a variable along with the frequency or number of times that value occurs.

tabla de frecuencias (p. 397)   Tabla que muestra los valores posibles de una variable junto con la frecuencia o el número de veces que ocurren.

G

greatest common factor (GCF) (p. 35)   For a set of two or more whole numbers, the greatest number that is a factor of all the numbers in the set.

máximo común divisor (MCD) (pág. 35)   El máximo común divisor de un conjunto de dos o más números enteros es el mayor número que es factor de todos los números del conjunto.

H

histogram (p. 397)   A graph used to show the frequencies for a set of data. The horizontal axis is divided into equal intervals. The vertical axis shows the frequency, or the number of items, in each interval.

histograma (pág. 397)   Gráfica que se usa para mostrar las frecuencias de un conjunto de datos. El eje horizontal está dividido en intervalos iguales. El eje vertical muestra la frecuencia, o número de elementos, que hay en cada intervalo.

I

improper fraction (p. 56)   A fraction whose numerator is greater than or equal to the denominator.

fracción impropia (pág. 56)   Fracción cuyo numerador es mayor o igual al denominador.

independent variable (p. 204)   The variable for which input values are substituted in a function.

variable independiente (pág. 204)   Variable que es reemplazada por los valores de entrada en una función.

inequality (p. 187)   A mathematical statement showing that one quantity is greater than or less than another. Inequalities use these symbols; $>$ (is greater than); $<$ (is less than); $\geq$ (is greater than or equal to); and $\leq$ (is less than or equal to).

desigualdad (pág. 187)   Enunciado matemático que muestra que una cantidad es mayor o menor que otra. Las desigualdades usan estos símbolos: $>$ (mayor que); $<$ (menor que); $\geq$ (mayor o igual a) y $\leq$ (menor o igual a).

integer (p. 84)   One of the set of numbers consisting of the natural numbers, their opposites, and zero.

entero (pág. 84)   Uno de un conjunto de números que consta de los números naturales, sus opuestos y el cero.

interquartile range (IQR) (p. 387)   The difference between the lower and upper quartiles of a set of ordered data.

rango intercuartil (RI) (pág. 387)   Diferencia entre el cuartil inferior y el cuartil superior de un conjunto de datos ordenados.

inverse operations (p. 163)   Operations that "undo" each other. Addition and subtraction are inverse operations. Multiplication and division are inverse operations.

operaciones inversas (pág. 163)   Operaciones que se "anulan" una a la otra. La suma y la resta son operaciones inversas. La multiplicación y la división son operaciones inversas.

L

least common denominator (LCD) (p. 51)   The least common multiple of two or more denominators.

mínimo común denominador (mcd) (pág. 51)   El mínimo común múltiplo de dos o más denominadores.

least common multiple (LCM) (p. 38)   For a set of two or more whole numbers, the smallest number that is a multiple of all the numbers in the set.

mínimo común múltiplo (mcm) (pág. 38)   Para un conjunto de dos o más números enteros, el menor número que es múltiplo de todos los números del conjunto.

M

mathematical property (p. 143)   A rule or statement that is always true.

propiedad matemática (pág. 143)   Regla o enunciado que siempre es verdadero.

mean (p. 363)   The arithmetic average of a set of data found by taking the sum of the data and then dividing by the total number of data items.

media (pág. 363)   Promedio aritmético de un conjunto de datos, que se calcula dividiendo las suma de los datos entre el número total de datos.

mean absolute deviation (p. 382)   The mean (average) of the sums of the absolute values of the difference between each data point and the chosen measure of central tendency (usually the mean).

desviación media absoluta (pág. 382)   La media (promedio) de la suma de los valores absolutos de la diferencia entre cada dato y la medida de la tendencia central (normalmente la media) escogida.

median (p. 367)   The middle number of a set of data in numerical order.

mediana (pág. 367)   Número que está en el medio de un conjunto de datos ordenados numéricamente.

mode (p. 353)   The data item in a set that occurs most often. A data set may have no mode, one mode, or more than one mode.

moda (pág. 353)   Dato que ocurre con mayor frecuencia en un conjunto. Puede que un conjunto de datos no tenga moda, tenga una moda o tenga más de una moda.

N

net (p. 317)   A two-dimensional drawing used to represent or form a three-dimensional object or solid.

red (pág. 317)   Dibujo bidimensional que se usa para representar o formar un objeto tridimensional o cuerpo geométrico.

numerical expression (p. 30, 131)   A mathematical phrase that uses numbers. Examples of numerical expressions are $2 + 3$, $35 \div 7$, and 62. A numeric expression is evaluated by performing any arithmetic operation indicated in the expression.

expresión numérica (págs. 30,131)   Frase matemática que usa números. Ejemplos de expresiones numéricas son $2 + 3$, $35 \div 7$ y 62. Una expresión numérica se evalúa realizando cualquier operación aritmética indicada en la expresión.

O

opposites (p. 85)   Numbers that are the same distance from zero on a number line but are on different sides of zero.

opuestos (pág. 85)   Números que están a la misma distancia del cero en una recta numérica, pero a lados diferentes del cero.

order of operations (p. 134)   A set of rules for evaluating expressions with more than one operation. The order is: do calculations inside parentheses; evaluate expressions with exponents; multiply or divide from left to right; add or subtract from left to right.

orden de las operaciones (pág. 134)   Conjunto de reglas para evaluar expresiones que contienen más de una operación. El orden es: hacer los cálculos que estén en paréntesis; evaluar las expresiones que tienen exponentes; multiplicar o dividir de izquierda a derecha; sumar o restar de izquierda a derecha.

ordered pair (pp. 109, 204)   A pair of numbers that locate a point on the coordinate plane. The first number refers to the horizontal position, and the second number refers to the vertical position. The numbers in the ordered pair are called the coordinates of the point.

par ordenado (págs. 109, 204)   Par de números que indican la posición de un punto en el plano de coordenadas. El primer número se refiere a la posición horizontal y el segundo número se refiere a la posición vertical. Los números del par ordenado se llaman coordenadas del punto.

origin (p. 109)   The point of intersection of the axes of the coordinate plane. The coordinates of the origin are (0,0).

origen (pág. 109)   Punto de intersección de los ejes del plano de coordenadas. Las coordenadas del origen son (0,0).

outliers (p. 364)   Data points in a set of data that do not fit the overall pattern of the data set.

valores atípicos (pág. 364)   Puntos de un conjunto de datos que no calzan en el patrón general del conjunto de datos.

P

percent (p. 247)   A ratio that compares a number to 100 and uses the % symbol.

porcentaje (pág. 247)   Razón que compara un número con 100 y usa el símbolo %.

perimeter (p. 294)   The distance around a figure.

perímetro (pág. 294)   Distancia alrededor de una figura.

polygon (p. 289)   A closed figure formed by three or more line segments that intersect only at their endpoints.

polígono (pág. 289)   Figura geométrica cerrada, formada por tres o más segmentos de recta que se intersecan solamente en sus extremos.

prime factor (p. 27)   A factor or a number which is a prime number.

factor prima (pág. 27)   Un factor o un número que es un número primo.

prime factorization (p. 27)   The prime factorization of a number shows the number as a product of its prime factors.

factorización prima (pág. 27)   La factorización prima de un número muestra el número como producto de sus factores primos.

prime number (p. 27)   A natural number greater than 1 that has exactly two factors, itself and 1.

número primo (pág. 27)   Número natural mayor que 1, que tiene solamente dos factores: el mismo número y 1.

prism (p. 321)   A three-dimensional figure with two parallel, congruent bases which are both polygons. A prism is named according to the shape of its base.

prisma (pág. 321)   Figura tridimensional que tiene como bases dos polígonos paralelos y congruentes. Un prisma recibe su nombre según la forma de su base.

proper fraction (p. 45)   A fraction with a numerator (the top number) that is less than the denominator (the bottom number); for example, $5 < 8$, so $\frac{5}{8}$ is a proper fraction. A proper fraction has a value less than 1.

fracción propia (pág. 45)   Una fracción con un numerador (el número de arriba) menor que el denominador (el número de abajo); por ejemplo: $5 < 8$, entonces $\frac{5}{8}$ es una fracción propia. Una fracción propia tiene un valor menor a 1.

Property of One (p. 45)   The Property of One states that if the numerator and denominator of a fraction are multiplied or divided by the same number, the value of the fraction is not changed.

Propiedad de identidad de la multiplicación (propiedad del uno) (pág. 45)   La propiedad del uno establece que si el numerador y el denominador de una fracción se multiplican o se dividen por/entre el mismo número, el valor de la fracción no cambia.

proportion (p. 238)   An equation stating that two ratios are equal.

proporción (pág. 238)   Ecuación que establece que dos razones son iguales.

Q

quadrant (p. 109)   One of the four regions that are formed by the intersection of the *x*- and *y*-axes of the coordinate plane.

cuadrante (pág. 109)   Una de las cuatro regiones que se forman por la intersección del eje de las *x* con el eje de las *y* del plano de coordenadas.

quadrilateral (p. 289)   A polygon with four sides.

cuadrilátero (pág. 289)   Polígono con cuatro lados.

quartiles (p. 386)   Values that divide a distribution into four groups, each having an equal number of observations.

cuartiles (pág. 386)   Valores que dividen una distribución en cuatro grupos, cada uno con el mismo número de elementos.

R

range (p. 380)   In statistics, the total length of the interval covered by the distribution. Range = maximum value − minimum value.

rango (pág. 380)   En estadística, todo el intervalo cubierto por la distribución. Rango = valor máximo − valor mínimo.

rate (pp. 223, 234)   A comparison of two different units or two different things measured with the same unit.

tasa (págs. 223, 234)   Comparación entre dos unidades diferentes o dos cosas diferentes medidas con la misma unidad.

rate of change (p. 202)   A relationship that compares the change in one variable to the corresponding change in a related variable.

tasa de cambio (pág. 202)   Relación que compara el cambio en una variable con el cambio correspondiente en una variable relacionada.

ratio (p. 215)   A comparison of two quantities. Ratios can be written as fractions (indicating a quotient), or using the word "to," or using a colon (:).

razón (pág. 215)   Comparación entre dos cantidades. Las razones pueden escribirse como fracciones (que indican un cociente) o usando la palabra "a" o usando dos puntos (:).

reciprocal (p. 72)   Two numbers are reciprocals if their product is 1.

recíprocos (pág. 72)   Dos números son recíprocos si un producto es 1.

rectangular prism (p. 321)   A prism that has bases that are rectangles. Its faces are also rectangles.

prisma rectangular (pág. 321)   Un prisma cuyas bases son rectángulos. Sus caras también son rectángulos.

reflection (p. 113)   A transformation in which a figure is flipped over a line, called a line of reflection.

reflexión (pág. 113)   Una transformación en la que una figura se invierte sobre una recta llamada eje de reflexión.

S

savings account (p. 411)   An account that pays interest on the amount of money in the account.

cuenta de ahorros (pág. 411)   Una cuenta que paga intereses sobre la cantidad de dinero en la cuenta.

simulate (p. 50)   To model a situation that can be represented with numbers, such as votes in an election.

simular (pág. 50)   Hacer un modelo de una situación que se puede representar con números, como los votos en una elección.

skewed (p. 359)   In statistics, the shape of a distribution that occurs when one side is longer than the other side.

distribución asimétrica (pág. 359)   En estadística, la forma de una distribución que ocurre cuando un lado es más largo que el otro lado.

solution (p. 149)   Any value that makes an equation or inequality true when substituted for the variable.

solución (pág. 149)   Cualquier valor que hace verdadera una ecuación o desigualdad al reemplazar la variable.

solution of an inequality (p. 188)   Much like the solution to an equation, a solution of an inequality is a number that makes a statement true when it is substituted for the variable in the inequality.

solución de una desigualdad (pág. 188)   Muy parecida a la solución de una ecuación, una solución de una desigualdad es un número que hace que una oración sea verdadera cuando se sustituye por la variable en la desigualdad.

statistical questions (p. 347)   A question that produces answers that vary from person to person.

preguntas estadísticas (pág. 347)   Una pregunta que produce respuestas que varían de una persona a otra.

stem plot (p. 355)   A data display that shows each data value in two parts according to its place value. The stem represents the first digit or digits, and the leaf represents the last digit of the number. A legend shows how to read the values. Also called a **stem plot**.

diagrama de tallo (pág. 355)   Representación de datos que muestra cada dato en dos partes de acuerdo con su valor posicional. El tallo representa el primer o primeros dígitos y la hoja representa el último dígito del número. Una leyenda muestra cómo leer los valores. También se lo denomina **diagrama de tallo y hojas**.

symmetrical (p. 359)   The shape of a distribution is symmetrical when the two halves are the same.

simétrico (pág. 359)   La forma de una distribución es simétrica cuando las dos mitades son iguales.

T

term (p. 137)   A number, a variable, or the product of a number and variable(s).

término (pág. 137)   Número, variable, o producto de un número por una o más variables.

theorem (p. 283)   A statement or conjecture that has been proven to be true.

teorema (pág. 283)   Un enunciado o conjetura que ha sido probado ser verdadero(a).

transfer (p. 412)   Moving money from one account to another; for example, from a savings account to a checking account.

transferencia (pág. 412)   Pasar dinero de una cuenta a otra; por ejemplo: de una cuenta de ahorros a una cuenta corriente (de cheques).

triangular prism (p. 323)   A prism that has two parallel bases that are congruent triangles. The three faces are rectangles.

prisma triangular (pág. 323)   Un prisma que tiene dos bases paralelas que son triángulos congruentes. Las tres caras son rectangulares.

U

uniform distribution (p. 359)   A distribution of data in which the values of the variable occur approximately the same number of times.

distribución uniforme (pág. 359)   Una distribución de datos en la cual los valores fr ls variable ocurren aproximadamente el mismo número de veces.

unit price (p. 236)   The cost of one unit of a product.

precio por unidad (pág. 236)   El costo de una unidad de un producto.

unit rate (p. 141, 234)   A rate expressed in terms of one unit.

tasa unitaria (págs. 141, 234)   Tasa que se expresa en términos de una unidad.

V

variability (p. 347)   The number of different answers that may be possible to answer a statistical question.

variabilidad (pág. 347)   El número de diferentes respuestas que pueden ser posibles contestar una pregunta de estadística.

variable (p. 136)   A letter or symbol used to represent a number in expressions or equations.

variable (pág. 136)   Letra o símbolo que se usa para representar un número en expresiones o ecuaciones.

visual representation (p. 6)   A visual model that uses pictures, graphs, number lines, or manipulatives to represent data in a problem in order to help solve the problem.

representación visual (pág. 6)   Un modelo visual que usa dibujos, gráficas, rectas numéricas u objetos manipulables para representar datos en un problema para ayudar a resolver el problema.

volume (p. 331)   The measure of the space occupied by a three-dimensional figure. Volume is measured in cubic units, such as cubic inches (in.^{3}).

volumen (pág. 331)   Medida del espacio que ocupa una figura tridimensional. El volumen se mide en unidades cúbicas, como pulgadas cúbicas (in.^{3}).

W

withdrawal (p. 412)   A withdrawal is money taken out of an account.

retiro (pág. 412)   Un retiro es el dinero que se saca de una cuenta.

Z

Z symbol (p. 84)   The symbol Z is often used to represent the set of integers. This is because in German, the word Zahl means "number."

símbolo Z (pág. 84)   El símbolo Z con frecuencia se usa para representar el conjunto de números enteros. Esto viene de la palabra alemana *zahl*, que significa "número."

Verbal & Visual Word Association

Definition in Your Own Words	Important Elements

Academic Vocabulary Word

Visual Representation	Personal Association

Word Map

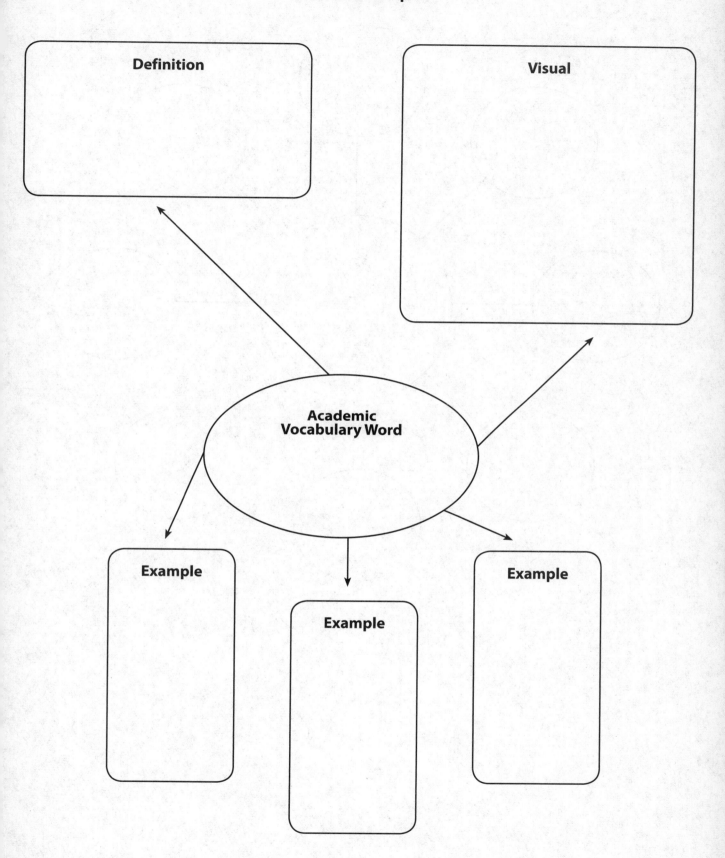

Definition

Visual

Academic
Vocabulary Word

Example

Example

Example

Eight Circle Spider

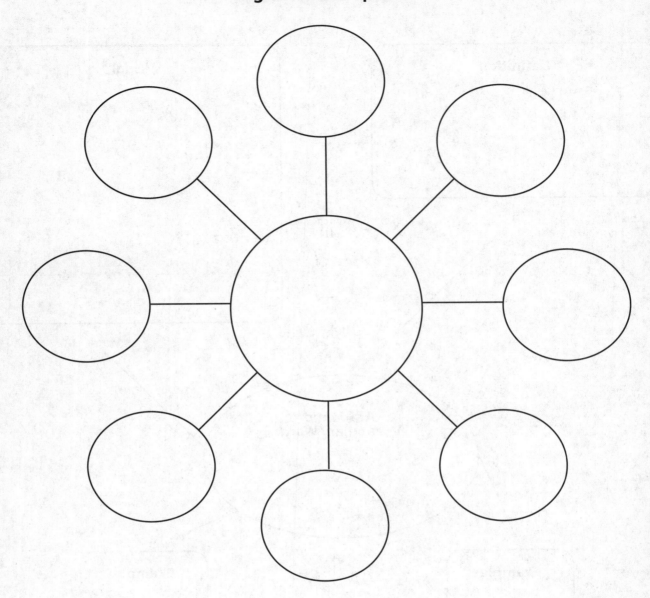

Index

A

Absolute value, 85
Acute angle, 281
Acute triangle, 282
Addition
  Associative Property of, 143–144
  Commutative Property of, 143–144
  decimals, 6–10
  integers, 93–99
  inverse operations, 163
  number line and, 93
  order of operations, 134
Addition equations
  Additive Identity Property, 163
  balance scale, 162–163
  isolate the variable, 162–163
  mental math, 160–161
  modeling and solving, 159–165
  solve algebraically, 163–164
Additive Identity Property, 144, 163, 169
Additive inverse, 94
Algebraic expression
  coefficient, 136
  compared to equations, 150
  defined, 136
  Distributive Property to simplify, 146
  evaluating, 136–138
  order of operation and, 137
  terms, 137
  variable, 136
  writing, 139–142
Algorithm, 8
Altitude, of triangle, 297
Angles
  acute, 281
  consecutive, 291
  obtuse, 281
  right, 281
Annex, 4
Area
  of composite figures, 293–296
  defined, 294
  of polygon, 297–300, 309–312
  of rectangle, 14, 140
  surface area, 317–320
  of trapezoid, 297–300
  of triangle, 297–300
Associative Property
  of addition, 143–144
  of multiplication, 143–144
Astronomy, 315
Average price, 265

B

Balance scale
  addition equations and, 162–163
  subtraction equations, 167–168
Bank accounts, 411–413
  checking account, 411
  debit card, 412
  deposit, 412–413
  savings account, 411
  transfer, 412–413
  withdrawal, 412–413

Bar chart, 353, 397
Bar graph, 397
Base, exponent, 30
Benchmark, 249
Bottle rocket, 236
Box plots, 391–396
Brackets, order of operations, 134
Business plan, 261

C

Cartesian coordinate plane, 109
Categorical variables, 351–352
Charts
  bar, 353
  relative frequency chart, 353
Checking account, 411
Circuit, electrical
  defined, 6
  node, 9
Class intervals, 401–403
Coefficient
  defined, 136, 178
  solving multiplication equations and,
    178–179
College, paying for, 416–417
Commutative Property
  of addition, 143–144
  of multiplication, 143–144
Compare
  decimals, 3–5
  defined, 145
  fractions, 50–55
  improper fractions, 60–61
  integers, 87–90
  mixed numbers, 60–61
  whole numbers, 3–5
Composite figures
  area, 293–296
  defined, 295
  perimeter, 293–296
Composite number, 27
Conjecture, 29
Consecutive angles, 291
Constant rate of change, 202
Contrast, 145
Conversion factor, 224–226
Conversions
  conversion factor, 224–226
  convert between measurements using
    ratios, 227–230
Coordinate plane
  distance and reflections, 112–114
  elements of, 109
  integers in, 109–112
  locating point on, 109
  ordered pair, 109, 204
  polygons on, 305–312
Counters
  to add integers, 93–95
  to subtract integers, 100–101
Credit cards, 414–415
Credit report, 414–415
Cross products, to compare fractions, 53
Crystals, 331
Cubed, 30

Cubes
  names of, 331
  nets and surface area of, 317–320
  volume of, 331–334

D

Darts, 133
Data analysis
  bar chart, 353
  box plots, 391–396
  categorical variables, 351–352
  distribution, 348
  dot plots, 354–355, 363–365
  five-number summary, 392
  frequency table, 397–398
  histograms, 397–404
  interquartile range, 386–389
  mean, 363–366, 370–373
  mean absolute deviation (MAD),
    382–384
  measures of center, 363–377
  median, 367–369, 370–373
  mode, 353
  numerical variables, 351–352
  outliers, 364
  range, 379–381
  shapes of distributions, 357–361
  stem plot, 355
  summarize center of distribution,
    370–373
  surveys, making, 347–349
  variability, 347–348
Debit card, 412
Decimals
  adding, 6–10
  comparing and ordering, 3–5
  dividing, 19–22
  multiplying, 11–14
  number line and, 4
  percent as, 251–258
  subtracting, 6–10
Denominator, least common
    denominator, 51
Dependent variables, 204–208
Deposit, 412–413
Descartes, Rene, 109
Dimensional analysis, 224
Discount, 265–266
Distance, on coordinate plane, 112–114
Distribution
  defined, 348
  interquartile range, 386–389
  mean, 363–366
  mean absolute deviation, 382–384
  median, 367–369
  outliers, 364
  shape of, 357–361
  skewed, 359–360, 372–373
  summarize center of, 370–373
  symmetrical, 359
  uniform, 359
Distributive Property
  multiplication, 145–146
  simplifying problems and, 145–146
Dividend, 15

Mixed numbers
    changing to improper fractions, 56–58
    comparing and ordering, 60–61
    defined, 56
    dividing, 75–76
    multiplying, 67–68
    number sentence and, 57
Mode, 353
Models
    to add integers, 93–96
    to subtract integers, 100–101
Multiplication
    Associative Property of, 143–144
    Commutative Property of, 143–144
    decimals, 11–14
    Distributive Property of, 145–146
    fractions, 63–68
    integers, 117–121
    inverse operations, 178
    mixed numbers, 67–68
    order of operations, 134
    symbols for, 144
Multiplication equations
    isolate the variable, 178–180
    modeling and solving, 175–181
Multiplicative Identity Property, 144
    dimensional analysis and, 224
Mural, 305

N

Natural numbers, 84
Net
    cube, 317–320
    defined, 317
    of prisms, 321–324
Node, 9
Number concepts
    absolute value, 85
    additive inverse, 94
    decimals, 3–22
    fractions, 45–55, 63–68, 71–74
    greatest common factor, 35–37
    least common multiple, 38–40
    mixed numbers, 56–61, 63–68, 75–76
    natural numbers, 84
    prime factorization, 27–32
    whole numbers, 3–22
Number line
    adding integers on, 93–95
    addition equations and, 160
    decimals and, 4
    inequalities on, 189–190
    integers and, 83–86, 87–88
    solving rate problems with double, 227
Numbers
    exponential form of, 30
    standard form of, 30
Number sentence, 57
Numerical variables, 351–352
Numeric expression, 131
    compared to equations, 150
    defined, 30
    evaluate, 30
    order of operations, 131–135

O

Obtuse angle, 281
Obtuse triangle, 282

Ohms, 6
One-step equations
    addition, 159–165
    define variable, 150–151
    multiplication, 175–181
    solving, 152–153
    subtraction, 166–174
    verbal model, 150–151
One-step inequalities, 193–196
Operations, inverse, 163, 169
Opposite numbers, 84–85
Order
    decimals, 3–5
    fractions, 50–55
    improper fractions, 60–61
    integers, 87–90
    mixed numbers, 60–61
    whole numbers, 3–5
Ordered pair, 109, 201, 204
Order of operations, 131–135
    algebraic expression and, 137
Origin, 109
Outliers, 364

P

Parallelogram, 289–292
    opposite and consecutive angles of, 291
    rectangle, 290–292
    rhombus, 290–292
    square, 290–292
Parentheses, order of operations, 134
Percent, 247–258
    benchmark, 249
    concept of, 247–250
    as decimal, 251–258
    defined, 247
    discount, 265–266
    as equivalent proportions, 261–262
    find part when given whole, 264–267
    find whole when given part, 268–270
    as fraction, 247, 251–258
    grid for, 248–250
    interest, 264–265
    markup, 266
    models to understand, 247–250, 261–263
    word form, 251
Perimeter, 140
    composite figures, 293–296
    defined, 294
Point, locating on coordinate plane, 109
Polygon
    area of, 297–300, 309–312
    on coordinate plane, 305–312
    defined, 289
Population density, 15
Positive rational numbers, 84
Powers, 30
Price
    average, 265
    discount, 265–266
    markup, 266
Prime factor, 27
Prime factorization
    defined, 27
    exponent and, 30–31
    factor tree, 27
    greatest common factor, 35–37
    least common multiple, 39–40
Prime number, 27

Prisms
    net for, 321–324
    rectangular, 321
    surface area of, 321–324
    triangular, 323
Product, 138, 139
Proper fraction, 45
Properties
    Additive Identity Property, 144
    Associative, 143–144
    Commutative, 143–144
    defined, 143
    Distributive, 145–146
    Multiplicative Identity Property, 144
    Property of One, 45
    Triangle Inequality Property, 278
Property of One, 45
Proportional relationships, 218–220
Proportions, 238
    as equivalent ratios, 261

Q

Quadrants, 109
Quadrilaterals, 289–292
    consecutive angles of, 291
    defined, 289
    parallelogram, 289–292
    rectangle, 290–292
    rhombus, 290–292
    square, 290–292
    trapezoid, 289
    Venn diagram, 291
Quartiles, 386–389
Questions, statistical, 347–349
Quotient, 15, 140

R

Range
    defined, 380
    interquartile range, 386–389
Rate of change, 202
Rates
    defined, 223, 234
    double number line to solve, 227
    of speed, 240–242
    unit rate, 223, 234, 236–239
    Venn diagram of, 235
Ratios, 213–273
    conversion factor, 224–226
    convert between measurements using, 227–230
    decimals, 251–258
    defined, 215
    equivalent, 218
    fractions, 251–258
    percent, 247–270
    proportional relationships and, 218–220
    proportions, 238, 261–262
    rates, 223, 233–235, 236–239
    ratio table, 218–220
    solving problems using, 223–226
    terms in, 215
    unit rates, 233–235, 236–239
    Venn diagram of, 235
    writing, 215–216
Ratio table, 218–220
Reading Math, 15, 52, 110, 162, 237
Reciprocals, 72